MOLLOY'S LIVE FOR SUCCESS

JOHN T. MOLLOY

bestselling author of **DRESS FOR SUCCESS** and
THE WOMAN'S DRESS FOR SUCCESS BOOK

ARE YOU A GOOD POWER PLAYER?

MOLLOY'S LIVE FOR SUCCESS

"*Molloy's Live for Success* promises to be the most valuable book ever written about success."

—*Cleveland Press*

"In this fascinating study of successful and unsuccessful people, personality images and body signals are examined in terms of appraising a person and setting guidelines for self-improvement. This book is excellent not only for those who want to get ahead, but also for everyone who wants to feel better about himself or herself."

—*Concise Book Reviews*

"The words 'success' and 'Molloy' are so inextricably entwined since the 'Dress for . . .' books that you almost cannot have one without the other . . . Molloy here imparts in riveting detail, from slant of shoulders to facial expression to nuance of fish knife use, the outward trappings he deems essential to the upwardly mobile executive. And the importance of it all is quite convincingly backed up by his research."

—*Savvy*

"Win at work. 'Success has more to do with perspiration than inspiration' is one of the gems in the pages of *Live for Success* by John T. (*Dress for Success*) Molloy. What makes this self-helper rise above the rest is its research. The experiences of 10,000 business men and women can't be all wrong."

—*Glamour*

MOLLOY'S LIVE FOR SUCCESS

JOHN T. MOLLOY

A PERIGORD PRESS BOOK

BANTAM BOOKS
TORONTO · NEW YORK · LONDON · SYDNEY

MOLLOY'S LIVE FOR SUCCESS

*A Bantam / Perigord Book / published in association with
William Morrow and Company, Inc.*

PRINTING HISTORY

Bantam / Perigord Trade edition / March 1982
Bantam / Perigord rack-size edition / August 1983

Library of Congress Cataloging in Pubication Data

Molloy, John T.
  Molloy's Live for success.
    1. Success. I. Title. II. Title: Live for success.
HF5386.M73 1981b   650.1   81-15056
  ISBN 0-553-23515-X (pbk.)   AACR2

Published simultaneously in the United States and Canada

PRINTED IN THE UNITED STATES OF AMERICA

O   0 9 8 7 6 5 4 3 2 1

To my son, Robert

CONTENTS

INTRODUCTION

This is the most important book ever written about success because it is based not on personal opinion, but on scientific research.

Nearly all books on success are founded on the ridiculous assumption that one man's personal experience or insight mirrors a newly discovered universal truth. This text, however, is based on interviews, conversations with, and observations of more than 10,000 American business men and women. The advice contained in this book is based on their combined experience and wisdom, not on my "omniscience."

I do not defend the premise that intimidation, craftiness, or dirty tricks are the keys to success. My research found no magic formula, no easy way. This book will not enable you to look at the world from a new angle and discover ultimate truth and easy victory. Instead, you will see the world as it is and learn to deal with it more effectively.

This book came about almost by accident. Five years ago, after my men's *Dress for Success* had been published, I had lunch with five of my friends: two successful executives from large corporations, two successful businessmen, and an attorney. They were discussing my book during the meal and complimented me on the fact that it was a useful and practical tool. When the subject switched (I don't remember exactly why or how) to the rash of success books on the market, these fellows expressed surprise at the shallowness and impracticality of the advice they gave. One said he had to let a young man in his office go because he came in and he acted like a boor. He found out later that the young man was following instructions in one of those kick-'em-in-the-teeth books. It was the general consensus that if anyone took those books seriously, their chances of getting ahead would be limited indeed.

Once they came to that conclusion, several of the fellows suggested I write an accurate book on success. I, half kidding, started to interview the five of them to see what suggestions they would give to young people. I asked them, if they were training young men and young women to succeed, what would they teach them? At the end of the meal, I had several pages of notes, most of which seemed very sensible, and I was hooked. After putting the same question to 995 additional executives, I came up with an outline for this very simple how-to book.

Almost all the men and women we interviewed agreed that success has more to do with perspiration than inspiration, more to do with energy than image. However, 98.5 percent of those interviewed also believe that successful image—including dressing correctly, moving correctly, and speaking correctly—is critical to getting ahead. They believe that a person who dresses conservatively, speaks standard English, and carries himself in an erect manner has a better chance of impressing people, and succeeding, than someone who does not. Sixty-two percent of those questioned also believe that possession of certain social skills is essential to success, and just about everyone we questioned agreed that understanding basic business strategy would be useful to any young man or woman, particularly at the beginning of his or her career.

In addition to these interviews, I applied rather sophisticated research techniques originally developed to determine the relationship of clothing to verbal and nonverbal success patterns. As a result, I made several discoveries. The first is, you're judged by almost everyone more on how to speak than on what you say. We found that men and women with poor diction and a limited vocabulary will not be trusted with an important assignment. And, while most executives were willing to admit that they would be hesitant to rely on someone who said "Toidy-toid Street and Toid Avenue," they denied that they reacted similarly to the socioeconomic level of body signals. However, our testing indicates that their reaction is exactly the same. If you walk into most executive offices with your head down if you're a woman, or your shoulders rounded if you're a man, you would be treated exactly the same way as if you had said "Toidy-toid Street."

Our research further discovered that the possession of the right visual and verbal skills is absolutely critical for advancement in most corporations and that lack of them excludes most young people from a shot at the executive ranks. The people who are being excluded are not only Joe and Jane Average, but also Joe and Jane Superior with MBA's from leading universities.

As I pointed out, we found no simple formula for success, but our research indicates that if a formula were developed, it would have to include looking, sounding, and acting like a winner. Therefore, the remainder of this book is dedicated to helping you do just that.

1

SUCCESS AND FAILURE

Although I spent most of my adult life researching image and its impact on how the world treats you, I never believed that success depended solely or primarily upon image. So I was not surprised when two research projects conducted by my company concluded that hard work, intelligence, and ability have a great deal more to do with success than does image.

Three years ago, in response to a series of questions sent to my column, I set out to identify characteristics common to successful people. In the process I learned more about failure than I did about success. I came to the conclusion, however, following interviews with sixty-two successful men and thirty-six who were failures, that failure and success are only opposite sides of the same coin. As a result, I decided to research them simultaneously and to correlate my findings.

Before I could study success and failure, I had to define them. I interviewed 300 people who represented a cross section of the American public and used their combined definition as the basis for our study. For the majority, a success is a person who has achieved his goals in life and a failure is a person whose background and ability should have enabled him to achieve certain goals but who tried and failed. This very reasonable and

broad definition allowed us to exclude from the ranks of
failure those who did not seek money, position, or power.
Although I fully realize that it leaves a lot of people out,
I think it is a fair definition.

A typical example of a failure would be a man of
fifty-five with an MBA from Harvard, son of a college
graduate, and of the middle class, who has been in
middle management positions for the past ten years. By
his own admission, his aim had been to be the chief
operating officer of the company by the time he was
fifty.

On the other hand, a man whose father is a policeman
or a plumber, who graduated from college at night, and
who works as the first man's assistant, cannot be considered a failure. In the opinion of those we interviewed,
he achieved as much as could be reasonably expected
from a man with his background. Although he might
have wanted to be president and daydreamed about it, it
wasn't a realistic goal and therefore he cannot be faulted
for having failed to achieve it.

These definitions created a very difficult problem for
our researchers. It's easy to identify successful people.
They've achieved things. You can go to their offices and
talk to them. They love to speak about their success. It
is extremely difficult, however, to find people who are
admitted failures. But that's exactly what we had to do.
We had to find someone who not only hadn't achieved in
life, but who also would admit openly that he had
intended to achieve. As a result, the number of failures
we questioned was relatively small.

Throughout a period of three years, I did manage to
interview twenty-four men and three women who fit our
agreed-upon description of failure. I also interviewed a
matching group of men and women who were achiev-
ers. We didn't simply match the groups, we matched
them individually where possible, one on one, on the
basis of age, sex, educational background, and industry.

We started every interview with the general question,
"What do you think makes a person successful?" We

made the question broad so that we would not prejudice the answers. Every one of the unsuccessful people who answered said his or her life was influenced by forces beyond his or her control. Here lies the key to failure. When a person denies responsibility for the movement and direction of his life, he almost automatically fails. Failures have several clichéd explanations for not achieving. Their favorite is not knowing the right people. Of the twenty-seven failures interviewed, sixteen used a version of the phrase, "It's not what you know, it's who you know that counts." The majority talked as if having the right family connections was the key to success.

Successful men and women, however, invariably stressed hard work and intelligence as dominant factors in their achievement. Successful people did not dismiss the value of having connections. On the contrary, they usually indicated that connections were essential. But they downplayed family connections, which are an accident of birth, and spoke of making good contacts and being liked by the right people. Connections are less an accident and more a product of effort.

The second cop-out that failures fell back on was luck. Here again the difference between successes and failures was a matter of perception. Successful people believe in luck, but they invariably implied that you can effect your own luck. Winners often combine the word "luck" with "timing," giving luck an added and somewhat controllable dimension. Losers, on the other hand, talk in terms of a roulette wheel and throws of the dice.

Typical examples of failures were two men who entered the railroad industry about twenty-five years ago. Neither had prospered the way he thought he should. They claimed that they didn't advance because they joined the industry at a bad time. When I questioned two successful men who started in the same industry at the same time, they indicated that their timing and their choice of industries had been poor. They admitted that advancing in the railroad industry during the past twenty years was very difficult and they said they had to work much harder to succeed than they would have elsewhere. Both said they very much regretted joining that industry. They admitted they had made a dreadful mistake but the mistake was theirs, which brings us back once again to the essential difference between them: winners take responsibility for their actions, even their mistakes; losers do not.

Winners do something else. They work. Losers talk a good job with little or no prodding. They will tell you how hard they work and how much they do. They are more likely to tell you how tired they are and how much they have sacrificed for the company. The fact is, they don't work very hard. They tend to be clock watchers. Even if they work for themselves, they will quit at five o'clock or a few minutes ahead of time. They simply do not put in the same number of hours as successful people. And when they are working, they are usually not accomplishing much. It is partially because of their work-stopping rituals—rituals practiced as often as possible. If the coffee cart comes, they stop; if a friend shows up at their desk or calls, everything stops. Work for them is an unpleasant duty. Even the conscientious types who perform their duty take any opportunity they can to escape.

There are several reasons why people don't work. The obvious one is that they are lazy. But the reason I put at the top of my list after talking to a number of people who are failing in life is that they do not enjoy work. And it isn't just that they don't enjoy their particular job. It is a myth that if you work at something you like, you will be able to succeed. This is true only if you work hard and take realistic steps toward success. One of the biggest groups of failures in our society are people who love professions in which they are never going to get ahead—unemployed actors, painters, and singers, for example. It's not disliking a specific job that gets them in trouble. The fact is, they don't like to work at all.

Many of them won't admit it. They know not liking to work is socially unacceptable. And if you ask about their work, they'll tell you they love it. One of the tricky things about interviewing winners or losers is that clever losers are likely to give the expected winning answers. Winners can afford to be honest about not liking to do this or that, but losers have learned to offer the standard responses everyone expects of them.

One way of spotting losers is to ask them to describe the last time they got real personal joy from their work. Usually, after a long and embarrassing silence, they will recall an episode from the distant past. Winners, on the other hand, always talk about something they did last week. There is also a significant difference in the type of incident they describe. Failures almost always tell stories in which they are good guys because they helped someone else. They will tell you how Mary couldn't get her typing done and how they stayed all night to help her finish, or about Sam across the aisle who was about to lose a tremendous sale until they helped him get it. Winners, on the other hand, are not as selfless. They tend to be at the center of their own efforts to succeed. They tell about problems they solved or products they sold. They are their own heroes. They benefit most from their own labors. Losers say, "No matter how much I work, someone else gets rewarded."

Most of the people I interviewed had no idea they were failing while they were doing it. They usually discovered it too late, and discovering it too late is a convenient cop-out. Acknowledging their failure would have required action, something to correct the situation. As I was interviewing these people, my grandmother's favorite saying kept popping into my mind. "God helps those who help themselves, and God help those who don't."

In one large manufacturing firm almost everyone knew that to become a corporate officer you had to work your way up through half a dozen jobs. The length of time spent doing any one of these jobs was critical. If you were being tracked for a top position, you spent eighteen months as a line supervisor, no more, no less. Two years or more spent on the post was a sure sign you were being passed over for a top spot.

The men on the line know which executives are headed for the top and which ones are going to be around for a long time. And they treat them differently. Surprisingly, they are more generous to those who will be around for a while than to the people heading for the president's office. Yet when I interviewed one of the men who held a line job for seven years, he said that he had almost quit six months before when he discovered he was not headed for the top. That's typical of a loser. He is usually the last one to know that he is losing. Some never discover it.

Losers rarely take work home or work in places and at times not specifically designed for work. They rarely use spare time as work time. If the plane they are catching is going to be an hour late, working in the airport will never occur to them. We did a small survey of the percentage of people in first class and in coach who worked on cross-country flights. It was a very simple unscientific survey. I walked through and counted the number of people working in each section. On daytime cross-country flights, 32.6 percent of the people in first class will be working; in coach, the percentage is 12. On seven separate flights I saw more than three times the percentage of people working in first class as in coach. The relationship is obvious. Since failures do not work at home, they don't think, they don't create, and they don't solve problems at home. They hardly ever come in the next day and say, "I was sitting in the bathtub and bang, something occurred to me." That's not what they do. That's the prerogative of winners.

The most universal characteristic of failures is their lack of energy. Of the twenty-seven people we put in the failure category, twenty-four displayed markedly low energy levels. I'm not quite certain whether the low energy level is a result of failure or the cause of it. We interviewed several people in subsequent research and found that when they succeed, they become more energetic. Successful people jog, play bridge, play touch football, attend art classes, read books on success, and so on, even after a ten- to twelve-hour day. Failures, however, tend to engage in passive, nonphysical activity. They sit and watch football games on television. Unsuccessful people go home after an eight-hour day and doze in their chairs.

This book is not going to help failures, because it requires action. For those of you with guts and energy, read on.

2

SOCIOECONOMIC LEVEL

Theoretically, everyone has two socioeconomic levels, a real one and a perceived one. The main factors in evaluating your socioeconomic level are your wealth, your job, your education, and your family background. Because there is no agreed-upon formula, these factors will have various weights depending on who's doing the measuring. If you ask college professors which factor weighs most heavily, they will tell you education. If you ask businessmen or the general public, they will tell you money. If you ask men in high-status, low-paying positions such as army officers, they will tell you position. No one denies socioeconomic positioning. What is argued about is how to establish it.

In some environments, establishing socioeconomic position is easier than in others. If you are the richest, best educated, most powerful man in a small town, you will be treated with great deference. If, on the other hand, you are an unemployed high school dropout in the same town, you're likely to be treated rather shabbily. This is a simple fact of life that no one questions. In such an environment it makes absolutely no difference how well you dress, what kind of car you drive, or even how you speak or carry yourself. Everyone knows who you are, what you've accomplished, and what you have. Therefore, if you spend most of your time in a closed environment such as a small town or a small company, your real socioeconomic position will determine how people treat you.

However, if you choose to live in the broader world where most power lies and must deal with relative strangers on a regular basis as you have to in a large city or large corporation, your perceived socioeconomic level will affect the way you are treated as much, if not more, than your real one. In fact, if there is any such thing as a real socioeconomic level, only a few will be able to identify it. Not one person in ten in this larger world will know how much money you have, what your educational background is, or even what position you hold.

Obviously, there is an overlap between real and perceived socioeconomic position. It depends not only on the perception of the viewer, but also on the information you present and how that information is packaged. Everyone we interviewed agreed that a professor earning $35,000 a year has a higher social status than a plumber earning $35,000 a year, because his job tells us that he has a better education and more prestige. However, if the same plumber takes his business and expands it to $250,000 a year, most of the people we interviewed indicated that he then outranks the professor. If that same plumber goes to a party and is introduced as a plumber, while the professor is introduced as a professor, the professor will receive better treatment. But if the plumber, without increasing his income, is introduced as a plumbing contractor, which really doesn't change what he does, he may be thought to outrank the professor. Your socioeconomic position will be determined not simply by your background, your wealth, or your job, but by how you present these elements to the world.

Tolltakers in a Northeast city are a superb example of the impact of title upon position. About twenty-five years ago during labor negotiations, a union leader had their title changed from "tolltaker" to "bridge and tunnel officer." Once their title changed, he insisted at subsequent negotiations that his bridge and tunnel officers learn to use firearms; he then insisted that they be issued firearms. Finally, he pointed out very logically that they were now law officers who were carrying firearms and they should be paid as law officers. Since the police made 30 to 40 percent more, he wanted a substantial raise. Although he didn't get exactly what he wanted, he came pretty close. This union leader understood the relationship of title, image, and money.

Some people who did not understand it were librarians from Texas. When we did research on their image for the Texas Library Association, we discovered the public held them in very low esteem. More than 70 percent of those questioned believed that it was not necessary to have a college degree to work in a library and that everyone who worked in a library was a librarian. The fact is that the minimum educational requirement for a librarian is a master's degree and that most of the people you meet in libraries are simply clerks.

The problem is not one of public ignorance but of poor image. The way librarians dress and conduct themselves gives the public the impression they are glorified clerks. As a result, they are one of the most underpaid groups of people in the United States. In fact, they are paid substantially less, despite their master's degrees, than most of the tunnel and bridge officers, who are generally high school graduates. And every time there is a budget crunch, the first to feel the impact are the libraries. One of the reasons is that the people who run them announce through their poor image that libraries are not important places because they are run by unimportant people.

This is a classic example of how the perceived socioeconomic image of a group affects its real socioeconomic position. Before you join a profession or an industry, identify its perceived socioeconomic position. This perception will affect the way you will be treated and paid for the rest of your life.

I'm not contending that position is strictly a matter of

salary. I make more money as a consultant than I do as an author and more as an author than I do as a nationally syndicated columnist. Yet I find when I introduce myself to people that I get better treatment when I tell them I'm a nationally syndicated columnist than when I tell them I'm an author. And again, I am more likely to get preferential treatment if I tell them I'm an author rather than a consultant. There is no strict one-on-one correlation. However, there is generally a relationship between the perceived socioeconomic level of your job and how much you're paid to perform that job.

I first started testing socioeconomic level while researching clothing. I found that people at various socioeconomic levels wore distinctly different types of clothing and that almost everyone recognized that difference. For example, eight out of every ten American males who come from an upper-middle-class background wear beige raincoats while eight out of every ten males who come from and remain in a lower-middle-class background wear black ones. If you wear a beige raincoat people will think you're better educated, more intelligent, more articulate, more reliable, and a harder worker than if you wear a black one.

Executives, professionals, and others in high-status, high-pay positions act differently than do blue-collar workers and people in low-status, low-pay positions. When someone acts like an executive or professional, he is treated with a great deal more respect than someone who acts like a blue-collar worker. Those surveyed readily admit that most people send mixed socioeconomic messages and that very few people can be classified as solely of an upper-socioeconomic or lower-socioeconomic level. Yet enough people do fall into these categories so that characteristics of each group can be identified. If you avoid the mannerisms of lower-socioeconomic groups and emulate those of the upper-socioeconomic groups, you will receive better treatment in this world. They also agree that the mannerisms of the upper-socioeconomic group can be listed and copied.

According to our research, members of upper-socioeconomic groups generally have possessions that indicate wealth and taste. They live in more expensive homes, drive more expensive cars, wear more expensive jewelry and clothing than do blue-collar workers, which facts simply announce they have more money. They also are more likely to have books and classical records in their homes, which fact indicates a certain level of taste. In addition, they will have works of art and antiques indicating both wealth and taste. Yet almost everyone agrees that simply having an expensive house and a big car doesn't make you upper-socioeconomic. They also admit it's a very good first step.

Upper-middle-class people have distinct verbal and visual signals. They tend to speak differently than blue-collar counterparts. Their choice of vocabulary is different, their accent and pronunciation is different. And they talk about different subjects. When we taped conversations of both upper- and lower-socioeconomic groups and played them back to cross sections of the public, almost everyone was able to identify the socioeconomic level of the people taking part in the conversation.

Visual signals, unsurprisingly, are as different and varied as verbal signals. Upper-middle-class people walk, stand, sit, and hold their heads at different angles than lower-middle-class people. There is also a previously unrecognized difference in the way they use and hold their facial muscles.

We accidentally discovered what has come to be known as "Molloy's Class Mask" while attempting to research the effect of eye movement on sales. We had taken video tape closeups of men and women while they were talking, hoping to show a correlation between eye movement and credibility. There was none. However, while looking at these pictures the researchers all agreed that they could, in most cases, identify the socioeconomic level of the people in the picture, even though they knew nothing about them.

When we showed these pictures to a cross section of

the public, we found that 41 percent of the people photographed gave off a socioeconomic message that everyone could identify and that more than 60 percent of them gave off messages that trained researchers could identify. At the time, I doubted that these statistics would hold true for the general public because at that stage in the research I believed that sales persons' faces are more expressive than others. This proved to be inaccurate.

To test whether everyone has an upper- or lower-socioeconomic class mask, we photographed just the faces of 500 executives, professionals, and blue-collar workers without their knowledge and showed them to 1,400 people. We told the respondents that we were testing their extrasensory perception. We asked them to guess what the person in the picture did for a living, his educational background, the type of car he drove, etc. The questions were designed to have them guess at the socioeconomic level of the person in the picture.

The number of people who guessed accurately the socioeconomic level of people under thirty was not statistically meaningful. Once a man reaches thirty, however, life seems to etch itself upon his face. Of those commenting on the pictures, 58 percent were able to identify accurately the socioeconomic level of the men in the pictures. It isn't until age forty that women are almost as easily identifiable. Irrespective of their sex, 53 percent of the photographs of men and women between the ages of forty and fifty were correctly identified by 78 percent of the people looking at the pictures. Ironically, once people reach fifty the numbers slide off again, because age, along with youth, tends to be a great equalizer. By the time a person reaches age sixty-five, the socioeconomic message in his face is as hard to spot as it was when he was under thirty. The reason the socioeconomic class mask is so important to businessmen is that when we showed the same pictures to a group of 100 executives, they picked out an amazing 83 percent of their fellow executives and professionals and eliminated the others. I can best explain this extraordinary accuracy by giving the comments they made as they went through the pictures.

"Yes, he's one of us. Yes, he's one of us. No, he's not one of us."

"He doesn't belong to the club. Yes, he belongs to the club. . . ." And so on.

What they were really doing was identifying their friends and people who looked like their friends. Obviously, carrying your facial muscles in a proper way is very important to an aspiring executive, particularly a young man who's dealing with the men at the top.

In the same way that class is not permanent in America, neither are class masks. They are products of habit. If you change your habits, you will change your look. We took twenty-five men, all of whom had been identified as lower-socioeconomic by almost everyone who looked at their video tapes, and with the guidance of an actor had them practice looking aristocratic. The technique the actor used was to have them think of themselves as judges, lawyers, or doctors, or he had them think of themselves as members of an old aristocracy, the duke of this or the prince of that. If that didn't work, he simply told them to look haughty and distant. After three two-hour meetings, most of those involved in the little class seemed to have mastered the upper-middle-class look. At least they could put it on any time they wished. As a group they promised they would attempt to maintain the look for at least three weeks. We told them we would be spying on them.

A week later we photographed them away from the controlled situation and all of the men except two had reverted to their old looks. Facial habits, apparently, are very deeply ingrained. Even if you are conscious of having a negative facial message, and you've been taught by an actor a method of turning it on and off, you will probably do it incorrectly unless you practice.

We developed a six-month program for practicing an upper-socioeconomic look. Fifteen men and three women took part. They met for one hour a week. It was a fun group; they did as much laughing as practicing. While they were away from class they attempted to maintain that look whenever possible. Several of the men bought wristwatches with alarms. When the alarms went off, the men put on the upper-middle-class look. After six months, ten of the eighteen had definitely changed their look.

A number of the men indicated that their new look had changed the way people treated them. One claimed a dramatic change. He had wanted to join a country club for some time and he knew several men who belonged. After three weeks of meeting him with his new upper-socioeconomic face, they asked him to join and they apologized to him. They said they didn't know why they hadn't asked him before. It just hadn't occurred to them. He thought he did know why.

Almost everyone we talked to agreed that the final indicator of class in America was the possession of certain social skills. Ninety-nine out of every 100 executives said that particular social skills were prerequisites to success in business and social life. They indicated that one has to have suitable table manners, know how to carry on a polite conversation, be able to introduce people without falling all over oneself, and be aware of simple rules of courtesy. Most agree that handling oneself well at a cocktail party or the dinner table is at least as important as handling oneself skillfully in a boardroom. In addition, there are social skills that some think are absolutely essential, while others think they are simply desirable. These skills consist of the ability to participate in upper-middle-class activities. Most believe you should know how to play golf and tennis. Half of them think that you should know how to sail. A few consider playing bridge essential. One mentioned hurley and another skiing, because in their social set these are absolutely essential skills. The social skills mentioned are invariably those that enable the person to participate in the activities of the rich and powerful. They enable you to belong to the right country club or yacht

Picture 1

A. Tough
   guy set
   jaw.

B. Mouth
   open.

The two most common characteristics of a
lower-middle-class face mask.

club and to socialize with people who directly or indirectly will be making key decisions about your business career.

The importance of these social skills was re-emphasized in interviews with the 100 top executives we spoke of before. All indicated that there were men with whom they had worked but would refuse to associate with socially. Every one of them admitted that socially ostracizing a man would make it more difficult, if not impossible, for him to move up in their corporation. Eighty-two said that if you can't socialize, you are not likely to succeed.

It is not only the men in the top corporations who react to upper-class and lower-class message senders. In 1973 we conducted a study with the aid of eleven client-corporations. We arranged with them to observe 312 new employees throughout a period of several years. All these young men and women had college degrees. The purpose of the first observation was to divide them into upper-middle-class message senders, mixed-middle-class message senders, and lower-middle-class message senders. There were only two lower-middle-class message senders in the first group. We eliminated them from the test. Apparently, lower-middle-class message senders don't get hired often enough to count, even when they have degrees. After three months, we made a second observation. At that time, we ascertained that 286 of the original 312 were still working in the same position. There were 184 men and 88 women.

The third observation took place five years later. We found that those we originally identified as upper-middle-class were earning $5,000-plus more than those identified as lower-middle-class. In addition, three people originally identified as mixed-lower-middle-class had now developed upper-middle-class visual and verbal patterns. All three had moved up successfully in their corporations as well. We also found that men and women from upper-socioeconomic backgrounds generally have better job ratings than the men and women of the lower-socioeconomic backgrounds. We discovered this is particularly true in those jobs in which the job ratings are more subjective. In scientific fields such as engineering and programming, a lower-middle-class background is not as much a barrier as it is in TV production, writing, and editing, the end product of which is difficult to measure.

We also found that upper-middle-class socioeconomic patterns are more important for women than they are for men. Without them, it's almost impossible for a woman to move up in most corporations. There was not one woman who changed her socioeconomic message level, and there was not one woman with a lower-socioeconomic message being groomed for a top management job. However, there were several men with lower- or mixed-socioeconomic messages still in the running for a top position.

The advantage for anyone working in corporate America to be sending off the right verbal and visual messages is obvious. The reason, however, isn't snobbery; it's sociological nepotism, more a subconscious reaction than a conscious one. I do not deny that snobbery exists, or that people are class conscious. This is a factor in most, if not all, corporations. However, there is something even more important than snobbery and that is conditioning.

In every upper-socioeconomic home I've ever been in the children have been told to sit up straight, use the correct table setting, behave themselves, and speak proper English because that is the correct or superior way of doing things. It is implied that people who do not master these social skills are inferior and that if they, the children, do not master them they will be inferior also. These admonitions are given by the most liberal parents because of their basic belief that their socioeconomic habits and patterns are superior to those of blue-collar workers. As loving parents they go to great effort to pass on upper-socioeconomic habits to their children. It is no wonder that their children, when they meet someone twenty, thirty, or forty years later, will be convinced that unless that person has positive socioeconomic patterns they are lesser beings.

An experiment that demonstrated precisely this was the report experiment. I hired an actor and an actress, showed them films of upper- and lower-socioeconomic body signals, and asked them to imitate them. In less than half an hour they were accurately turning it off and on. After they had accomplished this task, they accompanied me to twenty business meetings.

Each time I had them with me, I gave a final research report. Most of these reports were given to executives from upper-middle-class backgrounds. My standard procedure is to hand out printed copies before the meetings, to go over the report a section at a time, and then to open the floor to questions.

The young man and the young woman performed only one task. They passed out the research reports and sat next to me while I spoke. The only conversation they had with the people in the room was as a result of the basic social amenities, introductions and so on. On their visits to the first ten corporations, they consciously imitated lower-middle-class body signals. Although they did not use obvious lower-socioeconomic verbal patterns, they did let an occasional lower-socioeconomic sound slip in. They did not sound like James Cagney in a 1930s movie, they simply sounded like college graduates who came from a blue-collar background. When we visited the second group of companies, they changed their act. They became upper-middle-class. Here their presentation was a reasonable imitation of upper-middle-class men and women recently out of college.

Following the question-and-answer period at each company, I told them a little fib. I said I was thinking of training the young man and young woman who had left the room to deliver these reports. I explained they were both excellent researchers, understood statistical data, and would be able to report it accurately. I asked if it was necessary for me to deliver the report personally and requested their advice. Did they think these young people could do an adequate job?

Eight of the first ten were very negative. Most of the executives said that entrusting them with the report would be very foolish. Somehow they got the impression that these young people couldn't handle it and that my report would lose validity by being delivered by someone else. Among the second group of companies, the response was dramatically different. Six of the ten groups of executives said they didn't see any reason why I should have to report personally, that my time is too valuable. It seemed to them these young people could certainly do it for me. The four remaining companies who saw my assistants do an upper-middle-class act said that although they would prefer that I deliver the report personally, they would have no strong objection to the young people. In short, not one of the ten companies where the actor and actress conducted themselves in an upper-middle-class manner had anything but positive things to say about them. But eight of the ten, when they acted lower-middle-class, had nothing but negative comments. Obviously, these men would judge your competence at work by the socioeconomic message you send them. Class carries clout.

And class apparently counts heavily even if you have the right educational background. I observed 100 members of the MBA program at Harvard, Columbia, and Chicago as they went back and forth to class. I identified the program they were in by the books they carried. I may have been mistaken in 1 or 2 percent of the cases. Approximately 30 percent of the students had definite upper-middle-class body signals. The remainder had lower- or mixed-middle-class body messages. This may not seem important until I point out that of the 100 top corporate officers we observed—presidents, vice-presidents of large corporations, and presidents of moderate-sized ones, many of them graduates of these three schools—I found 96 percent had upper-middle-class body signals. In one column I wrote that I did not suggest that everyone in Harvard graduate school march to class with shoulders erect. I now withdraw that remark. I think it would be excellent advice for two thirds of the class.

Separate experiments we conducted indicated that the socioeconomic messages you give off directly affect your ability to be authoritative, to be convincing, and even to be sexy. Surprisingly, men and women who have upper-socioeconomic verbal and nonverbal patterns are more attractive to members of the other sex. We discovered this while attempting to discover if upper-socioeconomic messages made a woman more attractive to successful men and vice versa. The answer was definitely yes. Upper-socioeconomic messages make you attractive to everyone.

We used the same actor and actress we had used in the earlier research. We took them to singles bars and discotheques. They were accompanied by young college students acting as research gatherers. The male students went up to the men and asked them to judge the women in the bar on a one-to-ten basis with ten being the highest score. They were asked to judge all the women, not simply our plants. The female researcher went up to the women and asked them to evaluate the men. On the nights when our actress conducted herself in an upper-middle-class manner she rated a nine. Even more surprisingly, when the male actor carried himself in a lower-middle-class way, his score was four; when he carried himself in an upper-middle-class manner, his score was eight.

As a result of the tremendous difference in response, we asked several additional questions. First we asked them to guess the height and weight of the young man (he was five feet ten inches tall and weighed 143 pounds). When he carried himself in a lower-middle-class way, most of the women guessed him to be five feet nine inches and weigh 136 pounds. When he adopted his upper-middle-class stance, they immediately guessed his height as five feet eleven inches plus and his weight as 160 pounds. Even more interestingly, they described him as being "sheepish and ineffective" when he walked with his shoulders curved forward in a lower-middle-class way and "aggressive and masculine" when he carried himself with his shoulders and head erect.

Most of the women we questioned in the upper East Side bars were upper-middle-class. Nevertheless, the response was universal. We spoke to young ladies with Brooklyn accents and poor posture, who were obviously from blue-collar backgrounds. They were equally impressed by the young man's upper-middle-class stance as were their sisters from Wellesley and Vassar.

If you find yourself put off by the entire idea, don't be. It's actually very good news. Our research indicates that socioeconomic level in this country is not a product of background or of possessions. It is to a large degree a product of habit and perception. And since you can control the perception of others by simply changing your visual and verbal patterns and adjusting some of your social skills, you can change dramatically the way the world will react to you. You can enhance your chances of succeeding in America economically, socially, and even sexually. If you read the rest of this book and pay careful attention, there's no reason you shouldn't.

3

BODY SIGNALS

I have entitled this chapter "Body Signals" and not "Body Language" because I do not think the common term is accurate. The problem with the term "body language" is that it implies something that is not true. Body signals that I have studied in no way fit the accepted description of language. Language is usually defined as a set of verbal signals, each having a limited number of meanings affected by content, accent, emphasis, and other variables. Yet they are definite. So definite, in fact, that we have dictionaries. The problem with thinking of nonverbal communication as a language is that the elements do not have agreed-upon definitions, making a nonverbal dictionary impossible.

This misnomer has led serious researchers and not-so-serious pop-science writers astray. They have used legitimate research techniques and free-and-easy interpretation of questionable data to fit body signals into a language pattern. Their attempt to codify body signals has led them into a series of inaccuracies. The most common mistake is the notion that you can read a person's mind by reading his body language. This, of course, is ridiculous. It touches on hucksterism. Yet it is a common belief held by most laymen today. Many pop-science writers go so far as to imply that by reading someone's body language you can control him, that you can have a Svengali-like influence. They compound this idiocy by inventing the nonverbal dictionary. The most familiar entry is the folded arms definition, which states that a person whose arms are folded is signaling a break in communication. This may or may not be true. We found that just as often it means that the person is paying rapt attention or indicating that it's a bit chilly.

That definition does have, at least, some basis in reality. The researchers observed a number of people whose arms were folded and asked them what they were thinking. Their answers indicated that they were often cutting off communication. I believe that some of the research is inaccurate, but the attempt was honest. However, the people who look at research done with monkeys and superimpose their body signals on men are being ridiculous. The assumption that the society of the monkey and the sophisticated society of twentieth-century man are interchangeable is total nonsense. An obvious example disproves the monkey theory: among some of the monkeys observed, the dominant monkey proves he's dominant by staring and the submissive one admits he's subordinate by breaking eye contact. Although this can happen among men, the reverse is often true. Men who are in charge often break eye contact with subordinates as a way of cutting off conversation, ending a discussion, and imposing their will on others.

With monkeys, leaning forward in a ready-to-strike position is always a sign of mastery. With men, the opposite may be true. For example, at the end of *Godfather II* when the new leader is accepting homage from the other men in the organization, he leans back in an almost feminine stance, one that indicates that he need not physically defend himself, that he is above that. This is often the stance of men in absolute-authority positions. Only they are able to totally expose their bodies to theoretical attacks, because only they are perfectly secure. In fact, a stance that prepares a man to defend himself from physical attack is a lower-class message.

I am not for one second implying that all research on body signals is invalid. Most of the research is sophisticated, intricate, and fascinating. Although you can debate the validity of one approach or another, there is no question that some of the results are meaningful. The real problem with the research is that most of it is so sophisticated, intricate, and complicated that the results cannot be used in everyday life. Most researchers study body signals by playing back film or video tapes in slow motion. Many signals are so subtle, they are missed at real life speed, which makes the data they produce not very useful. If you spend twenty years studying the films, you'll probably have more questions than answers.

I do admit there is a limited vocabulary of nonverbal four-letter "words" and directional signals. If someone sticks his finger up in the air I know exactly what he's saying. And if someone puts up his hand in a halt motion or signals to the right or left, I again get a very simple message. But these simple signals that we all recognize hardly qualify as language.

I am not saying for one moment that you should not attempt to read body signals. With practice, you can become surprisingly accurate if you obey your instincts. You must remember that at least 70 percent of our nonverbal message sending is done with our facial muscles. Most of us are already skilled message senders and receivers. When you smile, frown, smirk, scowl, or even wink or react to others when they do, you're involved in the most sophisticated element in nonverbal communication.

Our research indicates that what most people call instinct would be described more accurately as an educated guess based on past experience. Actually, most of us are experts at reading body signals; however, we all can improve. The method we suggest includes using the new information brought about by research in combination with the instinct you've developed throughout a lifetime. Our research indicates that when you receive conflicting messages you are three or four times more likely to guess correctly if you obey your instincts. All this really means is that if you meet a man or woman with arms folded and a big friendly grin, you'd be a fool to assume you were being cut off.

We tested 162 people—100 men and 62 women—and discovered two facts: women's intuition is a myth—men guess as accurately as women do—and almost everyone can learn to read the nonverbal signals of people he deals with on a daily basis. Of those participating in these tests, 90 percent believed that the people around them gave off accurate and consistent nonverbal signals indicating mood and in some cases predicting specific actions. They all agreed that the information they gained was useful in solving everyday problems. Two men and six women told us they asked for raises when they knew their boss was in a good mood, and all except one woman received them. One man said he was now able to predict when his boss, who had a hot temper, was about to explode. He avoids him at these times. The usefulness of such an exercise was best pointed out by a woman attorney who said that many important people in her life had become predictable to a degree and, as a result, manageable.

One of the most interesting studies on body signals we did was part of a sales research project. We arranged to have video tape cameras secreted in seven different offices and tape people without their being aware of it. We had already identified the top salespeople in each office as well as the poor ones. The object of the research was to see if the good and poor salespeople had different sets of body signals. If we discovered a meaningful difference, we were going to teach the poor salespeople good body signals in hopes of increasing their sales.

We arranged to have the person in charge of each office turn the camera on during a different five minutes every day. The man in charge of the New York office apparently hadn't read our instructions and he turned the camera on for the same five minutes, sometime between ten o'clock and a quarter after, every day for three weeks. On the fourth week he was on vacation and he gave instructions to his secretary to turn the camera on. She was the only other person in the office who knew of its existence. She chose to turn the camera on between three o'clock and three-thirty every day because that was when she took her afternoon coffee break.

There was a dramatic difference in body signals from ten o'clock in the morning to three o'clock in the afternoon. In the morning, most of the subjects were erect, smiling, happy, alive, alert, and quick. In the afternoon, they were tired. Both men's and women's shoulders slumped. They held their heads slightly lower. They tended to walk and move more slowly. And while we didn't have one picture of a woman with her arms folded at ten o'clock in the morning, we had nineteen separate examples in the afternoon. We guessed at the time that this indicated that the women were more likely to fold their arms when they became tired. We confirmed this later when we were doing a similar study on store clerks and found that as the day went on, women store clerks were more likely to fold their arms.

We were also able to get women to fold their arms by simply dropping the temperature in the office a couple of degrees. It's one of the ways women keep warm. The store research uncovered several other oddities. There were three women who seemed to fold their arms all day on one day, and not on another. We found the three had one thing in common: they all had bad backs. When it rained, their backs bothered them and standing with their arms folded gave them a form of relief. Finally, we ran across a woman who walked around all the time with her arms folded. When one of our researchers asked why, she grinned a little and said when she was a young girl she was very busty. All the boys kidded her. She was so embarrassed that she started folding her arms and hunching her shoulders hoping that they wouldn't notice her bust. Although she was thirty-five and had four kids, she had never broken the habit.

So the next time you see a woman with her arms folded, you may assume that she has set up a psycho-

Picture 2

A. Male with arms folded (high on chest).
Message: defiant.

B. Woman with arms folded (low under breasts).
Message: defensive.

logical barrier and you may be correct. But you may just as easily assume that she is tired, bored, cold, has a sore back, or is busty and bashful.

We discovered that although you cannot control other people, particularly strangers, by reading their body signals, you can control the way other people will react to you if you control your own.

When we showed men pictures of women with their arms folded, the men, possibly conditioned by the current material on the subject, said the women were cutting off communication and being distant. When we showed the same pictures to women, they said that the women in the pictures were unsure of themselves, that their egos were not very strong, and that they were being defensive. When we showed men pictures of men with their arms folded, they said that they were cutting off communication and being negative. When we showed the same pictures to women, they said the men were being haughty, aloof, and more than 50 percent of them thought the men were being aggressive. Now, although there was no consistency among the four groups, there was tremendous consistency within the groups. In each group, more than 80 percent of those polled had a similar reaction, which means the science of sending body signals is far more practical than the science of reading them. If there is a Svengali effect, it's achieved by controlling the messages you send thereby controlling the way people react to you. Your body signals will determine whether you are believed, liked, admired, or thought competent. Obviously, upper-middle-class signals are a tremendous asset in business and social life.

We have been researching socioeconomic image for years. Our first research project dealt strictly with clothing. We found that if you changed people's clothing, their apparent socioeconomic level changed, the world treated them differently. When these people gave off upper-middle-class nonverbal signals, the majority of people from all backgrounds thought them more competent, intelligent, beautiful, and so on. We found the

same phenomenon takes place when you change someone's socioeconomic body signals. Men and women from
upper-socioeconomic backgrounds stand, sit, and move
differently from people from lower-socioeconomic backgrounds.

Men from an upper-socioeconomic background hold
their shoulders in an almost military fashion. While
their necks may be arched forward, their heads are
more likely to be erect. Their lower-middle-class counterparts invariably have their shoulders hunched forward and their heads down, forcing them to have a
rolling motion when they walk. Since 80 percent of all
the women in America carry their shoulders straight
and do not roll them, the angles of their head and their
neck tend to be the critical message centers. Upper-
middle-class women have their necks back and their
heads more erect.

Upper-middle-class and lower-middle-class people not
only stand and sit differently, they move differently.
Upper-middle-class people tend to have controlled, precise movements. The way they use their arms and where
their feet fall is dramatically different from lower-middle-
class people, who tend to swing their arms out rather
than hold them in closer to their bodies.

Studying these pictures will not enable you to go out
tomorrow and change your socioeconomic message. It
takes practice. There's an old joke about a young woman
who applied for a job as a cigarette girl at a fancy
nightclub. The owner, being cleverer than most large
corporations, decided to audition her. He let her have
the job for one night to see how she would do. At the
beginning of the evening she walked around with her
nose in the air, perfect posture, saying "Cigarettes and
almonds." About three hours later, her shoulders had
slumped over a little, her head wasn't in the air, and she
was going from table to table saying "Cigarettes and
ammans." Finally, at the end of the night, she was
sitting down, disheveled, yelling, "Nuts and butts." The

Picture 3

A. Upper-middle-class male.

B. Lower-middle-class male.

Key Difference: angle of head and shoulders.

C. Lower-middle-
class female.

D. Upper-middle-
class female.

Critical Difference: position of chin.

Picture 4

Front view of upper- and lower-middle-class men walking.
Upper-middle-class man (left)—shoulders straight,
arms in toward body, walk almost military. Lower-
middle-class man (right)—shoulders and body roll,
arms are throwing out, hips swing.

Side view of upper-middle-class stride (left): A. Head erect.
B. Shoulders straight. C. Hands cupped at side.
D. Approximately 12-inch stride. Side view of lower-middle-
class stride (right): E. Head and eyes down. F. Arms
swing. G. Long or erratic strides.

message, of course, is accurate in that in time our true character will show through.

Our studies indicate that you can chart an executive's background very accurately at the end of the day. I first noticed this when traveling with executives from various corporations. When I met them in the morning, everyone was erect and bright and executive-looking. But at the end of the day you could tell those from an upper-socioeconomic background by the way they carried themselves. They even lounged differently in the airport while waiting for planes.

All they were doing when tired was acting the way they normally acted. People under pressure often revert to past habits. Firemen in New York tell me that when they rush into a burning building, they are often greeted by a cacophony of foreign languages, that in life-or-death situations people often revert to their original verbal forms. We found that executives under pressure often do the same. We have at least two dozen examples on our tapes of men with apparent upper-middle-class visual and verbal habits who, when put under pressure at a corporate meeting, reverted to the language mannerisms of their youth. They instantly became blue-collar and, as a result, lost impact. Therefore, we must leave you with one final word of warning. If you come from a lower-socioeconomic background, even after you've mastered the upper-socioeconomic verbal and visual skills, you are going to have to control your temper and your emotions. If you explode, our research indicates you will do so in a lower-middle-class manner and, in doing so, kill your effectiveness.

Picture 5.

A. Erect.

B. Controlled.

Upper-middle-class men resting at the end of the day.

C. Bent over.
Disheveled.

D. Spread out.
Uncontrolled.

Lower-middle-class men resting at the end of the day.

4

VERBAL PATTERNS

Most Americans believe that a person's verbal patterns are the best indicators of class. Actually, they are a very inaccurate way of measuring a person's past or present socioeconomic level. Geography is as likely as class to play a dominant role in developing verbal patterns. The effect is not a simple one. Upper-middle-class verbal patterns in one area of the country will test as lower-middle-class in another, and vice versa. If you have been raised in New York City or the South, your verbal image in most cases will test very poorly when you leave home. A first-generation upper-middle-class New York City accent often tests as lower-middle-class in Chicago, Los Angeles, or Detroit. In the same way, an upper-middle-class rural southern accent tests as lower-class in just about every other section of the country. On the other hand, if you were born in Boston or a few other New England towns, you have a verbal advantage when you move. A lower-class Boston accent moved to the Midwest will usually test as upper-middle-class. Ironically, the best place for an American to be born is London. We tested a London cabdriver with an eighth-grade education and everyone assumed he was a professional man and a very competent one.

The technique we used to test the socioeconomic level of language patterns is simple. We gave identical statements to hundreds of men and women throughout the country. We selected people that represented various socioeconomic levels in New York, Boston, Chicago, Atlanta, Dallas, Los Angeles, and forty-six other locations. We taped them reading statements which we then played back to the people in their communities and other parts of the country. We asked those who listened to these tapes to identify the economic and educational level of the speaker and to guess what job he was most likely to have. We found there was a significant statistical difference in the way they identified speakers from different regions. Verbal patterns were almost as important as the real socioeconomic position of the speaker.

Most strong and easily identifiable regional speech patterns tested as lower-middle-class, but there were exceptions. Being a down-home Southerner in the South is not negative. You may have a rather strong southern accent if you live in rural sections of North and South Carolina, Georgia, and Alabama and test as upper-middle-class by the professionals and the executives in that area. However, if you leave the deep South, your deep southern accent will get you into deep trouble. A similar situation exists in Texas, where there is an upper-middle-class rural speech pattern. It is as down home as the lower-middle-class speech pattern, but the choice of vocabulary and tendency to use complete sentence structure evidently make it different. Upper-middle-class rural Texans have a speech pattern that is unique to their area of the country and is, if anything, a positive influence when used by them at local business meetings. However, when the Texan leaves home he has to leave his cowboy boots and his cowboy accent on the ranch or he will be considered a rube.

The lower-socioeconomic speakers tend to display several universal characteristics. They often shorten words and chop phrases. It's called skid talking in western Pennsylvania. Blue-collar workers in every section of the country are more likely to say "goin" than "going," "comin" than "coming." They are also more likely to say "comere" than "come here," displaying a general tendency to shorten phrases by hooking words together or dropping them. In addition, the letters *d* and *t* are often interchanged as in "de" instead of "the." Generally, lower-middle-class speakers also speak less. They are simply less verbal. They answer questions with single words or even shrugs while upper-middle-class speakers, if they do not use long sentences, will more often use complete sentences or at least complete phrases when answering questions. Lower-middle-class speakers will use an entire series of words that are identified as being strictly lower-middle-class. They will say "yeah" instead of "yes," "ain't" instead of "isn't," "nah" instead of "no." Although some of these words can be found in the dictionary, they do not pass in upper-middle-class society.

While I'm sure there is nothing in this chapter to surprise any speech teacher, the difference between our findings and theirs is that they measure speech patterns against some set standard. We let the general public measure the speech patterns and found that although there wasn't any norm, there were agreed-upon local and nationwide standards. We also discovered that the people who use upper-middle-class patterns reacted more positively to others who use the same patterns. They were more likely to think of them as authority figures or experts, which indicated that reaction to upper- and lower-middle-class speech patterns is not simply a matter of snobbery, but of conditioning.

One of the more interesting findings was that people who had easily identifiable lower-middle-class speech patterns often had upper-middle-class listening patterns. These were people with a great deal of formal education but limited business or social contact. Many dentists and doctors fell into this group. They were used to hearing people speak a standard form of English on television and radio and sometimes their friends had accustomed them to hearing a better grade of English. As a result, when we played back their conversational patterns to them, many of them were upset, surprised, and dismayed. A good many determined to improve their speech patterns immediately.

I recommend that everyone reading this book purchase or borrow a tape recorder and record your normal conversations. Put it at your dinner table, in the living room, when you're discussing finances, schoolwork, or local basketball games with your wife, your husband, your children, or your friends. Play it back in the privacy of your room. You may be astounded at what you hear and decide immediate improvement is necessary.

Before you undertake to evaluate your speech you are going to need guidelines. Dr. William Formaad,[1] who heads the Verbal Communications Department of Dress for Success, Inc., has prepared a simple test to aid you in this task. It is not meant to give you a comprehensive in-depth assessment of your speech profile, which would have to be done by a qualified speech specialist. If after taking this test you decide to engage a speech teacher, we strongly suggest that you check his or her academic credentials and insist on speaking to two or three recent clients. Unfortunately, this field is filled with unqualified people. A successful career in the theater does not qualify one for this technical field. Speech improvement is not only an art, but a science. The fact that I am one of the best paid and most-sought-after speakers in the country does not qualify me to give voice and elocution lessons, and for that reason I am very grateful for Dr. Formaad's assistance.

TEST

The following sentences are geared to test common articulatory deviations and mispronunciations. Read them into a tape recorder, pausing after each sentence.

1. Dr. William Formaad, Professor and Director of Communication Sciences and Disorders at Seton Hall University, Fellow of the American Speech and Hearing Association, Past President of New Jersey Speech and Hearing Association, Elected Member of NY Academy of Sciences and Elected Member International Association of Logopedics and Phoniatrics, author of *Articulation Therapy Through Play: A Multisensory Approach.*

1. I can't understand why the plans for the animal path were abandoned at the afternoon conference.

2. Jim said that he began to get tired and quite fretful at five to ten.

3. a) She says that he is as happy as he deserves to be.
   b) Bob and Doug will see you at the World Trade Center on February the third.

4. "Snow-White and the Seven Dwarfs" is playing at the Radio City Music Hall.

5. Jonathan Thorpe will leave North Dakota on Thursday, the thirteenth of this month. It's his birthday.

6. Robert Lee was looking for Rory's glass on the back left seat when the red light changed to green. Then Mrs. Lee made a right turn.

7. His incredulous look made us realize that he didn't enjoy the idea of it at all. The law was being flouted; he saw it with his own eyes.

8. Singing a song or two on our way to Long Island can be amusing.

9. a) Early in the morning, Earl will boil the oil.
   b) It's been a long time since I used a pen.

In sentence 1, listen for the A sound as can't, understand, plans, animal, path, abandoned and afternoon. Do you almost hear the vowel sound in air, hair, or bear? Nasality, flatness or vowel substitution when the underlined sounds are uttered? If you live in the East your mistake will probably be nasal; in the Midwest it's likely to be flat.

In sentence 2, does tired sound like tire, five like fie, quite like kwai? Do you hear the l in frightful, the m in

Jim, the *d* in sai*d*? Be sure not to slight your final sounds.

In sentence 3, do you give proper tone value (vocal fold vibration) to the underlined sounds?

In sentence 3a, does *says* sound like *cess, is* something like *iss* and *as* something like *ass*. . . . If they do you are "devoicing."

In sentence 3b, does *Bob* sound like a longer *Bop*? Does *Doug* sound like a longer *Duck*? Does *trade* sound like *trait*? Does the final *d* in *world* sound like a *t*? If so, you are once again guilty of devoicing.

In sentence 4, do you lisp a little? Does *Snow* sound something like *Thnow*, *Seven* something like *Theven*, *is* like *ith*, *city* like *thitty*, *music* like *muthic*? If so, you may be suffering from interdental lingual protrusion. Don't worry, it only means the tongue protrudes slightly or goes between the teeth where the s and z sounds are produced.

If *Snow* sounds like *Shnow*, *seven* like *sheven*, you are making your *s* sound like *sh*. The technical term is lateral emission lisp. Don't test this after a few drinks as you will fail.

You can test yourself with these additional sentences for the sh and zh pair and the ch and j pair:

> sh—zh   It was *Sh*irley's father who was fi*sh*ing on the televi*si*on commer*ci*al.

> ch—j   Did *J*udge *Ch*arles en*j*oy visiting his son's bea*ch* house?

In sentence 5, do you produce these sounds accurately? Does *Jonathan Thorpe* come out sounding something like Jonatan Torp? Do *this* and *that* sound a bit like *dis* and *dat*? Or do you favor another substitution in which case "bir*th*day" would sound like "birfday"?

In sentence 6, are you guilty of lallation? Do your *r*'s sound like *l*'s or *w*'s? Does *left* sound like *weft*? Does *glass* sound like *grass*? Does *red* sound like *wed* or *led*, or do *red, wed* and *led* all sound alike? Does *turn* sound a bit like *torn*? Speakers of English who learned English after speaking an Oriental language may have some difficulty in distinguishing between *l* and *r* because speakers for whom Japanese, Chinese, or Korean is a first language may not think of *l* and *r* as separate, different sounds.

In sentence 7, do you put in the r sound where it is not needed? Do you say the *idear* of it, the *lau* or *lawr* and/or *sawr*?

Does sentence 8 indicate that you suffer from the *ng* click? You do it when you say song and pronounce the *g*. If so, this is a very difficult flaw to spot yourself. Read this sentence to a few friends.

In sentence 9, does *early* sound like *oily*? *Earl* like *oil*? *Oil* like *earl*? *Boil* like *Berle*? *Berle* like *boil*?

Does *been* sound like *ben*? Does *Ben* sound like *been* or *bin*? Do *been* (*bin*) and *Ben* sound the same? Does *since* sound like *sense*? Does *sense* sound like *since*? Do *since* and *sense* sound the same? How about *pin* and *pen*? Do they sound the same, or can you pronounce them so that *pin* sounds like *in* and *pen* sounds like *men*. If your *in* sounds like *en* and your *men* sounds like *min*, you're in double twubble.

If you now believe that your voice and diction are not what they should be, you're faced with the difficult task of retraining yourself because both are products of longstanding habit. Correcting them will require an enormous effort. However, one of the factors affecting the socioeconomic level of your speech is your choice of vocabulary. Most of us use no more than 500 to 1,000 words when we speak. The choice of words you use is very important. It will affect your image in a significant manner. If you have a lower-class speaking pattern, you will use shorter Anglo-Saxon words almost exclusively. Although upper-middle-class speakers use these words, they also salt their sentences with polysyllabic words that are reserved for the active vocabulary of the upper-middle class. For example, while a blue-collar worker might say that a display was "flashy," the upper-middle-class speaker is likely to say "ostentatious." "Snotty" becomes "impudent" and "tough," "belligerent" and so on. If you have a limited active vocabulary, simply adding 100 to 150 words will automatically increase the perception of your educational level by three to four years and will make it far easier for you to deal with lawyers, bankers, and others of the upper-middle class.

Upper-middle-class speech patterns do not work best under all circumstances. We conducted tests on socioeconomic speech crossover. One of the most illuminating involved attorneys. We found that the active vocabulary of attorneys varied dramatically. Some used upper-middle-class words almost exclusively. These attorneys usually worked for prestige law firms and were most likely to be in corporate law. Usually, their performance before juries was absolutely horrible. We found a second group of attorneys from blue-collar backgrounds who never lost their blue-collar vocabulary. Except for technical legal terms, they stayed with the vocabulary of their youth. They were extremely effective with juries, particularly in big cities, but were ineffective when dealing with judges. The third group were verbal chameleons. They spoke one way when speaking to a judge and another way when speaking to a jury, even when they were conducting the same case in the same court at the same time. They adjusted their vocabulary and sentence structure to suit the people they were talking to. These were by far the most successful courtroom lawyers. We found the same was true of salesmen who dealt with a variety of people. Great salesmen change their speech pattern to suit the product they are selling and the people with whom they are dealing.

For some strange reason people with upper-middle-class speech patterns can, after only a few days' practice, cross over to lower-middle-class patterns on cue. The only difficulty for upper-socioeconomic speakers is in mimicking lower-class speech rhythms. Moving a speaker in the other direction takes months.

There is a tricky difference in rhythm between upper-socioeconomic and lower-socioeconomic speech. Upper-socioeconomic speech tends to be softer, easier, and broken into neater patterns. Lower-socioeconomic speech patterns tend to be jumpy and hesitating. In the same way that upper-socioeconomic people are used to answering in complete sentences, they are also conditioned to having people speak to them in the same fashion. If someone gives them a very short answer, they are not ready to respond and find the silence uncomfortable. The opposite reaction takes place when upper-middle-class people speak to lower-middle-class people. Lower-middle-class listeners are always irritated at their inability to say something because upper-middle-class speakers seem to be going on forever. Each group is annoyed by the vocal patterns of the other.

If you have to deal across socioeconomic lines, you must start listening very carefully to how members of the other group speak. If you are from a lower-middle-class background, you must be patient. Wait until people are finished and don't be annoyed by it. Realize it's a normal speech pattern. If you are from an upper-middle-class background, you have to pay careful attention, particularly to eye movement, which indicates that lower-middle-class people have finished their statement and expect an immediate response. However, although this is a critical part of the speech patterning, I do suggest that you not try it on your own or with a traditional speech teacher. You would probably be better off with an acting coach. And it will take a lifetime. As I said in the introduction, there is no easy way.

5

BEING LIKED

Bill stuck his head into my office and said, "Is this the place they're hiring researchers?" His hair was disheveled and he had an annoying silly grin on his face and I was tempted to say, no. But I said yes because at the time I was desperately looking for a project chief.

I had just received a research contract from a good client, had already hired fifteen professors who were themselves in the process of hiring students, and I needed someone to oversee the project. When I got to talking to this sloppy fellow, I found he was ideally qualified: master's degree in statistics, research background, experience in a clothing store. He was like a dream come true. The only problem with the dream was that I really didn't want to hire him. I put off hiring him until the next day, even though by any logical standard I should have taken him on then and there.

The job started two days later and I was called out of town unexpectedly and didn't get a chance to oversee it the way I wanted to. When I returned, to my delight and surprise the project had been completed. Bill had done a magnificent job. He had adjusted the data-gathering methods to suit the situation without my holding his hand. He had fired one professor who was not doing his job and hired another one who did. There was no question about it, the man was a first-class project chief. As a result, he became a semipermanent part of my organization.

When I discovered three months later that he had taken a job teaching in a local university, I was delighted. It enabled me to hire him on a regular basis and from that point on I did. But I must admit, I never liked him. I only hired him to work at a distance. I attempted to stay away from projects that he ran. I did not become involved with him personally for almost two years.

A client offered me a nice fat research contract, a cost-plus deal with a built-in bonus for results. They wanted me to put together a research team and to identify something that had never been researched before. The problem was that we had no method of going about it and, frankly, didn't know whether it could be done.

When my company runs across a new problem, we have a standard procedure for attacking it. We bring together our most experienced people, throw the problem on the table, and hope that they can, among them, come up with a solution. This project required two meetings. Bill was present at both. Unfortunately, the meetings were unproductive. I walked away thinking that my beautiful six-figure research contract was going to slide through my fingers because I couldn't figure out a way to do it, and yet I knew it could be done.

One of my best people was out of town and had to miss the meetings. He requested that I tape them, and when he returned I played them for him. Ten minutes into the first tape Bill made a suggestion that seemed to both of us to solve the problem. When I first heard his suggestion I guessed that I wasn't listening, but I wondered why everyone else had missed it. We let the tape run, mostly because we were sitting there eating sandwiches, when to my surprise, I heard Bill repeat his suggestion twice more. When we played the second tape, we found that he repeated the suggestion again. I was astonished and embarrassed that I had sat in on two meetings looking for a solution to a problem and ignored it when it was given to me. I instinctively recognized the reason. No one listened to Bill because no one really liked him. And I looked upon it as a personal flaw and made up my mind to listen to him in the future.

Our organization expanded during the next few years and we became more sophisticated and a little bit more affluent. We still held the same meetings but when someone couldn't make one, we video taped the important discussions. It was only after watching a couple of these video tapes that I realized why no one listened to Bill. No one looked at him when he talked, he annoyed people. If you listened to him, what he said didn't bother you. But if you watched him while he talked, it was very disturbing. His facial expressions often didn't match what he was saying. At times he would be animated when he should be bland, and at other times he would be bland when he should be animated. It seemed obvious he didn't know what he was doing. With a grin on his face, he made a comment about having to let half a dozen people go. The look was almost satanic in context, and yet I know he worked very hard to get another commission so that those people could continue to work. Obviously, he was sending out inaccurate messages. When he meant to say one thing, he actually said another to everyone and as a result turned them off.

He also had jerky, unsure movements. He pushed papers out on the table before they were expected or after they were needed. When he passed papers he shoved them at people rather than handing them to them. He seemed almost rude. In addition, when others were speaking he moved in his chair, looked away, rolled his eyes, fidgeted, and generally gave off the message that he was bored or inattentive when in actual fact, I could tell from his work that he was neither. His movements surprised the three of us who looked at them and tried to analyze them. They were completely unpredictable. We never discussed our findings with him because we didn't think there was any point. However, I realized that his inability to communicate accurately made him less useful to the organization and I avoided using him on jobs requiring public contact.

A couple of years later, I had a major project going in the Northeast. The contract had a built-in penalty clause tied to a time element. If we didn't finish in time, we not only wouldn't make money, we also could lose quite a bit. As things usually happen in those cases, a major snowstorm occurred just as we were completing the project. I gave up on the idea of finishing on time and went home. Bill, however, was as good a project manager as he'd ever been. He borrowed a four-wheel-drive vehicle, drove all day and all night picking up data forms from three states, brought them back, slept a couple of hours, and stayed up for twenty-four hours to finish the project. When I found out what he'd done, I was very grateful. He'd saved me a lot of money and I said to him, "If there is anything I can do for you, Bill, I will." And then it occurred to me that there was something I could do.

I told him that I was trying to do him a favor but he probably wouldn't like me when I finished. I was going to show him some tapes of himself because he had a problem. I played the audio tapes of that first meeting and then the follow-up video tapes and explained to him in detail what he was doing. To my delight and surprise he reacted fairly positively to the information. He asked me if he could use the company facilities to research himself. Of course, I said yes.

As a researcher, he started very logically. He researched his voice because we had developed proven methods for doing that. For years we had been helping politicians develop high-authority voices to match their high-authority message. His testing indicated that he had the same problem as most politicians. He tested as far more credible when he dropped his voice by a full octave. He brought it down almost overnight. He then set up a standard five-member research team and called a meeting during which he ran the video tapes. All the members, once they knew what they were looking for, immediately noticed the mismatched message system. Although he was one of the most professional researchers I have ever met and was fully aware that he needed an independent research team's reaction to test accurately, I think he regretted that we were there when he played the tapes, because as he played them he kept mumbling to himself, "My God, am I really doing that?" But he quickly settled down, started making notes, and wrote one of the finest research reports I have ever read.

I closed up the office that night and went home. At about eight o'clock I received a call from him. He seemed upset and I thought he finally had been embarrassed by the whole thing. But it wasn't that at all. When he had sat down with his wife and four sons to have dinner that night, he realized that two of his sons were sending off the same type of mismatched messages that he was. After talking to them for a few minutes, he discovered that they, as he had been, were very unpopular in school. They didn't have many friends, they found it difficult to make new friends and found it difficult to express themselves in a group. Life for them was as unpleasant as it had been for him. (He told me later he never felt so guilty about anything in his entire life. He knew how unpleasant it could be for a person who was disliked by almost everyone.)

He asked me if I would come over that night with copies of his video tapes and a recorder. He wanted to show them to his boys and explain to them that being unpopular was not part of their character, it was something he had taught them. He wanted me there to back him up and help him explain the difference to his sons.

Naturally, I went over right away. Although it was difficult to show the difference between message-sending systems to amateurs, particularly young boys who were used to their father's message system, we finally succeeded. They began to see that their father's and their message-sending systems were not what everyone expected. Once we had identified the problem we were halfway to a solution.

After I discussed it with Bill and the boys we decided to work together to correct their message systems. Our first job would be to identify the mistakes they were making. This turned out to be more difficult than we had thought, since the minute we turned on a video camera that night everyone started acting and sending artificial messages. We agreed we would have to video tape them over a long period of time so that they could become used to the camera and ignore it. They promised to eat dinner every night at the dining room table: the three family members with the broken message systems sitting at one end of the table and the camera at the other. The camera would run during every meal. We assumed that during the first couple of meals they would be uptight and acting and their message systems would be off, but we also believed, and we proved to be right, that they would eventually get used to the camera and forget about it and resume their normal message patterns.

I thought at the time that changing these message systems would be a very complicated procedure that would take many months, if not years. Happily, I was mistaken.

The cure didn't take nearly as long as we had thought. The minute the boys were aware of the fact that they were sending off mixed messages, they stopped doing it. Half of it stopped immediately. They began to correct themselves. One boy started carrying on animated conversations before a mirror. We found that he learned more quickly than the others. We asked both Bill and his other son to do this. It turned out to be an excellent technique.

If you have mixed-message-sending systems, get yourself a full-length mirror and talk to it and pretend that the mirror is carrying on the other end of the conversation. You will correct part of your negative message system within a week or two. It's a very simple procedure and it works almost every time. It worked not only with Bill and the boys, but also with many others.

The results were just spectacular. Bill reported that he was being treated the way he always dreamed of being treated. He stopped working for us several months later because he received two promotions at the university. He said that for the first time in his life people listened to him and promoted him.

He was even happier about his sons. One of the boys said that for the first time he got along with girls. He was fifteen or sixteen and for him this was very important. The other one, who was only twelve, said that for the first time in his life he was happy. When we first talked to him, he said that he thought that nobody in the world liked him, he wasn't going to like anybody, that everybody was his enemy and that they all could go to hell. To think that way when you're twelve must be terrible. He no longer thinks that way because his world changed.

Bill's story is very important because Bill does not represent a small minority. Approximately 10 to 15 percent of the population send off negative mixed verbal-visual messages. In addition to sending them, they teach them to their children.

We went to three rural school districts where parents and grandparents had attended the same schools as their children. We borrowed a series of class pictures taken eighteen to twenty-five years apart. These were pictures of the fathers and grandfathers of the children presently in school. We went out in the community and asked former classmates to identify those who were popular and those who were unpopular. We discovered that the men who were popular had popular sons and the men who were unpopular had unpopular sons. The correlation was not as high with women, but there definitely was one. Many of these youngsters were sending off the same mixed verbal-visual messages as their parents. If you have an unpopular message system, you are probably teaching this to your children.

As I pointed out earlier, it is a very simple flaw to correct and you can make the correction at almost any point in your life. We've had men and women in their late sixties who were sending out incorrect message systems and changed them with a little practice. It's not difficult at all. The minute you realize you're doing it, you're three quarters of the way toward cure.

You don't have to hire anyone, you don't have to go to a clinic. All you usually have to do is buy a big mirror and practice. It will take about six months for most who use this method to change their message system.

I personally consider this research project the most important I ever completed—not only because it helps people succeed, but for the first time I think I have helped people cope. There is nothing more delightful than working with men or women who have been unpopular and unhappy all their lives if after a few hours you can really help them. It is particularly delightful when they go from being unpopular to very popular, and many of them do. Because of their handicap, they had learned to compensate. They were often clever, witty, and friendly. When they started sending accurate messages, people began to like them.

Sending incorrect messages can be a fatal career flaw. You can neither convince nor command if you are sending off mixed messages. Of the 260 successful male and female executives we tested, not one was a mixed message sender. Obviously, poor message senders do not become successful executives.

And it is just as obvious that people who send off mismatched messages would make very poor salesmen. You would think they would avoid the field of sales, but you're wrong. There's a higher percentage of people with negative message systems in sales than there is among the general population. To make it even more difficult, salesmen tend to be blind to this particular fault. The reason for this blind spot is that being liked is so critical to their success, they hate to admit to failure in that area. I also believe that many people go into sales to prove that they're likable when they're not. It's ironic, therefore, that sales attracts people who can never sell. We have identified men who have been in sales for twenty to twenty-five years and were never anything but third-rate order takers because of this mixed visual-verbal message system. We turned 50 percent of them into salesmen in a matter of a couple of weeks by giving them a very small set of instructions and a large mirror.

One salesman came to us denying that he gave off visual-verbal mixed messages, even though our test showed clearly that he did. When we showed him his video tapes and taught him how to correct his message-sending system, his sales improved so dramatically that he turned his life around. After six weeks, he went from the bottom of his sales force to the sales honor list in his company. At the end of six months, he was one of the three leading salesmen in the company.

Therefore, I am going to suggest to everyone, particularly salesmen, conduct a simple test on themselves. First ask yourself, am I one of these unpopular people? You probably know whether you are or not. If you are not sure, mixed-message senders are very easy to identify. In every office and classroom there are one or two people who are not part of the group. They have been ostracized not because they are stinkers—some of the biggest stinkers we know are charming and we like being around them even though we may not trust them— but because they rubbed us and rubbed other people the wrong way. If you have been left out, you are probably a negative message sender.

We suggest you get your hands on a video recorder and record. The success rate with the video tape is 80 percent. You must become so used to the camera that you ignore it. You can use the same tape cassette over and over again. The quality may not be high, but that is not essential. It is better if you take pictures with both your family and friends because we found that many people send off different nonverbal messages when they are at home than when they are in public. However, if you can only test with your family, do; the information will be useful. Without training you will be able to spot whether you are a mixed-message sender.

Most of those testing themselves will discover that

they send off some mixed messages. Almost all of us have a few negative nonverbals. I know I became aware of the fact that I slouched all the time. I also found myself pointing with a pen when talking, a very annoying habit that turned people off. Some actually jumped back from me when I did it. I tried to correct both habits. Although I was not sending a total set of negative messages, I did have a few and I was able to correct them. I believe that all persons should test themselves.

If there are negative message senders in your company or your family you can help them only if you can spot them. They have certain telltale characteristics.

Mixed-message senders usually have a hesitant, tentative, nervous speech pattern. These developed because people often ignore them or cut them off. They don't complete sentences. They jump in and out of conversations erratically. They'll come into a conversation, interrupt people without meaning to, and then they'll stop when someone looks at them. They frankly act like the people they are—people who have received the nonverbal message all their lives, "Why don't you shut up, nobody wants to listen to you."

They tend to overstate and they repeat themselves. They are not used to others giving credence to what they say and they think repetition emphasizes. Instead of saying, "It is a nice picture," they will say, "It is one of the most beautiful pictures I've ever seen. It's a masterpiece. I really love it. It's in a wonderful frame." Most of this is unnecessary. They often finish their statments with a little smile or grin. They do it all the time. They don't mean anything by it. They grin when they say, "Good morning, how are you? It's a nice day. Pass me the salt." But they also grin when they tell you that they don't like the report you handed in. And that same little grin at that moment drives you crazy and makes them an enemy. In context, the wrong grin is aggravating, annoying, and destructive.

The other look they have that drives people right up a wall is the "I have a secret" look. They finish every statement by moving their lips slightly giving the impression that they're in on a joke that no one else knows. It drives the world crazy and gets them into trouble. Finally, we have the constant smiler. Women are more likely to do this than men. There are people who smile no matter what is going on. There is a news broadcaster in Binghamton, New York, who would smile if she announced World War III. She will never make it as a news broadcaster unless she breaks that habit because nobody is going to trust or believe her. Most of the time she just looks silly, but sooner or later that woman is going to be forced to announce that a bus with children went over a bridge and she is going to smile while doing it. That is going to be the end of her career.

Ironically, when these people match their verbal and nonverbal statements, they sometimes match the wrong ones. They will often have overblown unnecessary statements matched with overblown theatrical body motions. To some, they will appear to be putting on airs. Actually, all they are doing is trying very hard to impress you. Of course, for them that's impossible.

If you know one of these people, you can help him. Depending on your relationship, you can either give him a copy of this book or talk to him about it. But I must warn you that many mixed-message senders cannot recognize the mistakes they're making even when they're pointed out to them. So before you worry about your friends, you should worry about yourself.

Even if you are sure that you are not a mismatched message sender and you don't want to go to the expense of hiring, renting, or buying a video tape machine and camera, I suggest, if you are in a public contact business, that you sit before a mirror for an hour a night for one week and carry on a series of make-believe conversations. Ask your boss for a raise, ask him for a favor, try to talk him into doing something, talk to your children, give them an order. If you are a salesman, I would certainly expect you to give your sales presentation to several different types of people. Pretend you are at a party and carry on a conversation with several of your friends. Most people who do this find it very revealing, very enlightening, and sometimes shocking.

Before you attempt it however, we suggest you tell your wife and your family what you are doing because if you don't they may throw a net over you and you may have to practice talking to doctors in a padded cell where there are no mirrors.

6

THE
INTERVIEW GAME
OR
SELLING YOURSELF

I thought long and hard before settling on the title for this chapter. The word "game" bothered me because our research indicates that hard work, effort, and ability—not gamesmanship—are the critical factors in success. However, after I studied what really goes on during interviews, I could not think of any title more appropriate than the "Interview Game." The reason is simple. The people who run interviews make it a game and, what's more, a dirty game.

I interviewed two groups of personnel people while writing this chapter. The first group consisted of sixty-eight men and women from twenty-three different companies. I interviewed ten in their offices, the others at conventions. I found them far more open and honest in cocktail lounges over drinks than they were behind their desks. After a drink or two, they relaxed and openly admitted that they viewed an interview as a game in which an adversary relationship exists between the interviewer and the person being interviewed. The interviewers thought it was their job to catch people lying, to spot them when they were unsure of themselves, and to trap them into admitting personal weaknesses. They looked upon the whole process as a negative one. The only positive aspect of the interview as far as I could see was the ego trip taken by the interviewers. They invariably believed that they could spot a candidate who was lying or lacked self-esteem or who would be inefficient. Unfortunately, the people who get the products of their interviews don't agree with them. I know several large corporations which, after exhaustive studies of their personnel departments, decided they would be better off without them. The only problem is they don't know what to replace them with.

Personnel departments are grossly ineffective because they operate primarily on myth. The criteria they apply to job applicants is unrealistic and stupid and in many cases counterproductive. The only point on which I agree with the people who run personnel departments is that nonverbal messages are often more accurate than verbal ones. Years ago they discovered that job applicants were quite adept at lying and if interviewers listened to what the job applicants were saying they would be fooled much of the time. As a result, the people in today's personnel departments lean too heavily on nonverbal signals and whether an applicant gets a job or a second interview often depends on the nonverbal messages the applicant sends. Interviewers think nonverbal messages are invariably accurate and honest. Of course this is nonsense. One of the strategies I am going to teach you in this chapter is how to lie nonverbally.

I can see some people shuddering at such an immoral suggestion. I agree that nonverbal lying is immoral in most situations. However, not when you are dealing with personnel people who read nonverbal messages inaccurately and make them a basis for judgment. For example, 25 percent of the personnel people we talked to said they would refuse to consider anyone with a wet, clammy handshake for an important position. This is ridiculous, stupid, and unfair. A wet, clammy handshake is often an indication of nervousness and really wanting a job.

Which brings us to the second reason that playing the interview game is not immoral. The people companies hire often are the wrong people. We did a survey of 162 applicants in nineteen different companies. We interviewed them before they went into the interview and when they left. We asked them a series of questions to determine how badly they wanted the job and how much they really wanted to work for that company. We did not rate them on their ability, only their intentions. We found that the people who were most desperate to get a particular job, to work for a particular company, almost never got hired. They were invariably eliminated during interviews. We also discovered that many of the applicants who really didn't give a damn, who already had another job offer, or who were simply out practicing interviewing, scored very well. Obviously, this is not what most companies would want. This amazing fact was verified by a follow-up study in which we questioned people going for job interviews and found that those who already had job offers were far more likely to get a second one. They went into the interviews without the pressure of really needing the job and, as a result, they were more likely to be hired. Many of the nonverbal signs interviewers use to eliminate job applicants were simply signs of nervousness.

We also discovered that many of the nonverbal signs that interviewers believed signaled industry and self-assurance actually identified the applicant as being upper-middle-class. Most interviewers are not aware of this because 90 percent of professional personnel people come from blue-collar backgrounds.

As the system now stands, four types of people have tremendous advantages in job interviews. People who are good-looking have a three to four times greater chance of being hired for almost any position, whether it is typing, sales, or management; it makes no difference at all. If you're beautiful it helps. Second, people from upper-middle-class backgrounds have an advantage. They carry themselves and speak in a manner that tells the interviewers they are self-assured. Third, athletes have smoother, better-coordinated body motions and tend to pass the nonverbal sections of interviews far better than nonathletes. Fourth, actors who are trained at transmitting both verbal and nonverbal messages are absolute experts at getting jobs.

In fact, the actors we encountered were so good at getting jobs that we ran a research project using a half dozen of them, three men and three women. We took resumes originally rejected by client corporations, doctored them, had the actors spend a half hour in the library checking the careers that these resumes were geared to, and sent them out for interviews. They received job offers or offers for second interviews 38 percent of the time—an amazing batting average for people seeking jobs. Their success was based on three facts. First, they dressed the part. Second, they didn't really care if they got the job or not. Third, they knew exactly what the interviewers were looking for and they were able to lie verbally and nonverbally because that's their business. Play and pretend, apparently, is the main criterion for getting hired in America.

I must point out that in most cases in which these people received job offers or second interviews, they were interviewed by people who were professional personnel people. They didn't do nearly as well when they were interviewed by field people working in personnel for a stated period of time. The field people asked an entirely different series of questions and some of them immediately spotted the fact that the actors knew nothing about the field in which they were applying. When the actors were pretending to be engineers, and spoke to another engineer, they were often tripped up almost immediately. I believe this is one of the key weaknesses in personnel departments. The people interviewing often have no concrete concept of the requirements for the job. Since they can't ask factual questions, they set up an artificial criterion and make everyone pass through it on the assumption that if you can beat their criterion you can do anything.

The field men fell into two separate categories. In the first, they simply were brought in from the field to spend twelve to eighteen months in personnel. They usually were given a one-day orientation and then assigned to interview people applying for jobs in their speciality. A second type of field person was brought in and dominated by the vice-president in charge of personnel, put through a mandatory three-week training program, and absolutely forced, unless he had a very strong personality, into obeying the asinine rules which had been set up by the personnel department. In some cases they were even less selective and easier to fool than the personnel professionals. The field men and women left on their own actually applied very sensible criteria to applicants. When we interviewed them, we found they asked themselves several questions about most applicants. First, would this applicant get along with the people he has to work with? If client-contact was part of the job, how well he would relate to the clients was the critical question. If only co-workers were involved, how would he relate to them? Second, is this applicant technically qualified? We found field engineers paid a great deal more attention to the marks the fellow received in engineering than his overall grade average. The people in personnel, on the other hand, paid more attention to the overall grade average than to his marks in engineering. Third, is this person teachable? Almost nobody in personnel asked this question. But it was considered critical by the field people. Does this person look as if he's willing to learn? And the field people, who often had some limited management experience, asked what I considered the most practical question from the company's point of view: is this person worth the money we're paying him? This question was almost never asked by the people in personnel because they had no realistic criteria for judging it. The critical difference here is practical information on how the person is going to be used.

Since the actors did so well in the interviews and since 60 to 65 percent of all people being interviewed are going to have to pass through the personnel screen, we set up a training program for poor interviewees and used these actors as the instructors.

We collected twenty participants identified as poor interviewees—eleven men and nine women. All these people were seeking employment and we explained that if they would cooperate with us we would give them a free lesson on how to get through a job interview. Obviously they had a vested interest in joining the class. I started the session by explaining that we were working on the theory that interviewing was a game and that there were certain verbal and nonverbal rules that could be taught. The men and women doing the teaching were actors and actresses because they were experts at playing nonverbal and verbal games and they were attempting to pass on their expertise to the participants. I then turned the class over to the six actors.

They spent the remainder of the day role playing. First the participants acted out mini-interviews: walking in, sitting down, shaking hands, saying hello, smiling, not smiling, and answering certain stock questions. We took notes. Then the actors and actresses ran through each person's interview as they would have done it. Then we attempted to have the participants copy the actors. By the middle of the day we split the group of twenty into four smaller groups. By three o'clock many of the participants were as good as the actors doing the training. We stopped then because several of the actors had to leave, but we invited anyone who was interested to return the next day to attend a practice session. Only one person couldn't make it and she had a job interview. When we got there the next day we continued the mock interviews, this time under my supervision, with the two actors who returned as coaches. We added one additional training technique. The actors imitated the mistakes made by various participants while that participant played the part of the interviewer. Some of the students found this very helpful.

At the same time, participants met with one of my assistants in another room and she helped them rewrite their resumes. We hired a professional typist to type them and everyone in the class participated in the proofreading session.

These final resumes were also products of research. When we started, we originally intended to use standard guides on resume writing as the basis for our consultation. We found that most of them are written by university professors and personnel directors and are based on limited experience, educated guesswork, or myth. Therefore, we thought it necessary to do some basic research. We enlisted eight companies with twelve personnel officers and their staff. In addition, we enlisted sixty-two executives, who regularly receive resumes, and asked all of those participating to save all the resumes they received from June 1978 to June 1979. We asked each person who read a resume to sign it and make three comments. First, would they bring the person in for an interview? Second, list any mistakes in the resume. Third, list any positive points in the resume.

Surprisingly, the main reasons resumes and cover letters are discarded are spelling, punctuation, and sloppiness. Neatness counts. Often secretaries or clerks go through resumes and screen out those they consider inadequate. This type of screening takes place most often when an executive places an ad for a job in a newspaper and receives 200 replies. Knowing he cannot possibly read that many resumes or interview that many people, he usually has his secretary or some underling go through them to eliminate the unsuitable ones before he sees them. Often the person doing the eliminating has no real idea of what type of employee the company is seeking and will simply throw out those that look amateurish. Obviously, all the advice given by the so-called professionals on typing your own resume is total nonsense. If you are not a good typist, you are a fool if you don't have a professional do it. And even after a professional typist has finished, you should have several friends read it for punctuation and spelling. I also would suggest if there's a word in a resume that has two spellings, take the most common one. Secretaries frequently are unaware of more than one acceptable spelling for a word. We saw several cases of resumes being rejected on that basis alone.

The second most common reason for rejecting resumes is time gaps. Many college professors who write books on how to get jobs indicate that if there is a gap in your work history you cover it with a narrative resume. We found that in most cases narrative resumes don't even get you an interview. When they do, the first question asked is to explain the gap in your resume. If you hesitate, fumble, or fall on your face, you're caught. If you give a quick, glib answer, or lie, you're caught anyway because that's the one thing they check on. Most companies do not check very carefully on resumes and personnel directors are notoriously poor in this regard. But they will check on something you say that isn't on paper.

If you have an extended, unexplainable gap in your resume, you are frankly going to have to fudge. There are several ways you can go about this. You can take the job you had prior to your gap in time and extend it to cover the gap. You can take the job you had after the time gap and push back the starting date. Whatever you do, don't extend both. The fewer cover-ups you allow the better off you are. If you cannot extend the time you spent on a real job, you're going to have to create a fictitious position. The fiction that personnel people run across most often, and the one they're least likely to believe, is that you were self-employed. Unless you have extensive documentation to back this up, it will not work. The best way of covering a time gap is to have a real employer improvise for you. If your uncle, aunt, cousin, father, or anyone else you know, owns a small corporation, even if that corporation exists only on a letterhead, you can claim you worked for them—provided, of course, they're willing to back you up. If you don't know anyone who owns a company and if you spent a year or two at a country club such as San Quentin and you're absolutely sure that telling a potential boss would eliminate you from the job, you're going to have to do some creative writing. The best example I ever saw was a young man who did spend two years in prison. He looked up the name of an Iranian company right after the Ayatollah took over. He then checked and found out that no matter who you wrote to in that company, nobody answered. So he proceeded to create a position and a salary and filled it in on his resume. He even credited himself with completely reorganizing the accounting department, which elminated the third most popular reason for throwing resumes in the circular file. People who write resumes that simply indicate where they were without telling what they did, are hardly ever selected for interviews.

When you're filling out your resume, you don't list simply where you were, you have to list what you did. Putting down "Joe's Shoe Manufacturing Company from 1965–1970, salesman," is a very poor idea. If you put down "Joe's Shoe Manufacturing Company, 1965–1970, salesman" and indicate that you sold more shoes than anyone else in the company, that will catch everyone's attention. Even the fact that you didn't sell too many shoes isn't important because they're not even going to try to check on it. They already know Joe's Company won't give out internal information—what you've told is noncheckable. Then, if you spent from 1970 to 1975 in Sam's Shirt Company as their production chief, you list chief, and say you increased their button supply by 20 percent and cut their costs by 15 percent. Again, this may be complete nonsense, but it dresses up your resume even further. If you claim that when you moved to Harry's Suit Company you personally saw to it that all the

suits fitted perfectly, you have window-dressed your
resume to the point where people in personnel will be
delighted. It's known as a "can-do" and "has-done" resume; created terms for something that is probably fiction.

We know it's fiction because we went through 163
resumes and spotted a series of statements just like
those described. Because we have contacts in corporations, we were able to go back and check on forty-three
of them. We found that of the forty-three, twenty-four
were correct and the others were total fiction. Half of
the fiction writers were in good positions and perform-
ing on a very high level. In fact, three of them were so
high in corporations we decided that we better take that
research report and deep-six it. They were high enough
up that the truth wouldn't kill them, it would kill us.

The fourth most common reason for not getting an
interview is because the resume never even gets read.
Resumes that run more than a page, unless they are for
executive positions, are often ignored. We found a substantial percentage of personnel people who never read
more than a page. They gave us all sorts of excuses for it:
if the man couldn't summarize in one page what he did,
he wasn't doing it correctly; three- and four-page resumes were unspeakably long and unnecessary and proved
the job applicant didn't know what he was doing in the
first place. I suspect, after speaking to some of these
personnel people, that in their entire lives they never
read anything longer than a page.

The fifth reason resumes are rejected is that the resume
doesn't indicate you'd fit the job. This doesn't mean that
you're not qualified. In many cases, custom tailoring
your resume to suit a particular position will overcome
this. Having a custom-tailored resume always increases
your chances of getting the job provided that you make
very sure that the custom-tailored resume is as carefully checked as the mass-produced one for neatness,
spelling, and punctuation. As you move up the corporate ladder, custom-tailored resumes are far more pro-

ductive than mass-produced ones. I do not recommend mass-produced resumes for executive positions.

After you finish your resume, you should write your cover letter. The reason you write the cover letter after the resume is that the cover letter is an advertisement for the resume. In order to write the advertisement, you have to know the product. Good cover letters always have four characteristics. First, they're short. Second, they're simple. Third, they're catchy. And fourth, they're neat. The mistake people most often make in cover letters is simply writing a repeat of the resumes. The letter is supposed to tell a few things about you and get people interested enough to read your resume. The cover letter is an ad for the resume and it can be an ad for you.

I think the best cover letter I ever ran across came from a woman applying for a job as secretary at my company. She sent a letter that was perfectly typed and it said, "You know I don't have a great deal of experience, and I know I've worked for several companies in the last few years and that may not look good. But I guarantee you one thing. If I do come to work for you I'll work like hell!" First I was put off by her choice of language but then I was struck by the honesty, the power, and the forcefulness of the letter. It really had caught my eye. I took a chance and hired her. She did work like hell. She spelled like the devil, showed up when she felt like it, and gave everyone around her a lot of heat. As a result I had to let her go in a few weeks. But she did know how to sell herself in a cover letter.

Assuming you've written a suitable resume and cover letter you will be invited to interview with a number of companies. The minute you receive this invitation, there is a series of steps you should undertake. First, go to a library and do as much research on the company as possible. Find out what their problems are, what their goals are, who their competitors are. Find out as much as you can about their product line. If you can, read the financial statements. Make sure you find out who the president and the vice-presidents of the company are, or at least who's in charge of the area where you're interviewing. Check on whether that person has written anything. If he has, read it or at least skim through it. This will enable you to speak intelligently about the company and its top people during the interview.

The day before the interview, call and confirm the time, place, and the name of the person conducting the interview. With most organizations, calling ahead to confirm will be a plus on your chart even before you arrive. Before you leave for the interview, carefully scrutinize your appearance. Make sure you are dressed suitably, that your breath is clear, your shoes shined, and that you're not wearing too much lipstick or makeup. I know some readers may be insulted by this advice but my survey of interviewers indicates that 9 percent of the young men and women with college degrees eliminate themselves from job consideration by breaking basic grooming rules. I pointed out in my *Dress for Success* series that more than 30 percent are eliminated because of inappropriate clothing.

Make it a point to reach the building or the area of the interview ten to fifteen minutes ahead of time. Make this half an hour if you're interviewing in a major city where traffic can delay you. You can *never* be late for an interview. Being early serves two purposes. It guarantees you're going to get there on time and gives you a last chance to check yourself in the men's or ladies' room before the interview. Even if you were beautifully put together before you left home, it is easy to become disheveled on the way to an interview.

The interview starts the moment you walk into the waiting area. The receptionist in most corporate waiting areas will report to the interviewer on how you approach her and how you impress her. Make it a point to be polite and businesslike. When you've finished telling her you have an interview at one o'clock with Mr. So-and-so, she will probably ask you to take a seat; if not, wait half a minute and then simply do it on your own. If there's a place to hang your coat, hang it. If not, take it off and carry it over your arm. Most interviewers are more impressed by someone who is carrying a coat than someone still wearing one.

Once you have finished announcing yourself to the receptionist, sit down. Pick up one of the company magazines and start reading. Don't take out a book or magazine or anything else you brought with you. It is considered inappropriate. While you're sitting there try not to think about the interview. I know many books on this subject tell you to run over the interview in your mind but that should have been done earlier. Don't fidget. Try not to look overly concerned or nervous. Don't look up from your magazine every three or four seconds or the minute anyone comes into the room. Force yourself to read an article and try to become involved in it. If you must play little mental games with yourself while you're sitting there, tell yourself you're going to get the job. There's nothing the interviewer can do to stop you. He's very lucky that you've arrived. Try to build up your confidence rather than worry about making mistakes.

After you've sat there ten or fifteen minutes (they will often leave you waiting that long to see if you're going to become nervous or jittery), the official interview will usually start in one of two ways. The secretary may call to tell you the interviewer will see you and direct you to his or her office. Most probably, the interviewer will come out to meet you. When the interviewer arrives, stand up and walk toward him. Don't jump up and act nervous. Stand up and set yourself. This means that you pause a tenth of a second to pull yourself together once you get into a standing position. It's a trick that models use. When they get up out of a chair they pause for a split second to compose themselves, and rise to their full height before they walk. Do the same; it will give you a composed look. Walk directly over to the interviewer and shake his or her hand. If you're nervous and your hands tend to sweat, have a little bit of absorbent paper or cloth or something with powder or rosin on it in your pocket or pocketbook. Dry your hand just before you shake the interviewer's hand. If the interviewer comes out to meet you, there are two possible techniques he will use. He will either walk to his office and have you follow him or he will send you to his office. If he sends you to his office and tells you he'll be there in a minute, you must be aware of the fact that he's watching you. Your carriage is extremely important. You're going to be judged by how energetically you carry yourself. We had one gentleman who had a great deal of difficulty walking in a way that made him look energetic. One of the actors finally solved the problem. He had him walk down the hallway as if he were about to receive a gold medal in the Olympics. He imagined himself an athletic, energetic person about to be awarded a medal in front of a large, standing audience. With that in mind he walked more erect, more aggressively, and tested beautifully.

The interviewer is much more likely to send a woman ahead of him. He will often place himself in the doorway at one point so you have to squeeze past him. Many women become upset by this because it seems as if he's getting too close to them too quickly. It almost appears to be a sexual advance. I assure you they'll do the same thing with men. What he's doing is smelling you. He wants to see if you're wearing too much perfume or if you have body odor or bad breath. It is another one of those very unfair interviewing techniques.

When and how an interviewer watches you move is really not important. They're all interested in the same look. When we interviewed them they used such words as "alert," "aggresive," "forceful," and "energetic" to describe the ideal carriage. However, when we showed them pictures, we found the term they were really looking for was "upper-middle-class." They were not able to articulate this because people tend to be myopic when they look up the socioeconomic ladder and have 20–20 vision when they look down. Since nine out of ten personnel people come from blue-collar backgrounds, they do not recognize that the body carriage that is so attractive to them is the product of class.

If you fake a walk for the interview, you may or may not get away with it. Some people have a natural gift for drawing themselves to their full height and looking as if they walk that way all the time. Others make it look very artificial. We found that everyone who practices for two or three hours before a mirror can carry it off for those few moments. If you practice longer, as we suggested in our chapter on socioeconomic level, you will have no difficulty with it at all.

The other possibility is that you will be sent into the interviewer's office and you'll walk in and find him sitting behind his desk. If, when you walk in, he asks you to sit down, do so. If you find yourself standing in front of his desk without his looking up, he's trying to make you feel uncomfortable and test your reaction. The minute you do begin to feel uncomfortable, sit without his permission. Don't feel nervous about it. You've passed another part of the test. When you sit down, you have to remember to keep yourself erect. One of the things we found while training people is that if they had sloppy carriage when they walked, we could train them to walk erectly, but the minute they sat down, they slouched and destroyed their image. You must sit with your shoulders back if you're a woman.

Although you have taken the lead in the nonverbal part of the interview and seated yourself without permission, under no circumstances should you *talk* before he does. Wait for him to start the verbal part of the interview no matter how long it takes. There are some interviewers who will make you sit there an almost interminable period of time waiting for you to blow it. Don't.

By far the silliest piece of folklore and mythology in personnel departments is eye contact. Almost every personnel type I met swore by eye contact. They noticed immediately whether a man or a woman had good firm eye contact and they swore they could tell a great deal by the way a person handled eye contact. There may be some degree of truth in it. There have always been stories of shifty-eyed people. But I've taken this with a grain of salt for the past forty years. When I was three and a half or four, my grandmother, a lovely old lady who wished to lead me into good habits, told me there was no way I could look her in the eye and tell a lie. It wasn't a day or two later that I found out it was possible to do both things simultaneously. As a child I took great pleasure in proving it. I would take a cookie right in front of her, eat it, and then deny I had eaten it while staring her unflinchingly. I loved it, until she hauled off and gave me a whack where, as she said, it would do me the most good. After she gave me a little smack in the rear we laughed because we both understood that at that early age I had passed a milestone. I understood you could stare someone in the eye and lie. One of my childhood myths had been destroyed. Unfortunately for the people who are being interviewed and the corporations who are getting the product of these interviews, the people in personnel have not discovered that very salient fact.

The idea that you can't keep good eye contact while telling a lie is of course total nonsense. Good liars do it all the time. Several of the actors, when I told them this truism, practically fell off their seats laughing. They made a point during interviews of telling the most atrocious lies and staring at the personnel person very intently while they did it. They found that some of these men actually believed them.

As a result of this we sent several executives, who themselves were wonderful interviewers, into personnel. They, with even greater skill than the actors, lied like troopers and got away with it. They pretended to be electrical engineers with doctorates, sociology professors, psychologists, and almost anything under the sun and no one ever questioned them. Several of them were hired by their own companies for jobs they were certainly not qualified to do—which caused a bit of a stir in personnel. Most of the men had offers for second interviews. We found the best tactic during an interview is to look the interviewer directly in the eye. Interviewers insist it proves self-assurance, honesty, integrity. In our opinion, and in everyone else's, it's simply another example of the stupidity of the system.

Now I'm not saying that you can beat every interviewer playing by these rules. There are enough with the good common sense to play their instincts. They don't abide by the silly game I've laid out. But a large enough percentage of them have this fanatical belief in such an abysmally stupid system that it's almost a sin not to take advantage of it.

If you think the nonverbal part of the interview is stupid, the verbal part is ludicrous. During every interview you will be asked a series of indefinite questions. Why do you want to work for this company? Why do you want this particular job? Have you any plans if you get the job? It doesn't make any difference what question they ask. The answer they want is always the same. The answer is the "can-do" answer. They will smile and hire you if you say I want to work at this company because I can do X, Y, and Z. If you give them a realistic set of goals that fit the job, you're likely to get it. I believe I can help this company accomplish its sales goals. I believe I can sell widgets, computers, or anything else. This is what they're looking for, a can-do attitude. If they ask what you liked about your last company, answer that the job there allowed you to accomplish this, accomplish that, accomplish the other thing. If they ask you what you think your life has meant up to now, mention your wife, children, and painting your house, and you're not going to be hired. So you have to pretend that your family isn't the center of your life. They want to hear what you did on your last job and how you really made that company fly. Of course it's probably nonsense. But that's what's going to get you a job. Your answer to every question should be nothing more than a litany of things you have done or things you plan to do. When it's what you plan to do, be specific and realistic within the framework of what you know of the job they're offering. One thing you can't do is smoke, even if you're offered a cigarette. Offering a cigarette is another silly game. If you take it and light up, even after they do, you lose. You also don't criticize past employers. If you worked for the Mafia, you must praise them as equal opportunity employers.

When they ask about hobbies, you must tell them the only hobbies you enjoy are active ones. You're a doer. You don't read books, go to the opera, or watch television. You participate in sports, particularly status sports such as golf or tennis. You're not an observer, you're an active participant. In their opinion, people who read books and go to the opera are losers, while people who play golf and tennis are winners. Of course this is nonsense, but it's the nonsense they're looking for.

If you're still nervous about going to interviews, calm down. Interviewers are really nothing to be afraid of. The reasons you fear interviews are the same reasons egomaniacs behind the desk are having so much fun. They really think it's their game. You wouldn't be afraid of interviewers if you knew as much about them as I do. First, four out of five of the men in personnel graduated at the bottom of their class. They're not as bright as you are and they're not as articulate. They're simply playing in their own ball park. They often are the exact opposite of the people they pretend to be looking for. They're not go-getters. They're never going to be president of their company. Personnel tends to be a dead-end job. They play these little power games, and since it's the only power game they're ever going to play, they take it very seriously. But they are playing a game, and once you understand the rules you can beat them at it. If the information in this chapter does not give you all the confidence you need, we still have a solution. Hypnosis.

We sent several people to doctors who taught them self-hypnosis. They were people who became excessively nervous during interviews. I learned the technique some time ago while trying to improve my concentration. It's a wonderful way to calm yourself and control your emotions. Each and every one of our nervous job candidates, after a series of hypnosis sessions, was able to approach interviews from a new perspective and give a topnotch performance.

7

SALES

When we asked the wives, husbands, friends, and associates of some of the most successful men and women in America to describe them, the word they used most often was supersalesman. In spite of the fact that more than 85 percent of the people being described never held a job in direct sales, they sold all the time. They were more politicians than patriarchs and most of those around them responded to their charismatic personalities rather than their power.

When I told these executives that most of their associates saw them primarily as salesmen, they were in most cases flattered. In fact, two of them suggested an experiment. They sent select middle-management people through my sales training program to see if it would improve their performance. The results were so positive that several of our corporate clients now send all their middle managers to our sales training course.

I believe as do these executives that basic training in sales will enhance anyone's chances of succeeding. That is the reason that this chapter contains more factual data on how to sell than any five books I've read. While I advise that everyone read this chapter, I would suggest that anyone in sales read it a dozen times and anyone in sales training commit it to memory. The research on sales that follows represents a breakthrough.

The one thing that all the best and the worst sales forces have in common is that 20 percent of the people do 50 percent of the work. The reason for this is simple. If you take 100 salesmen with basic product knowledge and train them for five years, twenty will be very competent while the other eighty will be order takers. If you take the same sales force and put them in the field without training, at the end of six months to a year, twenty will be great salesmen and the other eighty will be order takers. Which is a bit surprising, because if you spend five years training men to be engineers, bricklayers, doctors, accountants, or almost anything else, you find that their achievement scores at the end of their training period will generally fall on a bell curve. Although some will perform at a higher level than others, the tremendous discrepancy that is seen in salesmen between those who are successful and those who are unsuccessful will not exist.

There is only one place where you will find similar statistics, and that's in our school system. If you look at good school districts, usually suburban ones, where learning and teaching do take place, you will find test scores

Picture 6

Bell curve. Shows even distribution of
learning in most training situations.

are similar to those in law, medicine, plumbing, and so on. There will be a small percentage of very talented students at the top and a small percentage at the bottom showing little academic talent. But most of the students will be clustered toward the middle. Those in the middle will be a product not of talent, but of training. They will achieve at a level sufficiently high so that most of them will be able to get into a college and just about all of them will perform well in our society. They will become solid middle-class citizens, and their educational abilities, no matter how limited, will be sufficient for them to survive. On the other hand, if you look at the worst schools in our educational system, those in ghetto areas where little or no teaching or learning goes on, you will find that a surprising 20 percent of the students score well on tests, that they progress fairly well through the educational system, and that they succeed at a level comparable to the 80 percent in the suburban schools. If you look at a curve of their accomplishments, it is almost identical to that of salesmen. The reason is simple. Teaching takes place in neither system. In the ghetto, as in sales, students tend to be looked upon as expendable. Those with natural talent survive while the others are thrown to the wolves. Both systems ruin the lives of 80 percent of the people who go through them.

While those teaching at inner-city schools can point to lack of money, background, and motivation of their students as a reason for failure, those teaching salesmen cannot. It is a flaw in the sales training rather than a flaw in the students. There are many reasons why sales training doesn't work. The main one is that professors in our major business schools have always looked down their noses at sales, sales training, and salesmen. They think of salesmen as men in loud suits telling funny jokes, peddling from door to door. Even at the best universities they are not aware of the sophistication of sales. They seem to have the mistaken idea that training in marketing produces an officer corps while sales training produces the infantry. As a result major business schools never encourage their people to go into sales and they have not bothered to research sales training. This puts the people doing sales training in a very unfortunate position. They are forced to guess at what works and what does not. With such a system they have limited success.

Another problem is that the trainers really don't believe in the training. We interviewed sixty-two sales trainers, guaranteed complete confidentiality, and signed nondisclosure agreements with built-in financial rewards if we revealed anything they said. As a result, we received very honest answers. Sixty of the sixty-two said that it was absolutely impossible to train someone who didn't have a natural talent for sales. Of the same sixty, fifty-eight said that even if they didn't train their best students, those with natural ability would catch on sooner or later. In their opinion, the whole point of training is to speed up this catching-on process. It has nothing to do with teaching how to sell, it's simply a way of teaching the students to use their natural abilities more efficiently and more quickly.

Sales training also fails because many sales trainers believe that there is but one correct way to sell. Most sales trainers we talked to have successfully sold insurance, computers, or used cars and they believe in their personal approach. Most of them thought that if a salesman or saleswoman did exactly what they told them to do, they would succeed. When we pointed out to them that the world reacts differently to different people, the majority dismissed that fact as being inconsequential. When we further pointed out that training women to sell the same way a man sells could be counterproductive, sixty-one of the sixty-two said they had heard that before, but in their opinion it was nonsense.

The only one who disagreed, to no one's surprise, was a woman. She said she was teaching women to sell the way she sold, and that they were far more effective than those trained by men. She believes that traditional sales training works only for men. Our statistics on women in sales back her up completely. The sales training women get in most corporations is counterproductive. If you take 100 women and train them to sell insurance, computers, or anything else, using the standard methods that most of the major corporations who spend millions on sales training use, only eight to twelve of those women will be productive salespeople. The rest will be order takers. If you take the same women and put them in the field without training, as is often done in real estate and insurance, they will outperform the males by 20 percent. Obviously, the sales training women get destroys their natural ability to sell. The present methods of sales training do not work with women because they are based on the assumption that women sell the same way men do, which of course is nonsense. The one characteristic we found to be common to all the great saleswomen was that they are all very independent women who take their training with a grain of salt.

Every one of them said that their male sales trainers told them to keep good eye contact or they would turn their buyers off, but the women knew that keeping good eye contact would turn their buyers on. Several of them pointed out that their instruction in nonverbal communication had them handling a contract in a way that was very sexy. But the silliest advice any of them received was to smile all the time. Two women, one who sold computers and one who was an attorney, said that if they smiled nobody took them seriously. One predicted the results of our research before we started. She said, "Smiles kill sales." If a woman smiles they ask her, "What's a nice girl like you doing in a job like this?" And since being taken seriously is the main problem women have in business, they must start by looking serious. Never smile for at least the first ten minutes of the first meeting until you've established the fact that you're a serious business person.

The universal advice from successful saleswomen is that women should pay no attention to their male sales trainers. They should obey their instincts when it comes to eye contact and body language. In addition, they think women have several advantages. A woman can be far more aggressive than a man when dealing with a male. In fact several of them suggest that their success was partially the result of the inability of most men to say no to a persistent woman. They also believe that most women learned basic techniques when they were young, while boys did not. The only warning they give to women is always be feminine. Don't try the macho close, which is, "I'm in charge here and you'll do what you're told."

Their recommendation is that companies design a new sales course for women. My recommendation is that companies redesign all their sales training. Our research found that sales depends as much on nonverbal communication as verbal and although some companies think they give nonverbal sales instruction, they really don't. The simplest proof is that they give the same training to women as they do to men. The instruction they give is based on untested assumptions and is often contradictory. In some sales training programs, individual instructors bring their own personality to bear. If you get one set of instructors you are taught to sit up straight while another swears you must lean forward to sell. Both are wrong. The truth is you must present a single socioeconomic sales message.

I do not contend that all sales training is a total waste of time. I am convinced that some of the better sales training programs do positively affect sales. But they do so without teaching anyone to sell. The success element has more to do with management than sales. The sales instructors are correct, they can teach a good salesperson to sell more quickly. I am not suggesting that major corporations close their sales training departments, but I do think they should upgrade and expand them. Some of their techniques are very productive.

The most successful technique in sales training is the motivational meeting. Outsiders may laugh at full-grown men and women running around in funny hats cheering for their company or department the way they did for their high school teams. They laugh because they do not understand.

It has nothing to do with teaching them to sell. Its object is to get people in the right state of mind so that they will sell. A man who sells 100 widgets a week may sell 110 if you can get him all excited about selling widgets. A second man who normally sells ten widgets may sell eleven if you get him excited. Motivation never makes a ten-widget salesman a 100-widget salesman and no one claims it does, but motivational programs have bottom-line value.

When we looked at the production of sales forces after a good motivational program, we found increases. The results could be traced in an S-curve with the first part of the S bigger than the second part. A 100-widget salesman, for example, might increase his sales by ten widgets a week for six weeks. At the end of this six-week period his sales would slump for about three weeks. But the down side of the curve was smaller than the up side, and, as a result, although he lost eighteen sales the last three weeks, he gained sixty for the first six weeks and therefore increased his sales by forty-two. With that type of increase, it is worthwhile for most companies to conduct motivational meetings on a regular basis. The end product—a motivated salesman and a motivated sales force—makes sense because motivated sales forces have a higher base line than unmotivated ones.

The next productive area of sales training is product knowledge. All the statistics indicate that once a man has basic product knowledge, additional technical expertise is not necessarily productive. Surprisingly, this is as true when selling computers as when selling insurance. Now I'm not implying that anyone can sell computers or insurance unless he understands the product. However, men and women are most likely to buy from salespeople who are on the same intellectual and technical level that they are. Knowing a bit more than your client does is good. Knowing too much more than your client does will kill a sale. Brilliant technical salesmen usually confuse the buyer, not sell him.

The third area of sales training that tested as being productive is time management. Salesmen, including some very good ones, are notoriously disorganized. When dealing with the entire sales force, this is the area that tends to have the greatest long-range positive impact. The area which will have the greatest impact with individuals, however, is client analysis. Teaching salesmen

Picture 7

60

18

Production curve after a successful sales motivation program.

to use varied approaches depending on whom they're dealing with is very helpful, particularly if the salesman handles a high-ticket item and sells to corporations. It can turn a third-rate order taker into a major producer in industries in which corporate approach is critical. However, we found only the very best sales trainers and training programs cover this subject adequately.

And finally, the heart and guts of present sales training courses is the prepackaged verbal presentation. Most major companies teach their salesmen a standard presentation. These standard presentations vary greatly; some are effective and some very ineffective. The most effective ones use sound teaching principles. They give an audiovisual presentation whenever possible, they keep it simple, and they steer their technical salesmen away from jargon. They organize the sale into a series of digestible intellectual bites. They think for the salesperson. They protect him from himself. They attempt to answer all the questions with the standard presentation. In addition, they have prepackaged answers to often-asked questions. One of their best sales techniques is called "straw man." The salesman leaves a hole in his presentation knowing the buyer will question that part. Naturally, he has the perfect answer.

There are two sound psychological principles that most great salespeople use. The first is the "Yes Principle." If you ask people to commit to anything, their first reaction is to say no. Therefore, you have to get them into the habit of saying yes first. Most readers will recognize the insurance version of the yes principle, because insurance salespeople are best known for using it. They will often ask a client such questions as: "You do want your wife and children to have the same life-style that they have now if anything happened to you?" Obvious answer: yes. "You would want your children to be able to go to the same fine schools they're going to now?" Obvious answer: yes. "I'm sure that you would want your wife and children to be able to live in this house if anything happened to you?" And this obvious yes answer leads to the critical question which is often a statement. "Therefore, you must want this policy that guarantees all that." To which a client is more likely to answer yes because he has given three yes answers in a row. This approach recognizes the fact that thinking and answering are matters of habit and if you can get people into a routine or path of positive or negative answers, they are likely to continue on the same path.

The second effective strategy is joining the opposition. Great salespeople almost never argue. No matter what the person they're selling to says, they begin by agreeing with it. If the buyer says that the house they're selling is the most expensive house they've seen in that neighborhood, they say, "Yes, it is very expensive and I can understand your not wanting to pay that much. However. . . ." Or if the buyer says that the house they're selling has beige carpets and they can't stand the color beige, the good salesperson will say that he or she dislikes beige, too, and understands how the buyer feels. However, beige would go with the furniture the buyer has now, and it's a universal color. The classic example of this technique was used time and time again by good salesmen when they answered the price question, "Why does yours cost more than the other fellow's?" A good salesman always starts by saying, "I understand your asking that question. It's a normal question. You should be concerned about price. The reason ours cost more is our product has A, B, C, and D and theirs does not." Poor salesmen invariably say, "The reason ours is more expensive is A, B, C, and D," without first agreeing that the question had legitimacy. One of the first rules of sales is never disagree with the buyer. Always start by agreeing with him and then show him why he's wrong.

Once a good salesperson has eliminated a prospect's objections, the intent is to get him to sign on the dotted line. Salespeople, at least the good ones, are always looking for commitment. If they are not sure that a prospect is ready to commit, they use a technique called the trail close. They ask the prospect if he wants his new product shipped by rail or by air, or whether he wants it in blue or green. No matter what answer he gives, if it indicates that he wants to buy, they hand him a contract. If the prospect objects, they continue to sell, always with the same object in mind: commitment. Good salesmen always ask for the sale and poor salesmen don't.

The techniques I have just described can help you sell

anything, including yourself. They can help you get a raise, a promotion, a new job, and they can help you get others to do what you want them to do, but they will help you only if you are in the lucky 20 percent. Our research finds that these techniques work only for 20 percent of most sales forces although 45 percent or more try to use them. The people for whom they work are no better-looking, no more aggressive, no more earnest, no more trustworthy than the people who don't sell.

Our research shows that these techniques work only when they are combined with the proper nonverbal selling system. The nonverbal element in sales is the real key to success. This discovery came about as the result of a major research project in which we video taped salespeople making actual and simulated sales presentations. My staff studied more than 1,800 hours of tapes in an attempt to identify the characteristics of each group. The study was conducted with the cooperation of thirty-four companies. Some of the companies put cameras in their own offices and photographed people trying to sell to them. Others set up elaborate simulated sales sessions and had them video taped by professionals in studios while others sent us homemade video tapes.

Our original plan was to have only the people on my staff look at the video tapes. We soon discovered that people in specific industries saw things in presentations that people outside the industry did not. We therefore revised our research method for the first time. Instead of having the tape sent to us, we first had them viewed by people in the same industry, usually the executives in charge of the sales force, and had them comment on the verbal and nonverbal characteristics of their good and poor salespeople. Sixty percent of the information we have in this chapter is based on their comments.

When the tapes were sent to us, our researchers looked at them and reported on the differences they noticed between the good salespeople and the poor ones. We followed a standard procedure. First, the tapes were played without sound. This helped our researchers isolate the nonverbal elements of the presentation. Then they listened to the verbal presentation without the picture. Finally, they looked at the video tape with picture and sound and made an independent set of comments each time.

We found that this research procedure had several built-in flaws. The main one was that it broke the researchers into visual and verbal camps. They tended to defend their positions. Our solution was to take the original seven-person research team and divide it. We added two additional researchers, which gave us three three-person teams. Each team specialized. If the team saw the visual part of tape four, they would get to hear only the verbal part of tape five and the combined assignment on tape six. We didn't want them defending any one point of view. We wanted independent analysis of each part that was not prejudiced by what they had previously seen or heard. This produced more realistic results.

The first thing that struck everyone who looked at the tapes was that the good salespeople were calmer. Their body movements were smooth and unhurried. They made no jerky motions, particularly when they were handing a contract or a pen across the table. They didn't surprise anyone, they did everything gradually, they never pulled a rabbit out of a hat. When they went into their briefcases to get a paper, they knew exactly which paper they were picking up, yet they flipped through one or two before slowly picking out the one they needed.

We also identified people who never sold. We called them the jumpies. The jumpies were people who seemed to be very nervous. They moved their hands and mouths too quickly. They gave the impression that they were upset and they communicated this to the buyer.

There is a phenomenon called mirroring. If one person in a room shows signs of nervousness, there is a very definite possibility that the other people in the room will pick it up, particularly if the nervous person is talking. Therefore, if a salesperson is nervous, jumpy, and on edge, the buyer will be put on edge and obviously that's not good.

After three years, we decided we were raising almost as many questions as we were solving. For example, when we first started looking at the tapes, they contained apparently conflicting information. We saw that one group of very successful salespeople tended to, if not touch their clients, come very close to them when they were closing a sale. When we questioned these salespeople, they all made similar comments. They couldn't sell anyone they couldn't touch or get close to. At the same time we noticed that one of the things that killed sales was poor salespeople moving into someone's territory. Although we knew that good salespeople closed in, we didn't know when or how.

As a result, we were forced to do a study on body space and its impact on sales. We gave actual purchasing agents and people who were playing buyers in simulated sales situations one of two devices. One was a hand-held device with a button. The harder you pressed the button, the higher the needle registered. The other was a brake pedal with the same type of apparatus. We told them when they were annoyed to squeeze or press the device and the more annoyed they became the harder they were to squeeze or press.

We then had salespeople approach them and studied their reactions. We found that when a good salesperson appeared they were much less likely to squeeze the button or press the brake. There were a variety of reasons but the main one was that good salespeople have a sixth sense. Without ever knowing the brake was being pressed or the button was being squeezed, they sensed when they were offending people and backed off. Good salespeople didn't come physically close to their clients until they could do it without offending. Sales for them was a process of getting closer, of breaking down barriers. Poor salespeople, on the other hand, invaded other people's territory, touched them in ways that they found objectionable, and turned them off completely.

The sixth sense we talk about is one that can be developed through training. We use several methods. The one that's simplest to describe is one in which we have a salesperson approach an instructor who signals him when he is giving off positive verbal and nonverbal messages. After fewer than a dozen exposures, most salespeople begin to get a feeling for what they can and cannot do.

If you're a salesperson, or someone who has to sell his ideas for a living, you must practice creating a good first impression. Our testing indicates that less than 20 percent of the male and 30 percent of the female population create a positive first impression. We have all met people who immediately make everyone feel good. The object is to become one of those people. The best method for practicing is to get a full-length mirror and try very hard to look upon that person in the mirror as your student. The first twenty-five times you see yourself in the mirror, or the first two or three days, you're not going to like what you see. However, you will begin to get used to that person in the mirror and once you do, you will be able to correct that person's negative message sending. You will discover that you would rather that person hold his or her head at a slightly different angle. You will discover that that person smiles a little too much or not quite enough. You will discover that that person leans forward when shaking hands, which annoys you. You will discover that that person stands at a funny angle or that person's clothing doesn't seem to hang well and simply by observing them you will begin to correct those faults.

In addition to practice with a mirror, you're going to have practice with people. The ideal group is a dozen people, six men and six women, because this will give you more reactors. A reactor is someone who plays opposite the salesperson and reacts to him. During the sale they are to interrupt with constructive criticism. When you shake hands they might say, "Why don't you make it a bit firmer?" Or, "Your grip is a bit too strong for a woman." They are to interrupt you continually, have you repeat an action until you satisfy them. Their job is not to criticize you, it is to coach you. They're to look upon their job in the same way that a golf pro would look upon his. They are to tell you to raise your hand a bit or lower your eyes a bit. If you practice with enough people you are going to get conflicting information. This is because there are several variations of nonverbal messages that you can send out and that one variation will work with one type of person while a second variation works with another. In the same way you now adjust your verbal presentation to suit your client, after training you should be able to adjust your nonverbal presentation.

When two people sit or stand facing each other, the distance between them affects their comfort and their credibility. If two men who are the same size, the comfortable distance for one will be most comfortable for the other; at that point, both will have their highest credibility rating. If the same man meets a woman, he should stand or sit four to six inches closer. Women, when they talk among themselves, stand and sit closer and a man who sits or stands back seems distant. He is less intimate and, as a result, less credible. The reverse is true when a woman is selling to a man. She should sit four to five inches farther back than she would if she were selling to a woman. Her comfort distance is an intrusion upon his territory. If a man is standing and selling to a man who is noticeably shorter than he, he should back off three to four inches. Most of the time this will relax the shorter man. When he's dealing with a woman, the opposite is true. If a man or woman is shorter than the person he or she is selling to, whether the buyer be male or female, the seller should stand as close as possible without arching the neck at an artificial angle, which would cut into his or her credibility.

Picture 8

A. Ideal sales distance when one man sells to another.
Slightly more than an arm's length.

B. Ideal sales distance when one woman sells to another.
Definitely shorter than an arm's length.

C. A man must move in when selling to a woman.

D. A woman must move back when selling to a man.

There are no exact measurements. The distance at which people feel comfortable varies dramatically. The size or the sex of the person and where the meeting is taking place will determine the distance that works best. The most reliable method of estimating distance is from the other person's perspective. You should not guess at what distance you feel the most comfortable. You should try to look at the other person and see where you think their barriers are. Place yourself outside their barriers and make them feel comfortable. If you do, you'll be right 80 to 90 percent of the time. If you're in an office, the general rule is that two thirds of the desk is his, one third is yours. If, however, he has major barriers at the front edge of his desk, such as pen and pencil sets or a plaque that makes it almost impossible for you to put anything on his desk without moving them, you must first ask permission.

If you sit at the side of a person's desk, the amount of territory that is usually his is shown in Picture 12. If you meet someone in a public dining area where neither of you has territorial rights, you can split the table in half. If you sit at the side of a neutral table, the territorial line almost divides the space equally.

We also discovered that physical setting changes a person's concept of body space. For example, a buyer sitting with his back to a corner cannot be approached from his protected sides. You must advance directly across the table. His body space will be determined by the psychological fortress in which he has placed himself. His physical environment becomes an extension of his personal environment.

Sometimes our created sense of space extends beyond the body. If a man or a woman comes from a large city, never touch him or her. If a person comes from a small town, he has a greater sense of space but is less threatened by people invading it. It is for this reason that most people in small towns look upon people from Chicago, New York, and other large cities as being cold and distant when actually they are trying to repect the other

Picture 9

Territories in a client's office—
one-third yours, two-thirds his.

Picture 10

Territories in a client's office—from side triangle.

person's privacy. Ironically, they are being their friend-
liest when they seem least friendly. On the other hand,
people from small towns who come into big cities are
often thought to be rude and pushy when, in actual
fact, they are attempting to be friendly. Touching for

most big-city people starts three to six inches from the body. That is the area they consider intimate body space. If you have lived in a large city, you will notice that people, even in crowded subways and elevators, maintain this three- to six-inch distance whenever possible. When it becomes impossible, they feel uncomfortable

Picture 11

Territorial division in a neutral setting—
desk split horizontally in half.

Picture 12

Territorial division in a neutral setting—
desk divided diagonally.

and become very quiet. If you, without a legitimate reason, come within three to six inches of a person in a big city, you will instantly turn him off. In order to survive in big cities, people have to defend their individuality and this is one of the ways they do it. The only time you get a similar reaction from people in a small town is if you come close to their eyes or their sexual organs. They then feel threatened and become defensive.

The primary rule for a salesperson is never threaten anyone to whom you're trying to sell. This is why most great salesmen, particularly those who are tall, lean back when they stand. Great salesmen are hardly ever physically aggressive, enabling them to be very aggressive verbally. It also explains why lower-socioeconomic body signals tend to be negative in sales. A lower-socioeconomic stance is an aggressive stance, which physically threatens people and kills sales.

Another sure turn-off for most people is being ignored. All great salespeople are great listeners, or at least they seem to be. They give the impression that they are interested only in the customer. When the buyer talks, the salesperson gives rapt attention. You can learn to look interested if you practice in a mirror. However, the body signals are standard. For a man the angle of rapt attention is with shoulders and head arched slightly forward. For a woman, the body angle is greater than for a man. If she sits at the same angle that a man sits at she will appear disinterested. We expect women to lean farther forward when they are listening. Naturally, the normal position for a woman when she's selling is different from that of a man.

There are several mistakes that women make when sitting down. One, they will sit too close to the edge of the chair and two, they will sit with their legs bent to one side. The only effective sitting position for a woman is one with her legs crossed. This requires that a woman wear a skirt at least two inches below her knees.

As in most research projects, one piece of information often led to another. For example, we found that left-

Picture 13

A. Male at rapt attention.
   Can sit up or even lean back.

B. Female at rapt attention
   Must lean forward.

handed people are more likely to be good salesmen than
those who are right-handed. We immediately pulled the
tapes and started playing left-handed versus right-handed
to see if there were any obvious differences; there were.
Left-handed salespeople, if given a choice, would sit or
stand to the buyer's left, while right-handed salespeople
would sit or stand to the buyer's right. When we asked
them why, they said they felt more comfortable there.
However, when we tested the buyers, we found right-
handed buyers, who make up the majority, usually prefer people on their left. Therefore, if you deal with a
right-handed buyer, you should sit or stand on his left,
and if you deal with a left-handed buyer, you should sit
or stand on his right. Salespeople pick the side on which
they feel most comfortable rather than picking the side
that makes the buyer feel most comfortable, thereby
breaking one of the basic principles of sales. Good salespeople make their buyers feel good.

We noticed that left-handed people also handle pens
and contracts differently. While righties often pushed
contracts straight across the table, lefties almost invariably handed the contracts at an angle that tested as
being less offensive. You can get into a person's body
space if you come in sideways moving away from that
person. We found the way left-handed people held pens
also gave them an advantage. They tended to point the
pen at themselves when explaining something on a written contract. Right-handed people often aimed the pen
at the buyer making the buyer feel very uncomfortable.
People do not like having things pointed at them.

We also discovered that you could tell whether your
sale is going well by starting to move in on the buyer.
This is the nonverbal counterpart of the trial close we
discussed earlier. One of the keys of completing a sale is
to physically move in on the other person. If you start to
move in and you are rejected, there is a good chance the
sale is not working and you should postpone asking for
a commitment. Good salespeople, if they are rejected,
change direction nonverbally. We noticed that when this
occurred they also changed the nature of their verbal

Picture 14

A. Head or body tilted to the side.

B. Sitting on the edge of a chair.

Wrong positions for women.

Picture 15

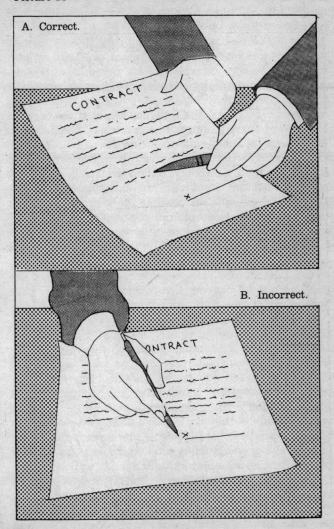

Right and wrong way to handle a pen and a contract.

presentation. They read nonverbal rejection correctly as a signal that they were doing something wrong. They backed off and began moving slowly in again, only this time on a different track.

One of the best methods for moving into someone's territory is to get him to invite you. If you can get him to hold a piece of paper, write his name, read a paragraph, or do anything else that forces him to partake in the physical activity of a sale, you have overcome a major hurdle. If you can't get the buyer involved, you are going to have to move in on your own. The best way is to sneak in. Don't pull a contract out of your attaché and throw it on the desk. Take it out, put it in your lap, and hold it there a minute. Let him see it in your lap, let him get used to it. Then move the contract very nonchalantly onto the table. If possible, do it when he is not looking. Good salespeople never surprise their clients. In fact, if they can arrange it, they will start the sales presentation with a contract lying on the table so the client becomes used to looking at it. One of the key commandments for sales is never surprise anyone, not even with your clothes. Use a very normal, everyday vocabulary; it creates trust.

Which brings us to a very important point: good salespeople have a matched visual, verbal, and product presentation. One of the main flaws with sales presentations created by major corporations is that they are invariably written with upper-middle-class verbal patterns. Sometimes they do not match the products they're selling, which is unfortunate, but most of the time the real problem is they do not match the socioeconomic verbal and nonverbal signals of the salespeople. Very simply, the presentation doesn't sound as if it's coming out of the salesperson's mouth. It sounds as if he's reading something and, as a result, the buyer gets a mixed verbal-visual message which is the surest way to kill credibility. If you are selling an upper-middle-class product with an upper-middle-class sales presentation and you have lower-middle-class verbal-visual patterns, you should take one or two steps immediately. Change your presentation so it matches your normal verbal and visual patterns or change your patterns so they match the presentation. It is preferable to change the presentation because changing your verbal and visual patterns will take many, many months. The other you can do almost overnight.

What you must do is take your presentation and read it onto a tape recorder and then say every sentence over in your own words. Say it as you would say it when speaking to your neighbor. Avoid vocabulary that isn't a normal part of your everyday speech. Do not say "the automobile will positively impact your image," if normally you would say, "the car will make you look great." Only after you've taken this step should you work on upgrading your socioeconomic message system. We don't want you to starve to death while you are doing it.

Good salesmen and good saleswomen do a sales dance. They move to the other person's vibes. They go into the sales situation with the idea of controlling the sales dance. They lead. The whole object is to get the other person to follow. They use all sorts of devices to get the buyer to move the way they want him to move. They first get him to move physically. They never try to sell a product by verbal means only. They're always trying to sell themselves, then their product. Good salespeople recognize that they have to move the buyer's body to move the buyer's mind, which brings us to two major breakthroughs in research.

First, all the research on body signals until mine was based on the premise, stated or unstated, that the mind controlled the body. If a person folded her arms, she was turning you off. As we indicated in an earlier chapter, it's not necessarily true. Our research indicates that in most sales situations it's easier to change someone's body position than to change their mind. And this is the preferred technique used by most good salespeople. They found through trial and error that if you once get a person to change their body position, the mind will follow.

When successful salespeople run across someone who is being offensive or whose physical bearing sends off a very strong negative message, they immediately get off the subject of the sale. They change their verbal tack. They relax their bodies in hopes that the mirror image effect will take place and the buyer will relax his. If this does not work, good salespeople will attempt to change the buyer's position. They will ask the buyer to hold or pick up an object, to help them with a sales prop, to get something from his desk, to get them a piece of paper, or to lend them a pen. Anything to change his physical position. They may also try to change his physical attitude by changing his mental attitude. This is the theory behind the traditional salesman's adage, if you can get a man to laugh, he isn't going to be sitting there staring at you as if he hates you. The object is to put the buyer in a friendly, positive position. When we questioned the better salespeople, some consciously realized what they were doing and others did not. One of the best examples of involving people in a sale came from a real estate saleswoman. She had every paper in her office rolled up in rubber bands like old maps. She said that it was much easier to sell a piece of property after she had the diagram for two days because by that time it would have been rolled long enough so that in order for her to spread it out, the potential buyer had to help hold down the edges. Once she involved the buyer in this way, she was halfway to the sale.

This is a very important lesson for nonprofessional sales people. We photographed at least fifty corporate meetings where people were selling on a one-to-one basis. The unsuccessful businessmen and women usually stood back from the person they were selling and talked at him, a very weak method. The effective business people sold the same way crack salespeople did; they involved the person to whom they were selling in physical activity. They got their prospect, who was often their boss, personally involved in holding charts, pointing to slides, moving his chair, or even passing out papers. By getting him involved, they enlisted his physical aid and they put him psychologically on their side. These people were successful three or four times more often than the people who talked at other people. If you ask your boss to give you a raise, okay a new project, or change your desk, you are selling and you should involve him.

Where you sell can be as important as how you sell. The ideal sales environment is not an office, but a conference room. The table is oval because the curved edges blur territorial lines and make it easier for the salesperson to pass a contract or other printed material to a prospective buyer. In an ideal sales environment the client will be relaxed. He will not get the feeling he's in your office but in his own. One of the ways of accomplishing this is getting him to sit facing the door while you sit with your back to it. This will give him a feeling of safety and command. The best colors for sales conference rooms are beige and blue. They have a relaxing effect.

If you have to sell in your office there are a few essentials. First, if the office is small and it can accommodate only your desk, your chair, and two chairs for guests, the guest chairs must be the right type. There are two types of sales chairs: one with wheels and one with wheels and a swivel and they both move. If you seat a person in a chair that does not move and you come on too strong, he can become extremely defensive which will kill the sale. If you seat him in a chair that does move, he can simply move away from you for a second (a signal you can look for) and that will relax him. Swivel chairs make sales (Picture 17A). Even in a small office there are two possible arrangements: the authority design (Picture 17A) and the nonauthority design (Picture 17B).

A more efficient sales office is the slightly larger one in Picture 17C. In Picture 17C, as in A and B, you always put the prospect in the movable chair. In Office C, the officeholder has two options: to sit behind his desk, be an authority figure, and sell from that perspec-

Picture 16

Ideal sales environment. Beige walls, well lit, swivel
chairs with wheels, oval desk.

tive or to sit on the couch and give the prominent position to the buyer (Picture 17C).

In Picture 18, the two chairs next to the couch and the chairs in front of your desk should be on wheels or swivel and, here again, you may choose where you wish to sit (Picture 17C).

If you are entering the client's office, walk in without hesitating. Never speak until you reach the person's desk. Always introduce yourself with a firm handshake. When you're signaled to sit, sit down, but pause a second beforehand so you don't look rushed or harried. If you have your choice of seats, choose the seat on the left unless you know the person is left-handed, in which case choose the one on the right. If there are barriers in front of his desk that make it impossible for you to place items there, ask to move your seat around to the side. If you have to sell directly across a man's desk, remember the third of the desk closest to you is your territory but ask permission before moving on the remainder of the desk. And finally, don't come in and try to take over immediately. Take command of the situation gradually. If you come on too strong in the beginning, you will offend most buyers.

If you are going to sell to a person in her home, the first thing you do is ask her if you can use the kitchen or the dining room. Most serious family discussions are carried on in those places, not in the living room. The living room is a place for formal entertainment and she will be on her guard there and sit at a distance. In most living rooms the couches and the chairs are four to five feet apart. Your chance of selling anything to a person in her home triples if you can get her into the kitchen. Once you do, however, do not choose a seat. Let her assign you a seat because in most homes the husband and wife have their own seats and will be offended if you take them.

No matter where they sell, good salespeople are professionals; they act like professionals and they think like professionals. They look upon sales as an honored

Picture 17

Three variations of small office. A. High authority office.
B. Best sales office. C. Multiple function office.

Picture 18

A. Sales setting.

B. Authority setting.

Ideal office design.

profession, which it is. They legitimately try to help their clients whenever they can and they are constantly involved in self-improvement. Good salespeople take sales courses, read books such as this, try the information out to see if it works, and judge for themselves. The poor ones will invariably reject new ideas. They do not believe anything will help because up until now nothing has.

One of the reasons some salespeople can't sell is they have an image of themselves as hucksters. They try to deny this image by taking a dignified, dull approach. It never works. Enthusiasm is one of the characteristics of good salespeople; being excited about one's product and showing real interest is critical to making a sale. Nearly 75 percent of the best salespeople told us they couldn't sell a product they didn't believe in. We wondered why until we started looking at video tapes. When they lied, we could spot it. The salespeople from one large company who didn't believe that their product line was competitive, projected all the classic lie signals when comparing their line to their competition's. They put their fingers up against their noses, they covered their mouths, they looked down, they avoided eye contact. They practically wore signs that said, "I don't believe in my product."

Ironically, confidence men, who you would think couldn't possibly believe in their product, do. I questioned five who were in prison for working various confidence rackets, and four of the five said that when they were talking about a stock or a property, they were convinced they were telling the truth. Two of them said they often forgot they were lying. They would get so wrapped up in their story that they would begin to believe it. One said the only way he could con people was to believe in the con himself. What he described was close to the Stanislavski method of acting—when he was working a mark he looked upon the con as the real world and believed in the part he was playing.

Unlike the people who worked for the company mentioned earlier, confidence men, when their veracity is attacked, react as if they're telling the truth. Unlike the four salesmen from that company, they defend their claims.

In addition, when a buyer attacked one of their claims, they didn't defend them. Good salespeople have a common way of handling an attack. When they believe in their product they let the attacker know in nonverbal ways that they don't agree with him. They erect nonverbal defenses. They hardly ever contradict someone, at least not in the middle of an attack. Instead, they deny the validity of the attack through a series of body signals. When they're sitting at a table, good salesmen steeple and good saleswomen low-steeple.

When sitting in a chair without a desk, good salesmen cross their legs and fold their hands or fold their arms. Good saleswomen will steeple in their laps or fold their arms. These are very critical moves because if someone is attacking your product or your beliefs, and you remain sitting in an open position, you announce nonverbally that you agree with them. No matter what you say, they will never take you seriously.

Poor salespeople and salespeople who are lying often give off the same nonverbal signals for different reasons. People who don't believe in their product and people who don't believe in themselves oversell because they try too hard. They overstate nonverbally. Instead of gestures and expressions being used as positive sales tools, they become negative ones. Poor salespeople offend by gesturing past their normal territorial lines. This is the surest way of killing sales and half the poor salespeople in America do it. See Pictures 20 and 21.

The information in this chapter is quite extensive but it represents only the tip of the sales-research iceberg. Although it will help individual salespeople and some sales trainers, it will not really qualify anyone to teach nonverbal sales. It takes us three to six months to train an experienced sales trainer to teach nonverbal techniques. Anyone who attempts to do it without this train-

Picture 19

A. Man high steepling. B. Woman low steepling.

Picture 20

Standing salesperson's safe gesture territory.
Usually about 14 inches.

Picture 21

Sitting salesperson's safe gesture territory.
Usually ends inch or two past the knee.

ing may be doing you more harm than good. Rereading
this chapter will do you more good than listening to one
of the self-styled experts that this chapter will undoubtedly produce.

8

COMMUNICATION

If you can't communicate, you can't command. This was the consensus of 2,628 successful men and women we questioned throughout the United States—2,212 were executives in large and moderate-sized corporations and the remainder successful either in their own businesses or in fields outside the normal business spectrum such as the arts. Surprisingly, even though the corporate executive thought of communication as the most essential success skill, the men outside the corporate world were, if anything, more insistent that ability to communicate was the key to their success. In fact, one of the chief reasons they gave for their success was their ability to communicate effectively with their clients in large corporations.

The second point of agreement was that educational institutions, even those with very good reputations, do an abysmal job of training young people to communicate. The only disagreement is on the extent of the problem. One said that in three years she hadn't met a young man or young woman who could communicate, while another said that about 60 percent of the college graduates who came to work for her were adequate communicators. On average, two thirds of those interviewed agreed that 70 percent of the young people they met weren't able to communicate adequately. This included, in their opinion, graduates of major universities, including those with master's degrees and MBA's from some of the best schools in the country.

You cannot dismiss their charges as simple broadsides from the older generation. Their charges are very specific. The majority of these very successful people indicate that 60 to 70 percent of the people who join their corporation right out of an American university aren't able to write well-constructed business letters and that close to 80 or 90 percent of them need instruction on how to write a simple business report. One gentleman for whom I have a great deal of respect said that 90 percent of the business reports written by the people who were with his corporation for less than three years had to be rewritten before they could be presented to clients. This is in spite of the fact that his corporation pays very well and is able to attract the top graduates from the top schools.

While the majority of men and women in corporate America are convinced that young people coming out of the universities cannot write adequately, they admit that most of them eventually master basic writing skills and that they can be trained. The real problem for a substantial percentage of these executives is teaching young people to speak clearly. Most of them say that fewer than 20 percent of the people they work with are capable of giving a concise, clear oral report and that they have far greater difficulty training people to do this than to write a simple letter.

The men and women who run corporate America are so dismayed by the quality of our university graduates that several very large corporations have set up remedial courses for their up-and-coming young executives. Others have taken to sending their engineers and technical people back to universities to take liberal arts courses in the hope of improving their communication skills.

When I first started researching corporate communications I assumed that when executives complained about a lack of ability to communicate they meant that their subordinates couldn't write and speak clearly. Working on that assumption, I requested several corporate clients to send me a series of written reports produced by their people with comments on the quality of the report. I also asked them to send me video tapes of corporate meetings and to accompany the tapes with comments by the man in charge on the strengths and weaknesses as communicators of various people at the meetings. In an attempt to have a uniform measurement, we asked them to grade the reports of the people writing or speaking on an A, B, C, D, F basis with the marks having the same value they had in college, A being superior, B being above average, C being average, D being inadequate, and F being failure.

When we received the reports, we found the grades not only surprising but also confusing. There was very little, if any, correlation between the grades the executives gave to their subordinates and the ability of their subordinates to use language well or even accurately. It was apparent from this that when the executives spoke about communication, they were speaking about something other than the ability to handle language. Only in one third of the cases was poor language skills the dominant factor. In the other two thirds, the consensus among the researchers who read the reports and looked at video tapes was that the corporate executives were really commenting on the inability of their subordinates to present or sell ideas in an acceptable manner.

After spending nearly 600 research hours reading reports, looking at video tapes, and analyzing them, we set up interviews with sixty-two, or one third, of the executives who had sent us the original reports. We still had not analyzed the problem correctly. At this point we were looking into the possibility that the breakdown in communication was as much a fault of the executives as it was of the subordinates. We started by testing the listening and reading skills of the executives who had, in our opinion, inaccurately graded their subordinates. After doing so, the researchers believed that they understood what the subordinates were trying to say. We therefore started by testing the executives on their comprehension. We found that in 98 percent of the cases the executives understood the content of the report at least as well as our researchers. When they spoke of someone being an inadequate communicator, what they were really speaking about was that person's inability to sell ideas or the fact that the format the person used to report the ideas was, in their view, inappropriate.

The importance of the format surprised me. We found, for example, that in the same corporation engineers giving reports to different department heads were required to go about it in a totally different manner. One department head wanted every detail covered in the report. He wanted analyses of why the report was being done, complete background on the subject under discussion, and a review of the literature, and he expected the report to run twenty or thirty written pages. In addition, he wanted an oral presentation that covered almost every detail in the report. The man who ran the department right down the hall wanted just the opposite. He wanted short, comprehensive reports discussing only the elements that were new. He said he already knew what was going on in his department. He didn't need an analysis of the situation, and he didn't want any young engineer wasting his time. The reports that got an A in one department, got an F in another and vice versa. Therefore, the first rule for anyone giving a report is to ask those who requested the report what form they would like it to take. If it's a written one, ask for examples of written reports that they thought were good and possibly even examples of one or two they thought were poor. Then you can give them exactly what they want. Superiors usually will be happy to give you this information. If it's an oral report, the most critical question you must ask is, "How much time am I going to be allowed?" One of the key mistakes made by young people preparing a report for a meeting is to assume they will have the entire length of the meeting in which to deliver it. The fact that a meeting takes half an hour doesn't mean you're going to have half an hour. Ask exactly how much time you're going to be allowed and ask how much detail will be required. If the time is inadequate, state so before the report is given. This advice is so simple that many people may overlook it. However, if you remember only one part of this chapter, remember this.

The trickiest report to give is a technical one to non-technical people. A key industry problem today is that everyone is a specialist—at least everyone seems to be. Both society and industry have become so complicated that the generalist is obsolete. All of who are technicians in our own field are now obliged to communicate our expertise to nontechnical people. The kind of writing that I do in this pop-science book is the most needed communication skill in industry today because often the people who are going to make judgments about your specialty, or about you, will not have an adequate technical background for doing so. Today's executive must package his technical information in a way that can be understood by nontechnical people.

Even if the people you're talking to are technicians themselves, there is often no overlap in fields. The engineer down the hallway who happens to be your boss may have only a limited knowledge of your specialty. If he is going to judge your work, you must find out exactly how much he knows before you report to him. The man in charge is often a generalist with an MBA, an accountant who came up through the finance section, or an attorney who believes that all points are debatable. You're going to have to package your information so that these people without any technical background can digest it. But simplify does not mean water down. You can never present your information in a way that will invalidate it. This is a very tricky procedure.

If you are assigned to give a report in your field, whether it's banking, finance, or engineering, to members of the general public or to members of a committee who are not experts in your field, you must keep several factors in mind. The questions that will occur to nontechnical people are not the same questions that will occur to your co-workers, so you cannot test your report by reading it to another expert in the field or to someone else in the office. You are probably better off reading it to your wife, your children, or your neighbor, or, if need be, hiring someone to listen to you.

Before this book went to press, in fact before I handed it to a publisher, I hired six tenth graders with a B average to read the manuscript. I paid them to take a test and gave them bonuses for correct answers. After I analyzed the results, we discussed the book. The sections which they obviously had not fully grasped, I rewrote. Theirs is the base at which I'm aiming. These were intelligent young people who were capable of understanding rather complicated material if it's presented correctly. The first rule for those who write or speak about technical subjects is the KISS rule: Keep It Simple, Stupid! Don't try to impress people with your writing ability or dazzle them with your vocabulary or your technical knowledge. The essence of being brilliant is not making a simple subject complicated, it's making the complicated subject simple.

There is one other rule for people writing or speaking to those outside their field. Jargon is for jerks.

In our study of corporate communication the average grade on oral and on written reports was C, but the average grade for the combined report was D. The combined one is much more complicated. If you have to give such a report, there are certain basic rules. One, make sure that everyone has his own copy of the printed material. If they're looking over one another's shoulders, you will lose them. You can't speak to someone who's looking elsewhere. Two, make sure they're all facing in the same direction. If they're sitting at a long table, even if you have to ask the boss to move, you must speak from the head of the table. Everyone has to be able to look at you and at the report without turning in his chair. Three, every verbal-visual report should be written in the following form: the top sheet should be a highpoint sheet; under it you should have an outline of the report or a content sheet; beneath that, the report itself. It may have any of a dozen formats depending on the nature of the information. If your company has a mandatory form for reports that does not include a highpoint sheet, make one up and give it out with the report. If you can, place it physically on top.

The reason for placing the highpoint sheet on top is that you do not want people to open the report while you're speaking. You want them to be able to look at that highpoint sheet and follow what you're saying. The highpoint sheet should be an outline of your presentation. If you absolutely must ask people to read sections of the report, try to get them in and out as quickly as possible. For example, if they must open the report during your presentation to familiarize themselves with statistics or other written material that cannot be presented on a chart, your problem is to get them to open the report, look at the necessary section, and, when they're finished, to shut the report and place it face up on the table. There are several techniques you can use. The simplest technique is to say, "Gentlemen, go to page ninety-seven. When you're finished, shut the report so we know when everyone is ready to discuss this section." This forces someone who wants to continue reading to close his report because you're not going to say anything until everyone has indicated he is finished. Everyone will feel group pressure to close the report and rejoin you. Two, make sure that on page 97 you have only the information you want them to read. Even if you have to do some rather extraordinary juggling to do this, it is worth the effort. Three, if you have to have them go into the report several times to read one or two paragraphs and you don't want them reading the entire page, make sure the appropriate paragraphs are marked off or underlined. Then you can tell them, "Read the underlined section on page sixty-two," and this will lead them to do just that and stop when they're finished. The one thing you cannot let them do is continue reading the report and ignore you. If you find them doing that, you must take control. You must say, "Gentlemen, please. I must bring you back to page one. You can continue reading the report later." Even if you're the youngest man in the firm and you're talking to all the vice-presidents, you must still be in charge. It is one of those times when it's not only okay for you to be authoritative, it's expected.

Remember, when you give an oral report you're not simply passing on information. If you were, you could hand out a printed form. You are there to sell, to convince the people that your point of view is correct. If you present your information in a deadpan manner, without exuberance or belief, you will lose your audience. If you let people interrupt you, you will lose your audience. If you read a written report you will lose credibility and your audience because there is a difference between the way people speak and the way they write. If you stumble or hesitate, you will lose authority and your audience. If you present complicated technical information in a way that your audience cannot comprehend, you will lose your audience. And if you lose your audience, you are talking to yourself.

All speakers must remember that audiences have personalities and react as a group. They react not only to what you say but also to how you say it. They not only listen to you but they also look at you. If your expressions and your gestures do not match your message, they will turn you off. Therefore, before you make a presentation to an audience, you should first make it to a mirror and then to family or friends. You should do it over and over again until you have it down pat. This is important. When we questioned successful businessmen and women about presentations they made, most of them indicated that these were critical crossroads in their lives and careers. The importance of preparing for such presentations cannot be overemphasized.

No matter how well you know your subject, preparation is necessary. Never speak off the cuff.

There are only two types of preparations: notes or a speech outline and a fully prepared speech. If you know your subject better than anyone who is likely to be in your audience, you may use notes. If not, a written speech is preferable. If you hope or expect to get press coverage, hire a professional speech writer. As a former reporter I can tell you that amateurs are never quotable.

Remember that all the preparation in the world is of no use if you forget what you were going to say, and it happens to the best of us. You must therefore not only have notes or a text, you must also follow it even if you have memorized your speech. The point of having notes or a text is to keep you from getting lost. If you have to start flipping through your papers, you will look like a fool and the audience will disregard you.

If you choose to read your speech, it should be typed all in capitals and triple-spaced on legal-size paper as shown on pages 138 and 139.

Of course, the preparation of a speech goes far beyond the printed form or even the subject matter. You must tailor your presentation to your audience.

Before you can do that you must determine what type of audience you will be talking to. There are really only five types of audience: the intimate audience, the boardroom audience, the classroom audience, the small formal audience, and the large formal audience. Each one has different characteristics and each must be treated in a different way.

The intimate audience is one you can speak to in your normal conversational tone without the help of mechanical aids. Usually this limits the number of people to six or seven. When speaking to such a group there are several factors you must keep in mind. First, always position yourself so you can see everyone and everyone can see you without twisting or turning. Avoid sitting in the middle of a couch or in the middle of a group; always move to the end. Twisting and turning will make you look confused, weak, defensive, and will cut dramatically into your authority and credibility. There are two basic positioning tricks you can use. First, you can move back from the group slightly so that everyone faces you when you speak. Or you can raise your head above the rest of the group. If they're all seated on a couch and chairs, you can sit on an arm of the couch. When talking with such a group, remember that you are better off if the majority of the people agree with you. With intimate groups, whoever controls the majority controls the atmosphere for acceptance. If you've ever been the only Democrat at a meeting of Republicans, the only Republican at a meeting of Democrats, you know exactly what I mean. Never bring up an important topic when you think you're outnumbered in an intimate group.

The boardroom audience is a small group of fewer than fifteen people who cannot hear you when you use a conversational tone. Speaking to a boardroom audience, you have to either speak up or stand up. We would suggest you do both. With the boardroom or conference audience, however, you still maintain a friendly, if not conversational, tone. Do not start to preach and avoid exaggerated gestures. If you are going to give a report in a boardroom or conference room, and it must be given from your seat, you should attempt to sit at either end of the table. If you cannot sit in one of those positions, sit to the right of the person who's running the meeting. If you cannot get that seat, stand up and move to the upper-right position when speaking. If you need an excuse to stand there, bring in a chart and place it there before the meeting begins. Never speak from the middle of the table or from a seated position unless you have absolutely no choice.

The standard classroom setup is a group of seated people with a person standing on the same level and speaking without the aid of a microphone. The standard audiovisual aids used in this environment are charts, blackboard, and chalk. The style used is almost identical to that used in a boardroom setting, possibly with a little more emphasis and formality. You must use restrained gestures since the audience can see your face very clearly. You will be more effective if your verbal and nonverbal messages are kept on a personal level. The standard academic classroom, however, is not a very efficient communications forum. A far better arrangement is the horseshoe (see Picture 23). This form of classroom was researched not only by my organization but also by several *Fortune* 500 companies. We came to the same conclusion: the horseshoe gives the instructor a number of advantages. First, the instructor can choose to stand outside of the horseshoe and deliver an authoritative lecture. In this position he is a high-authority figure similar to a teacher in the traditional classroom. The instructor may also walk into the horseshoe and, by doing so, automatically make himself a part of the group and create a rapport with it. Our research indicates that once you step within the horseshoe, the number of questions you get from the audience will automatically double. The instructor may go one step further and have a chair placed on the invisible line that closes the horseshoe. He can not only walk in, but sit down, putting himself on a level with the audience and creating an even more intimate rapport. Skilled instructors move in and out of the horseshoe forcing the audience to respond differently from moment to moment. If at the beginning of his presentation, the speaker finds his audience too distant, he may move in. If, during the question period, they begin to debate his answers and he doesn't want a debate, he may stand up, walk back past the invisible line, and again take the authoritative position. Because of its great flexibility, I suggest that anyone speaking with fifteen to fifty people use the horseshoe format.

This text is marked to suit my speaking style and interpretation. Each speaker should mark his own text, novices with the help of a friend or coach.

I AM DELIGHTED TO BE HERE
THIS EVENING . . .

KEY: | indicate a breath   <u>ALL</u> for emphasis
      || full pause   ══ more emphasis
      ||| pause for emphasis   ≡ maximum emphasis

FOUR SCORE AND SEVEN YEARS AGO/OUR FATHERS BROUGHT FORTH ON THIS CONTINENT/A NEW NATION CONCEIVED IN LIBERTY/AND DEDICATED TO THE PROPOSITION THAT ALL MEN ARE CREATED EQUAL.//NOW WE ARE ENGAGED IN A GREAT CIVIL WAR/TESTING WHETHER THAT NATION, OR <u>ANY</u> NATION SO CONCEIVED/AND SO DEDICATED,/CAN LONG ENDURE./ WE ARE MET ON A GREAT BATTLEFIELD OF THAT WAR.// WE HAVE COME TO DEDICATE A PORTION OF THAT FIELD AS A FINAL RESTING PLACE FOR THOSE WHO HERE GAVE THEIR LIVES THAT THAT NATION MIGHT LIVE.

IT IS ALTOGETHER FITTING AND PROPER THAT WE SHOULD DO THIS./BUT,/IN A LARGER SENSE,/WE CANNOT <u>DEDICATE</u>/— WE CANNOT <u>CONSECRATE</u>—WE CANNOT <u>HALLOW</u>—THIS GROUND./ THE BRAVE MEN,/LIVING AND DEAD, WHO STRUGGLED HERE/ HAVE <u>CONSECRATED</u> IT/FAR ABOVE OUR POOR POWER TO ADD OR DETRACT.//THE WORLD WILL LITTLE NOTE/NOR LONG REMEMBER/WHAT WE SAY HERE,/BUT IT CAN NEVER FORGET WHAT THEY DID HERE.

IT IS ALTOGETHER FITTING AND PROPER THAT WE SHOULD DO THIS. BUT, IN A LARGER SENSE, WE CANNOT DEDICATE—WE CANNOT CONSECRATE—WE CANNOT HALLOW—THIS GROUND. THE BRAVE MEN, LIVING AND DEAD, WHO STRUGGLED HERE HAVE CONSECRATED IT FAR ABOVE OUR POOR POWER TO ADD OR DETRACT. THE WORLD WILL LITTLE NOTE NOR LONG REMEMBER WHAT WE SAY HERE, BUT IT CAN NEVER FORGET WHAT THEY DID HERE.

IT IS FOR US THE LIVING/RATHER/TO BE DEDICATED HERE TO THE UNFINISHED WORK/WHICH THEY WHO FOUGHT HERE/ HAVE THUS FAR SO NOBLY ADVANCED./IT IS RATHER FOR US/TO BE HERE DEDICATED TO THE GREAT TASK REMAINING BEFORE US—/THAT FROM THESE HONORED DEAD WE TAKE INCREASED DEVOTION/TO THAT CAUSE FOR WHICH THEY GAVE THE LAST FULL MEASURE OF DEVOTION—//THAT WE HERE HIGHLY RESOLVE THAT THESE DEAD SHALL NOT HAVE DIED IN VAIN//—THAT THIS NATION/UNDER GOD/SHALL HAVE A NEW BIRTH OF FREEDOM—/ AND THAT GOVERNMENT OF THE PEOPLE, BY THE PEOPLE, FOR THE PEOPLE, SHALL NOT PERISH FROM THE EARTH.

Picture 22

Boardroom.

The small audience is an audience in which anyone can easily see the speaker's face and read its expression. Speakers in front of small, formal audiences are usually on raised platforms and often behind podiums. With the small, formal audience, a clever speaker wears a lavalier mike, which gives him the option of standing behind the podium or moving out to the side. Moving from behind the podium breaks down a barrier between him and the audience. Before small, formal audiences, speakers are required to be slightly more effervescent and demonstrative than they are before a classroom audience. Once you are on a raised platform, the audience expects a more formal presentation. They expect exaggerated gestures, and they will not give you as much credibility if you do not use them. The same gestures and movements that would have seemed excessive in a boardroom are totally appropriate on the stage. Most businessmen, because they are used to speaking before boardroom groups, maintain their style on the stage. As

Picture 23

Speaker's
Position

Horseshoe classroom.

a result, they are dull and boring. The minute you are
raised on a stage you must raise your voice when you
speak and you must raise your arms when you gesture.
You cannot talk to the audience as if you were talking
to a small group. Even though you have known the
people all your life, there is an expectation that once
you are on the stage you must be a bit of an actor. The
expectations increase by tenfold when you speak to a
large audience of 200 people or more. Once you step on
a stage before that many people you are an entertainer.
Whether you are running for the presidency of the United
States or you're talking about nuclear physics, your
first job is to keep your audience entertained. You cannot pass on useful information or convince them to vote
for you unless they want to listen to you. Large audiences have a personality all their own. They expect people on the stage to be entertaining. That is why good
speakers (almost) always tell jokes. But jokes are not
enough. You must entertain them with the subject mat-

ter. You must be exuberant. You must pause longer
than you would normally pause for everyday speech.
The restraint normally associated with executive speech
patterns must be thrown out the window. If it is not,
you will be another executive bore on the stage. If you
are taking speech lessons, quit. Go and take a course in
acting. The rules for using your hands and gesturing
on the stage are more akin to acting in *Othello* or *On
the Waterfront* than they are to giving a speech in any
other format. Good speakers are actors, entertainers,
and hams and unless you can become one, you will
never be a good speaker.

Once you've decided what type of audience you are
dealing with and how you're going to deal with them,
decide on the mechanical aids you're going to use. The
first and most obvious is a microphone. If you're speaking to fifty people or more and you do not know the
room, insist on a mike. Sometimes extremely small rooms
have dead spots, and without a mike, you'll be dead. You
can always choose not to use it, but have a mike ready.
Always keep your mouth at least six inches from the
mike. Some mikes will pick you up even if you talk from
the side, others will not; they are very directional and
you must test this ahead of time. If you are not used to
handling a mike, ask for a lavalier mike. These are
small mikes that are hung around the neck or pinned to
your tie or shirt and pick up perfectly at that distance.
If you're going to be using charts or slides, wear a
lavalier mike. It will free both your hands.

Use charts with groups of twenty-five people or fewer.
When you have more than twenty-five people in the
room, transfer your information to slides. The best slide
projectors are carousel slide projectors and most hotels
and companies have them. The only tray you should
ever use is the eighty-slide tray. The larger one that
carries more slides sticks too often. If you use slides,
you must know ahead of time if you're going to have
front or rear projection. Rear projection requires glass-
mounted slides; regular slides will burn out. You can

never put any printed material on a chart or a slide that you are not going to read to the audience because there is a percentage of people in the audience who will not be able to read it without your help. Extensive printed material on slides or charts infuriates audiences.

Naturally, if you're going to use slides, you need a slide projector. The rule for using slide and movie projectors, video cassettes, and other mechanical devices is based on Molloy's Law of Mechanical Devices. It states: if a machine can break down it will and it will do so at the most inappropriate moment. Therefore, you must be sure you have a backup item for each mechanical device you need. That means you need two of everything—slide projectors, movie projectors, whatever. If the person running the conference tells you that you really don't need a second one, that he has someone there who's an expert, pay no attention to him. Insist on a backup. You must also have backup for your presentation, a five-minute story that will fit in at any point in your speech when the entire system breaks down. And, of course, you must be prepared to go on without your audiovisual aids because there are times when it will just be impossible to fix them, even when you have a backup system.

Finally, the greatest breakdown in corporate communications that I've seen is communications between speakers and those who are setting up meetings. Do not believe hotels. They will promise you everything and leave you up the creek. If you are going to speak at a hotel, make a list of the audiovisual equipment you need and have someone in the hotel sign the list. In addition, be sure you have the name and telephone number of someone who will be available when you're going to speak, particularly if you're going to be speaking at night when there will be no one there to correct mistakes.

This entire chapter up to this point has been based on the premise that communication is message sending. But to a very large extent it is also message receiving.

All the great communicators that we witnessed at corporate meetings, and in person, have one thing in common: they are extremely sensitive people. The stereotype of the American executive presented on television and in the movies as a hard, crass, unfeeling clown is untrue. He is a very discerning human being; that is one of the keys to his success. He is sensitive to everyone around him.

While watching the video tapes of corporate meetings we noticed that the executives in charge answered questions differently depending on who asked them. We found that executives read between the lines—not the lines on paper but the lines on people's faces. They pick up very subtle messages. An executive in a major computer company ran seven meetings for our video tape system. During two of these meetings he was confronted by his chief engineer, an argumentative man who insisted on his own way. In those first two meetings the man in charge, in no uncertain terms, said he was in charge and that was the end of that. The third time he was challenged, he didn't back off but simply walked around the question, said we'll come back to it later and very gently patted his adversary on the head. When we went back and asked him why, he said he sensed that the man was upset that day and didn't want to push him. When we talked to the man, we found that on that day he had been in a car accident on the way to work. Although this is a rather surprising example, it is not uncommon.

The men who run corporate America are great people-watchers. However, watching is not the main difference between the good and poor communicators. The great communicators are all listeners. They listen carefully, patiently, even kindly to their subordinates. They encourage people to speak to them. They hardly ever step on a man's ego or a woman's sentence. Even if they don't like a suggestion, they treat it with respect and they treat the people coming to them with respect. The really great communicators are great receivers as well as great senders of messages.

9

POWER

My first job after college was as a management trainee for a large department store chain. I was immediately introduced to the company SOB and, unfortunately, spent my first three weeks working for him. To give the devil his due, he was a very efficient department head. He demanded, and got, first-class performance from the people who worked for him. His department was one of the most productive, efficient, and certainly one of the most profitable in the store. He kept it that way by intimidating everyone. One of his favorite targets was new young men so, naturally, he leaned very heavily on a friend and me.

Everyone in the store, at least those working under him, reacted to him in the same way; they respected him grudgingly, obeyed him fearfully, and hated him intensely.

After two months I decided to leave retailing for insurance. I put out my feelers while working for Mr. Charm and had received a couple of replies. Although I hadn't told my superior, I casually mentioned it to one or two of my co-workers. On the Friday I had chosen to hand in my resignation, a couple of friends and I were having lunch in the company cafeteria. One of the secretaries from the executive offices came in and gave us the bad news.

Mr. Charm was about to be put in charge of several departments and everyone there was going to be work-

ing for him, some of them permanently. The news elic-
ited grumbles, curses, and a decision by three other
trainees to quit the same afternoon. It only caused me to
change my mind about giving two weeks' notice. I decided
to leave then and there.

But as in most groups of equals, some are more equal
than others. One of the management trainees apparently
needed a lot less training for management than the rest
of us. He was the only one who didn't talk about quitting. Instead, he sat for a while and listened and then
suggested that if we all got together, we might get Mr.
Charm instead of Mr. Charm getting us. He pointed out
that since four of us were going to resign, resigning as a
group might have greater impact. He went on to suggest
that since I had already decided to resign before the bad
news came and had nothing to lose, I would be the ideal
person to carry the message.

I remember giving him a little grin because I knew I
was being used and I wanted him to know I knew.
Under different circumstances I might have objected
vehemently, but in that instance, I didn't care. In fact, I
liked the idea. Getting even with Mr. Charm would be a
real pleasure. He had made a point of embarrassing me
for no legitimate reason every day I worked for him.

Instead of resigning that afternoon, I arranged an
appointment with the president of the company for Mon-
day morning. When I got to his office I handed him my
resignation along with those of my three co-workers and
told him that I was quitting because of the man he had
put in charge. There was no way he could talk me out of
it but he might be able to convince the others to stay if
he changed his mind about his selection for the new
division head. I also pointed out that although there
were six or seven other management trainees who had
not handed in their resignations, from what I understood, they were looking around.

The president of the store gave me a speech about
snotnoses interfering in management and told me I did
not have to give him two weeks' notice but I could leave

at the end of the day, which I did. He then proceeded to act as if my announcement had no impact at all. However, when I checked back three weeks later, I found that our friend was still running only one department instead of six and that another man had been given his promotion.

The most important thing you must know about power is how to use it and when to use it.

One year before writing this chapter I gave a two-day seminar based on our power research to forty-six young men and seventeen young women, all of whom had been identified by superiors as poor power players. Nine months later I contacted these same managers and asked if the course had been effective. They reported that the course had been extremely effective, that thirty-nine of the young men and fifteen of the young women had improved their power profiles. They were giving orders and, in some cases, for the first time, they were being carried out by their subordinates. Although admittedly none of them were as yet polished power-users, they were certainly more effective than they had been. More significantly, twenty-six of these young men and thirteen of these young women were now being considered for first-run management positions, whereas only nine months before all of them had been out of the running.

The report we received about the young women indicated that their improvement was far more dramatic than that of the men. Apparently, women in their normal socialization are not taught about power. Most of them had never played team sports in which they had to take charge, interact under pressure, or lead a group, which is where most young men learn to lead and to follow. As a result, the women had little or no practice in exercising authority. However, once they were taught the fundamentals, they exercised power with as much proficiency and know-how as any man.

The information in this chapter works. It will give anyone who reads it carefully a new weapon system. But before passing on the weapon, I would like to remind the reader that most men who have handled this weapon

have considered it a two-edged sword. Just about everyone who has been in power has come to realize its
dilemma sooner or later. The literature is full of quotes
about its dangers from those who have exercised power.
I have chosen two from opposite ends of the spectrum so
that the reader will understand how universal the fear
of power is by those who have wielded it. Jimmy Walker,
the very colorful mayor of New York, who sought power
for glamour, borrowed a quote from someone else when
he said, "Be nice to the people you meet on the way up,
because you are going to meet the same people on the
way down." Napoleon, who sought power for its own
sake, expressed exactly the same idea somewhat differently when he said, "Any leader who makes enemies of
people he meets while gaining his leadership is a fool
and will not be a leader long." If you read and believed
all those books and articles that suggest that the way to
the top is over the bodies of everyone you meet, you'd be
very wise to make a painful reappraisal of your present
work-style.

Nevertheless, most of the executives we questioned
said the main problem their subordinates had with power
wasn't that they overused it, but that they didn't know
how to use it. They agreed this was particularly true of
women. This fact was confirmed by the women executives we talked to, who stressed that the chief stumbling
block in most young women's careers is their inability
or unwillingness to use power. One woman, the vice-
president of a major marketing firm, phrased it rather
comically: "If you can't kick tail, you're gonna get your
tail kicked, particularly if you're a woman." The men we
questioned did not think that power is a sexual problem
but a universal one. The president of a large manufacturing company said, "If a man can't use power on those
occasions when he needs it to get the job done, he's not
going anywhere." The head of a marketing department
in a *Fortune* 500 company commented with a touch of
sarcasm, "In this company and in every other company,
in spite of all the fancy glass doors and the $400 suits,

there are those who are doing and those who are being done to. If you don't know how to play the game, you are going to fall into the latter category." The man who seemed to hit the nail on the head was an executive in a large computer company. He said, "If you can't get the people under you to do what you want them to do, even when they want to do something else, you don't belong in the executive suite and you probably won't get there."

In spite of their hard-boiled realism, most of the executives were very charming. The real killers are always charmers. They seldom use raw power in business. You know they have it, but you don't get the feeling the ax is about to fall on your neck. They relax you, they talk to you, they persuade you. Their main weapon is leadership, not raw force. They get people to want to do what they want them to do. Nevertheless, these very polished ladies and gentlemen said that this chapter is critical to a book on making it, because they recognize that their power of persuasion rests to a large degree upon the knowledge of the people being persuaded, that even if they don't go along willingly, they are going to go along anyway.

I know this flies in the face of most of the management courses being taught today. The majority of recent MBA's we interviewed were convinced that management by objective is the new pathway for business success. A percentage believed that business is being democratized too slowly, and when they get in they are going to let people set their own goals and through this they will achieve increased production and a wonderful new lifestyle. Actually, all of the new techniques in management are useful, but they work only when the man or woman in command is really in command. This was the unanimous opinion of every executive we questioned. Further, they agreed that sooner or later in all business persons' lives, they reach a point where they have to know how to exercise raw power. If they know, they succeed. If they don't, they fail—at that moment, and possibly forever.

Although power has been written about by almost everyone, data on the most critical aspects of the subject is extremely difficult to find. The psychological studies that I read were often so theoretical that they were useless. They were more often than not based on the premise that one management technique is superior to others, and they usually reflected the personal opinion of the author. Many of them were little more than essays couched in psychological and semiscientific terms. In the few places where hard data did exist, it dealt almost exclusively with men, and even then, much of the information was contradictory.

The studies we found most significant dealt with men wielding almost absolute power in limited environments: the presidents of corporations, the heads of countries, the owners of companies. They were people who made decisions that no one in their environment dared to question. When I first spoke to them, they started giving me the same information they gave to previous researchers. But when I told them that as president of my own corporation I now acted dramatically differently from the way I did before the corporation succeeded, and when I went on to explain that as a fellow power-user I did not for one moment believe what they were telling me, most of them immediately changed their stories. For example, just about all of them told previous researchers that the way to get ahead in their corporation was to stand up for what you believe in, defend your position, take a chance, be a gambler. If you have a problem, go directly to the top. That's what they wanted from the people who worked for them, being fully aware that communication is essential to the man at the top and that if he cuts himself off from the people under him and doesn't keep the lines of communication open, it will interfere with his ability to run a corporation. Therefore, they said their object was to keep the lines of communication open. At the same time, they admitted that when they were subordinates, they backed down often when they were right, they sidestepped certain subjects, and they didn't circumvent their bosses to get to the big boss as they were suggesting those under them do. Because if they had, and their boss found out, he would have cut their throats and they would have never made it to the top. In fact, they didn't act at all the way they were suggesting that their subordinates act.

They went on to state the obvious: often, if you win the battle, you lose the war and, with it, your career. Taking the ball and running with it is nice in theory, but in fact, you have to find out who has the ball and who is willing to run with you. They talked openly to me because before the interviews I not only signed non-disclosure agreements, I also showed them that in nineteen years of research I never betrayed a client's or a subject's confidence. One of the things that all readers must keep in mind when they see the statements of the great and powerful, is that people who are great and powerful know how to look out for themselves, they give researchers the information they want the researchers to have. They don't bother to talk about unpleasant or uncomplimentary facts. They are never going to mention that in order to get to the top, they had to kowtow on the way up. In order to get along, you've got to learn to go along, and they never said they lied to their bosses because they don't want their subordinates lying to them. Almost every man I spoke to at the head of a corporation told me that at one point in his career he worked for an idiot, and he looked out for that idiot in order to take care of himself. In short, he saved the idiot's career in order to save his own. The man who came closest to telling the unvarnished truth said, "The only system-ized training for leadership I encountered was at West Point." He learned that in order to give orders, you had to take orders. He said that what it really comes to is that "you have to take a lot of bunk before you can give any bunk." The key to power is knowing when to back off. You have to know when to say, "Yes, sir," "I'm sorry, sir, I'll do it your way," because, according to all of the executives we questioned, unless you learn very quickly to bow to power, you are not going to have any. Power is given by the boss *above* to people the boss thinks are going to help him. If you keep that in mind, you'll have the real key to power.

The most surprising bit of information we uncovered was that the majority of executives agreed it was easier to exercise power at the top, than it was in the middle. They suggested that if I wished to help power-seekers I study the exercise of limited power, since the skill needed to exercise limited power is substantially different from that needed to exercise power at the top. The authoritarian positions that a top man can take will not work in the middle. Several of them suggested I look at people in their organizations, particularly those in beginning and middle management positions, who were handling power efficiently. I asked if I could also look at those who were handling it inefficiently, and when they agreed, we began our studies.

We attempted, under a variety of conditions, to observe men and women identified by their superiors as good and poor power players. First, we observed them during critical power situations, corporate meetings, giving reports, etc. We also sent our researchers to them in various guises. They identified themselves as clients, co-workers, subordinates, and superiors and noted the reaction of the successful and unsuccessful power players in social business activities. We noted with whom they went to lunch, where they went to lunch, whose company they sought and whose company they avoided, how they dressed, and so on.

We also enlisted the cooperation of several of our client corporations. They agreed to have a number of their executives report on inefficient and efficient power-users. We asked for reports in specific areas. We wanted a general description of each person involved, his job title, category, and power relationships. We wanted descriptions of their relationships with the people around them, both past and present. We also requested physical descriptions of the people and their environments. We asked them to supply us with pictures when they could, and most of them did. Finally, we asked for a summary of their command habits, how they gave orders to their secretaries and other subordinates on a daily basis. We asked for word-for-word playbacks when possible.

We also requested reports on critical challenges to their authority. We asked the executives to make careful notes the first few days anyone was in a new job. We wanted specific information. We wanted to know which signals they sent off when they were challenged: their voice quality, intonation, language, and sentence structure. Again, if possible, we wanted word-for-word playbacks. We also wanted to know the nonverbal signals they sent out when they were challenged: where and how they stood, sat, moved; how they used their heads, hands, angles of their shoulders, their bodies; where they placed their feet; anything and everything. We asked that those making observations draw little pictures if possible and note the position and exact movement of specific parts of the body.

At the same time, we were conducting a survey of communications with various corporations. As part of that study, we had clients video tape corporate meetings. These tapes soon revealed that the corporate meetings were dramatic scenes of infighting. We decided at that point to analyze certain sections of the tapes and use them as part of the study of power.

The first fact we discovered about power is that it is a way of life rather than a response to a particular situation. Power people have definite personality profiles. They are private people who maintain psychological barriers between themselves and their co-workers, their subordinates, and their superiors. Most of the people around them know very little about their personal lives, and power people do not volunteer any information. They never allow themselves to be the butt of jokes, nor do they allow others to impose on them, even in minor ways. They will take offense if anyone takes even slight advantage of them, particularly if it is done publicly. They understand that power is a habit and in all their relationships they maintain a power profile. This usually means they have little or no social relationships with their subordinates, even incidental ones. If they had been having lunch with the same four people for three years and they become an assistant department head, they stop those lunches and start lunching with the other assistant department heads. Not doing this is one of the main mistakes women make. They attempt to maintain former relationships even when their position is changed. When choosing who among their equals they should associate with, they choose very carefully. If they are real power players, they will never associate with a competitor. In offices where there are two obvious power players, each of them gathers around him little groups of friends. Power players always attempt to enlist the most able people and avoid anyone who is incompetent.

Their relationship with their subordinates is simple. In minor ways they continually reinforce their positions. Their actions identify them as the boss. Our video tape studies show that, particularly at the beginning of meetings, they give subordinates trivial assignments: "Move that chair over here, Tom." "Mary, please get me a cup of coffee." In their everyday relationships with subordinates, particularly women, men often establish themselves as father figures, kind but demanding, big daddy looking out for the small and helpless. Once this parent-child relationship is developed, there is no way the power player can be challenged, even on minor issues. These relationships are not necessarily unfriendly, nor do they always involve executive plotting. They are often products of personality types or male-female stereotyping. They are also often the basis for real friendships. A classic example is the relationship between Mary Tyler Moore and her boss, Lou Grant, on the TV show. As his assistant, she had no power or authority to challenge him, because he fathered her and allowed her no leeway.

During their entire time on the air she always referred to him as "Mr. Grant." The show's writers had excellent insight into power relationships.

Another favorite method for power players to remind subordinates that they are subordinates, is by judging them. They judge their work, the way they dress, how they stand, the kind of restaurants they frequent. They never relinquish their right to judge. That doesn't mean they're continually sniping at subordinates. On the contrary, power players are praisers. If you do an excellent job, they will pat you on the back in front of other people and you will feel great. This accomplishes two goals. It encourages you to work harder and it reinforces the relationship. They not only pat people on the back psychologically, they pat them physically. Power players constantly engage in physical activities that identify them as the dominant person in the relationship. They approach a secretary's desk and without asking permission, take something and start reading it. They do the same with subordinates. They often come up behind subordinates and look over their shoulders. When they do, they will usually comment positively and negatively on what they see. There is a judgmental quality to everything they do. Under certain circumstances they will often compliment subordinates on tasks that are relatively meaningless. Some of the better power players we witnessed even set up artificial goals and deadlines so that they could praise someone for reaching them and condemn them for not doing so. They spent much of their time establishing and reinforcing the command relationship.

The only time you can identify a great power-user is when he meets with a challenge. Poor power-users immediately go for the throat. They start World War III, they commit to unnecessary confrontations. Good power-users avoid confrontations. They get their way without a fight. They nibble away at their opponent. When an efficient power-user becomes a department head and finds out there are two or three people in the department who are likely to challenge him, he sets up small power confrontations, things that his subordinates are not going to argue about. He will go to a troublemaker's desk and tell him to come to his office immediately. After rushing him into his office, he will make him sit down and wait before giving him a meaningless assignment. When the subordinate is out to lunch, he will go to his desk, take the assignment from it, read it, correct it, and return it. It's all part of the power game.

Good power players play the same everywhere. They plan. The rules they apply in offices work equally well in schools and at home. We found teachers working in very rough schools who had few authority problems in their classrooms. Inevitably they were the ones who used their positions to advantage. They were not necessarily the biggest teachers or the loudest teachers or the toughest teachers. They were the ones who knew how to manipulate people. They never allowed direct confrontations with student troublemakers during the first few days of school. They made it a point to give assignments that everyone, including the troublemakers, were required to do—usually a simple assignment during class. Then they made it a point to judge, criticize, and assist the troublemakers, establishing their relationship as a teacher before any confrontation could take place. By helping the students, which was their job, they were establishing their authority in such a way that the student couldn't argue about it. Before confronting anyone who is likely to fight with you, it is sound advice to give that person several small orders where there is no real possibility of a confrontation developing. Once you have established a pattern, discipline problems are not likely to arise. In a survey of the parents of teen-agers we found that those who were good authority figures tended to establish their authority in minor ways. Parents who insist their children be in at reasonable hours, clean their rooms, and look decent before they leave the house, hardly ever had major authority problems. Mothers are particularly effective at this. Mothers who straighten their sons' ties, make sure their hair is combed, comment about their shoes not being shined, are really very effective authority figures. Parents who argue only over major issues almost always lose.

Our research also indicates that where an authority relationship is broken down, it can be re-established. The technique that seems to work best is for the authority figure to give a series of small, inoffensive commands, being careful to choose areas in which there will be no argument. The next step is for the authority figure to make minor territorial invasions: take things off a subordinate's desk, straighten your son's room, and so on. Subordinates are much more likely to obey orders after a series of minor, seemingly meaningless victories by the person in authority.

We tested this particular procedure in three different schools with half a dozen teachers who were having serious authority problems. With a few noted exceptions they were able to establish their authority over groups, if not over every individual within the group. We also had a great deal of success teaching these techniques to young executives who were having authority problems with other workers. My guess is that to re-establish parental authority would be trickier, would take much longer, and would be a much more difficult process. But the rules of power and authority operate the same in the home as they do in the office and the school, so similar techniques should work over a period of time.

The habits of powerful men and women can create significant difficulties for their subordinates. In a later chapter we will point out that one of the best ways to move up in a corporation is to find a powerful man and attach yourself to him. That way, you are likely to move up when he moves up. You must also understand that powerful men and women are going to impose on you. Throughout these relationships, you must maintain your dignity or they will lose respect for you. The path to power is across a tightrope. Most of the men we questioned were now at the top and said that at various stages in their careers they put up with what they considered abusive treatment because they had no choice. They advised that when you are not sure what to do, go along with your boss. They also insist that you must draw a line somewhere. Never let your boss make a fool of you in public. The president of one corporation told me that he had a boss who poked and punched subordinates all the time. He absolutely insisted that the boss not do that to him. He told his boss that being poked and punched drove him crazy and he couldn't stand it. He pointed it out, he didn't argue about it with him. He was careful to pick a time when his boss seemed to be in a good mood. As a result, he was made an exception to the punching and pushing and he maintained his dignity while others did not. The vice-president of another corporation told the same story with a different ending. He had a boss who shouted at people all the time. He insisted that the boss not shout at him and swears that this cost him his promotion. He spent eighteen months instead of twelve in personnel, and he feels that this is the primary reason he is not president of the company today.

These obviously contradictory tales, I am sure, leave the reader with a series of questions, and that is exactly where you should be. I want you to know there are no correct answers; no absolutely right or wrong ways to handle any situation. If you don't know which way to go, don't fret about it. Some of the most successful men in the country admitted that during their careers they had been in situations in which they had to close their eyes and pray that they were doing the right thing. Sometimes they won and sometimes they lost, and sometimes, as they were going about it, they didn't know whether they were winning or losing.

One fact they all agreed upon: if you work for a powerful man and you try to play power games with him, you are in all probability going to lose.

If your boss looks upon you as someone who will not support him, he is going to get rid of you. The executive of a major insurance company said it best, "The mutuality of interest, rather than manipulation, generally moves people up the corporate ladder and helps them succeed." The president of one of the top 100 corporations in America, certainly the most powerful man I interviewed for this book, and a man who is constantly being described in major business magazines as a corporate giant, gave me this quote. He said, "John, tell the young men and women out there that the most important thing they are going to have to do is bite their tongues and say, 'Yes, I made a mistake,' even when they are not sure. If they are not sure, duck when their boss swings. I had to eliminate two people from contention for top positions in the past few years because I found them playing silly games. Tell them not to come into a corporation with the idea of playing those games. Come in with the idea of cooperating with the people in charge. If that means acting like a pussycat, well, on occasion, they're going to have to do that, because if you take two men making ten decisions, they are going to disagree at least four or five times. Which means there will be constant fighting if no one is in charge. Occasionally, if you are a subordinate, you have to act like a pussycat, because that's the way the world works."

While you occasionally have to act like a pussycat with your superiors, apparently you should always be a tiger when dealing with your subordinates. Our research does not suggest that you always use an iron fist, but it does suggest that there be an iron fist in the velvet glove. Surveys of superiors, co-workers, and subordinates indicate that most employees are happier, more productive, and more effective when working for high-authority figures. This does not for one moment assume that the Draconian methods are always in order. All employees should not be treated identically. Different personality types require different management techniques. An employee who lives on rules and regulations and keeps saying ought and shall, will respond to well-structured sets of orders. At the same time, the man working next to him may be a self-motivated status seeker who will respond only to some democratization of management. The fact remains that both of these employees will be more effective and certainly happier working for someone they know is a decision maker and in charge. Unfortunately, many of the management courses put the cart before the horse. Teaching management techniques to people who don't understand the mechanism of power is very much like teaching strategy to someone who does not understand how weapons work. For this very simple reason, this chapter teaches you how power works rather than the theory of power.

In most social and business situations, having upper-middle-class speech patterns is absolutely essential to have a power image. It announces to those around you that you are a member of an elite group. Even though we found successful men in their own businesses who had obvious lower-middle-class speech patterns, they were effective only when dealing with others with lower-middle-class speech patterns or with young people. When they had to deal with people who used upper-middle-class speech patterns, they were noticeably ineffective.

The simple declarative sentence is the bedrock on which power language is built. It is a basic, bare bones language with few modifiers. Power people, although they use complicated sentence structure and a rather extensive vocabulary to prove they are upper-middle-class, avoid these structures during critical power situations. They also avoid modifiers that weaken their statements.

Our research indicates that women are four times more likely than men to modify their statements with weakening phrases. They often start sentences with such phrases as "I think" and "I believe." Both signal uncertainty. Another weakening female habit is asking for consensus, for example, "shouldn't we all," or "isn't this the right thing to do." These are actually not calls for consensus but a call for debate. Men, on the other hand, in the same situation are much more likely to say, "now that we have solved the problem, let's do X," or "now that we have eliminated the objection, let's do Y." Even when both are married to management by objective techniques, men and women handle consensus differently. Men are likely to seek consensus through direction. "Now that we have eliminated the objections let's go on and do 1, 2, 3." Women will seek consensus by question. "Don't you think we should be doing 1, 2, or 3?" And the consensus through questioning never arrives.

Power people not only use different vocabulary and sentence structure, they use their voices differently. Ninety-five percent of the men in America can increase their verbal power image by lowering their voices from a half to a full octave. Ninety-five percent of the women, on the other hand, can increase their verbal power image by dropping their voices a full octave and slowing them down a great deal. Most women, particularly when excited, speak much too rapidly and lose effectiveness as a result. A woman must take special caution never to raise her voice to a screech or a squeal level. Once she does she appears to have lost control and with it she loses her power. While a man can shout and scream to increase his power on a particular occasion, women almost never can do that effectively.

As we pointed out previously, power people are at their best during critical power situations. It means they use their best power voice as well as their most effective mannerisms. Men drop their voices the half octave and women drop their voices a full octave, when challenged. Some women who are consummate power players have true power voices as do some men. A power voice is not only slower, it has a different intonation. It is almost solemn. This solemnity is helpful to the power image of a man and absolutely critical to the power image of a woman. When we play the order-giving voices of some of the best women power figures without pictures, those listening describe their voices as steely, icy, precise, and distinct. However, if you are not a power figure in your environment, you cannot pull off that solemn tone. It works only if you precondition your audience to take you seriously. If you have not, you risk being laughable. Your verbal power image must match your nonverbal power image.

The men who run military academies will tell you that authority is as much nonverbal as verbal. The basic authority stance is almost military in nature: the shoulders squared, the head erect, the jaw muscles tight, the mouth closed and unsmiling, feet planted firmly on the floor, and eyes steady.

If a person sits down he sits in exactly the same manner. The head remains erect, the facial expression does not change, and the feet remain firmly planted on the floor. The military are taught to keep their head and eyes unmoving. This is critical for power. The entire look is one of control. The authority figure creates a certain sense of immobility. Powerful people, when they are making critical statements, usually move their lips very little, some actually whisper. Although there are exceptions, they tend to be rather stonefaced. This does not mean that they lack energy or that they are dull. On the contrary, their statements usually are very vibrant. The power of their statements comes from the pent-up power of a motionless body taut and ready to spring.

Powerful people's moves are orchestrated. They are very deliberate and know what they are doing. They move straight forward and back. They hardly ever sway and they never move from side to side. The most effective power players use the implements on their desk effortlessly. Pens, pencils, contracts, or pieces of paper become power props. They always seem to know where everything is. They do not have to break critical eye contact or move and lose their sense of immobility to find something. When we questioned two expert power players about this both of them said they memorized where everything on their desk was located. And they did so deliberately. They believe it gives their movements a smooth, flowing, unhurried look. This unhurried character of their movements gives the impression of being relaxed while the tautness in their face muscles gives the impression they're ready to spring. This is not something you can turn off and on. It takes a great deal of practice because there is no artificiality in their movements or in their voices. Power is essentially part of their personality. For this reason you cannot simply put on a power voice and copy the power movements in this book. Power takes practice. If you attempt to emulate the power body language I've just described only when you are challenged, it will probably hurt your image more than it will help. If you wish to do it successfully, you are going to have to buy a full-length mirror, sit in front of it, and carry on make-believe conversations and give make-believe orders hour after hour. It will work even better if you purchase a video tape machine, tape yourself, play it back, and criticize yourself very harshly. Our study indicates that the study of power is closer to learning golf or karate than it is to studying philosophy. You have to develop a good power reflex, not an intellectual grasp of the subject. I repeat, power takes practice. But there are elements of our study on power and authority that you can apply immediately. They deal with presence, props, position, and territory.

One of the essential elements of power is presence, which depends on size, weight, and positioning. If you are six feet five inches tall you have a greater sense of presence than someone five feet five inches. Years ago, a study was done that indicated there was a greater correlation between the success of students graduating from the MBA program at Harvard and their height than between their success and their grades. The reason is simple. Big men have a greater sense of presence and a greater sense of power. Therefore, it is to your advantage to add to your sense of presence. There is an entire series of techniques for doing this.

You can start by wearing what is commonly called serious clothing. Very dark suits, in charcoal-gray or navy-blue pinstripe, with white shirts or blouses and obviously expensive accessories will add to your psychological sense of power. You can further add to your sense of presence and power by sitting in a large chair

Picture 24

A. Man with hands on hips—power stance.
Woman with hands on hips—non-power stance.

B. Man with one hand on hip—power stance.
Woman with one hand on hip—non-power stance.

C. The most effective male and female power stance. Straight, feet slightly spread, erect, almost military.

as long as the chair is not so large that it overwhelms you. One of the critical mistakes made by women who move into executive positions is that they sit their 120-pound frame in a chair that belonged to a 220-pound man. The enormous chair makes the 220-pound man look much more powerful, while it dwarfs the woman and makes her look like a little girl in her daddy's chair and obviously cuts into her effectiveness. If you take that chair and you put it behind a desk, you have again added to your weight and to your sense of presence and to your sense of power. If the desk and the chair have a window behind them or a series of pictures that frames the chair and gives it a throne effect, that too adds to the sense of power. If the chair behind your desk is set so that it is two or three inches higher than the chairs in front of the desk, you have changed the relative eye position of people in the room and you again, by changing your position, add to your sense of power. If you are a short woman you must make it a point to have your chair higher than the chairs of people sitting in front of you or they can come in and intimidate you in your office. You never want that to happen and naturally if it is your office your sense of territory adds to your power.

While some props add weight, others add status. There is a famous story of a stockbroker on Wall Street who had a picture of Rockefeller on his wall. He never told people that he knew Rockefeller but people assumed he did. He became very rich because his clients assumed he had information he didn't have. A very fancy and expensive desk is a more common status prop, as in an office with a view. All of these things add to your power and authority. In most large corporations the size of your office and your desk is determined by your position and there is little you can do to change it. However, if you are a young attorney in business for yourself, it might be wise to invest in a larger office and slightly larger desk if you expect to be giving advice to the rich and the powerful or to executives who have been conditioned to think that the size of your office is a reflection of your power.

Position is also a critical power factor. The person who has a superior position will often dominate the conversation. As we pointed out in the section on chairs, the position you should seek is an elevated one. If there is a stage, you can stand on it and sit on it. You automatically have an advantage. As someone who speaks 100 times a year to various groups and opens the floor to questions at the end of my presentation, I assure you that the kinds of questions I get and the way people accept my answers are dramatically different when I am on a raised platform from when I am on the same level as the audience. Height is not only power, it is also apparently credibility. So if you are at a meeting, stand up when you speak. At a long rectangular table, which you find in most conference rooms, the best position is at the head of the table farthest from the door. The second strongest position is on the right of the man at the head of the table. The third power position is at the other end of the table. You can not only add to your power by choosing the right chair, the way you position yourself in the chair will affect your apparent power. When you're seated either to the right or the left of the president of the company, if you angle your chair slightly away from him and face down as if you were joining him you reinforce your power image.

This position works because it associates you with the president. There is a whole series of nonverbal moves you can use to associate yourself with people in power. At corporate meetings we observed that most skilled power players sat as near the prime power person as possible, preferably to the right. When they could not sit there, they sat next to another power figure. The one exception to this rule is, of course, when the meetings are held in a subordinate's office. The polished power players will inevitably stand in the back and when they think the moment appropriate will start speaking from the back of the room and everyone will turn around and refocus on them. Presidents of companies and other top honchos are usually smart enough not to sit in front of a subordinate's desk. Even when seats are available they avoid them.

The final ingredient in power is territory. The territorial aspect of power is most effective when dealing with equals. Any powerful superior can intimidate an officeholder by purposefully invading his territory without permission. By walking up behind him, leaning over him, or even sitting on his desk, a superior can say he is in charge. He nonverbally says, "I have the right to invade your property. It is my sign of power. You are almost impotent." Beware if you invite a superior into your office. You may regret it. On the other hand, being in your office behind your desk gives you a definite advantage when you are dealing with equals. All the studies indicate that when equals gather, whoever owns the office owns the meeting.

I read in several books that when you are dealing with someone and you want him to back down, the best place to meet is in his office. This is true if only two people are present. He is more agreeable and easy to manipulate than he would be in your office. However, if there are other people present to witness his humiliation, he is far less likely to cave in. Because he is on his home ground he feels the psychological strength of territory. All animals, including the executive animal, will defend their territorial rights with tremendous vigor. Territory, however, is not just your desk, office, or home. It can be your restaurant or even your city—especially if during the meeting you pick the power position. If in your restaurant you are sitting with your back to the wall so the backs of those talking to you are exposed, you are in the power position. If you deal with someone who is very clever and refuses to meet you in your restaurant or your club or even to let you pick your own seat, you will have to meet him on neutral territory. However, if you show up at a neutral office with five people when the other party shows up with two, the neutral office becomes your territory because your people dominate the environment.

Your people can dominate the environment in several ways. The status of the people you bring with you or even their size can be a critical factor. If you arrive in almost any Washington office with your Congressman at your side, you automatically have more power than a man who shows up with his personal aide. There was an old-fashioned union leader in Chicago who insisted on negotiating with management in a neutral setting with two assistants. The corporate executives usually showed up with their accountant and lawyer. He ran a very tough union. He brought the two biggest, roughest-looking men in the organization. It was their job to sit there and intimidate the other side, which they did, and by doing so they made that neutral territory the union's.

Having a territorial advantage can be very useful. But you should remember that when you are in someone else's territory you have to be very careful. There are several best-selling books on the market that suggest that when you go into someone's office you throw your coat over his chair, spread your papers over his desk, and take over. We found these tactics counterproductive. We sent researchers into several dozen offices in which they followed the advice in the best-selling books. What happened most often was that the officeholders became very defensive or as mad as hell or both. If the researchers had been genuine businessmen and had had a deal with the men and women who owned the offices, those men and women would have killed the deal. The lesson is obvious. Being pushy and being powerful are not the same.

So I end this chapter with the same advice I gave at the beginning. Be careful how you use power. It's a two-edged sword.

10

OFFICE POLITICS

I talked to more than 2,000 executives about success and failure and only two of them ever used the term office politics. Both were women. Apparently, the term is not part of the lexicon of the male executive, but they did give a great deal of advice on the subject.

The first, most practical, and cynical piece of advice came from fellows who were friends of mine and as a result were being very frank. Their universal cry was: "Get yourself a rabbi." Now in business circles, getting yourself a rabbi has nothing to do with being Jewish. The term "rabbi" is used to describe someone on top who helps you when you're having a problem. Your rabbi is your mentor, your leader, and your guardian angel.

The term originated in Tammany Hall around the turn of the century. Between 1903 and 1918 a large number of Jewish immigrants arrived in groups from Russia and landed on the lower East Side of New York. The only thing they seemed to have in common was that each group was led by a rabbi. The rabbis were leaders because often they were the only person in the group with an education. As a result, their advice was sought not only on religious and personal matters, but on social and business matters as well.

When these men moved into a society run by Tammany Hall, it became obvious to them that if they were going to help their people, they had to deal with Tammany. Many of them became ward leaders and agreed to deliver so many votes in return for favors for members of their congregation. They negotiated for jobs in city government, admittance to schools, and so on. However, there was an equally large group of rabbis who, for a variety of reasons, would have no part of Tammany. As a result, one group of immigrants tended to do much better than the other.

The reason was Tammany's first rule. Tammany took care of those who took care of Tammany. It had only one other rule: if you wanted a favor from Tammany you went down to the club and you asked. The man who ran the club on the lower East Side in New York was an Irishman by the name of O'Brian who was a typical old-line Tammany boss, not very polite, but very effective. When someone who looked Jewish entered his club, before he'd get more than a foot in the door, O'Brian would yell: "Who's your rabbi?" If he gave him the name of one of the rabbis who was cooperating, O'Brian would invite him in and see what he could do for him. If the rabbi, however, wasn't on his list, he unceremoniously threw him out. Naturally, over a period of time he screamed "Who's your rabbi" at many people who weren't Jewish. But everyone soon got to know what the term meant. Instead of giving the name of a rabbi, they'd give the name of their Tammany connection. As a result, "Who's your rabbi?" became the question you asked people when you wanted to know if they knew anyone at the top.

The term and its original meaning were gradually picked up by men in business who still use it today. According to them, if you are going to spend your life working in corporate America, the first rule is the Tammany rule: get yourself the right rabbi.

I asked them the obvious question: what about the young people who want to do it on their own, consider having influence at the top an unfair advantage, and would rather not seek it? The majority said that that person wasn't likely to succeed, because he or she didn't deserve it, he or she was too stupid. The first rule of success is, if you have an edge, use it and if you don't have one, find one.

Since the best rabbis are blood rabbis, the executives we questioned universally advised that if you have an uncle, a cousin, or a father already in management in a firm, you attempt to join the same firm. They strongly recommended uncles and cousins with different last names because although nepotism is one of the key factors in corporate success, it is a taboo subject. You are absolutely forbidden to speak about it. Which means if you get a job from your uncle or cousin, mention it to no one. If your uncle or cousin is really important, everyone will know anyway. There is a second nepotism rule: never complain about nepotism in your company because you never know whose relative you're talking to. The reason for the second rule is that in about one third of the corporations in America being related to the right people is really the best way and in some outfits the only way to get ahead.

If you don't have a blood rabbi in a key position, use family friends or old school ties. These can be equally useful. Often men from one or two schools will dominate entire corporations and entire states. In some companies and industries, your religious or ethnic background can be a critical factor. A good rule of thumb is if 60 percent or more of the men who run a corporation or industry are members of an ethnic or religious group, don't go to work for that company or industry unless you're also a member of that group. If prejudice is not a factor, nepotism probably is; and where one starts and the other lets off is hard to pin down. If you don't take it into consideration when you join a company, if you think that all that is a thing of the past, you're kidding yourself.

Most of the people reading this book can do nothing about their families, their religion, or their schooling. It is behind them. This does not mean that you cannot have a rabbi. If you don't have a connection, you have to make one.

After you join a company, look around and choose a boss who looks as if he's moving up. Do more for him, produce for him; if you can, become his essential right arm. Work especially hard when he gives you a job. Be willing to work overtime and when he asks, travel to Paducah. Do everything you can to enhance his career. If you pick the right man, he's going to take up with him the people who helped him move. If you're one of them, you're on your way.

Upwardly mobile executives wish to gather around them coteries of younger people who will support them. The size and the number of people who want to work for you may be a factor in your upward mobility. In order to be upwardly mobile, you not only have to get a rabbi, you have to eventually become one. But before you can become one, you have to pick the right rabbi. If there are four assistant department heads and you become the protégé of the one who's never going to get promoted, you may end up being frozen under him. Therefore, you must pick very carefully.

There are several ways of spotting winners. In most companies you can immediately identify the people on their way up because everyone knows who they are. They're brilliant, hardworking, or connected. Spotting the brilliant and hardworking is fairly easy. Spotting the connected, although tricky, is possible. Before you make your move, before you join the team, find out who's who and who has the power. One of the best ways of doing this is to listen very carefully to office gossip. Get to know the office gossips and pump them. Find out who knows whom, who is related to whom, and who's been sleeping with whom. If there's a secretary who's been in the company for thirty years, she'll know where all the skeletons are buried. Get to know her. This information is critical. Unless you know who they are, you can't join the right team. Watch for little things. Take note of who lunches with whom, who drinks with whom. And if there's a young man who plays golf regularly with the vice-president of the company, don't dismiss it. Be very nice to him. The rule is: "Look before you latch on." Most of the executives we talked to said that the success books written today miss a very important point. In most cases, it's mutual interest rather than manipulation that helps people get ahead. You must recognize that other people in the company have interests in common. The minute you go into a management position, check very carefully on the people who work for you and the people on whom you're going to be reporting. Look at their personnel files, find out who got them the job, check their letters of recommendation very carefully. If you don't know the name of the person on the letter of recommendation, see if you can find out. As one partner in a major accounting firm said, "If you've got a young man working under you as an accountant who can't count past ten without taking off his shoes, and you find that one of the top partners in the firm wrote his letter of recommendation, you had better be very careful about what you write in his job appraisal. You are not going to recommend him for a top slot, but you are going to phrase his evaluation in such a way that they can read it any way they want." The minute you put in writing that that young man is the stupidest person in the company, he no longer is. You are.

Once you've settled into the corporation and decided who you wish to follow to the top, decided who your friends and allies are and who your potential enemies are, your job is to catch a rising star. And keep your enemy list as small as possible.

In order to attach yourself to a rising star, you should attempt to draw favorable attention to yourself. No matter who your rabbi is, you're better off if you can make your presence known to as many men at the top as possible. If they simply know your name, you have an advantage over someone they don't know. After all, on the occasions when they need someone quickly, the first name that pops into mind is the person they will use. The men and women we discussed this with said there is a whole variety of ways to go about getting yourself known. The first and simplest is that if someone compliments you for doing a wonderful job, tell him not to tell you but to tell your boss. And don't simply tell him, give him a practical way of going about this. Have the name and address of your boss readily available and suggest that he write a letter. You can point out to him that it's the only way your boss is going to know what you're doing and that you'd appreciate it. A lot of people will take your suggestion and send that all-important complimentary letter which will be put in your file.

If you can't get a key letter that way, try the trade-off system. Inevitably, you're going to have clients come to you who want you to do more for them than you do for everybody else. Your company normally performs services 1, 2, 3, and 4, but they're going to request that you do 1, 2, 3, 4, and 5. And they're going to request that you do 5 free. If you can possibly perform 5, do it. However, explain in great detail to these people that it is not standard company policy, that you're going out of your way, that you are going to spend Saturday doing it because it would be unfair for you to do it on company time. Since you're doing all this work, you'd appreciate it very much if they would let your boss know. You can give them a little song and dance about your boss not appreciating what a good job you're doing out in the field and ask them to write a factual letter simply restating what you've done for them and to thank your boss for it. If they're clever, and most people are, they'll very quickly get the message. One hand washes the other. You take care of me and I'll take care of you. That's a basic business technique.

Such a letter in your personnel file is extremely important. It can be critical to your chances of advancement. It is one of the best props you can have in that file and will do you more good at promotion time than almost anything else. If you can arrange for just two complimentary letters a year, you'll have an advantage over everyone who's doing just as good a job as you, and a few who are probably doing a better one but haven't documented it. If you've read as many personnel files as I have, you understand that many times the appraisals are written in such a way that you can read anything you want into them. The people writing the appraisals are trying not to commit themselves one way or another. They do a lot of fast footwork. Therefore, anything definite in the personnel file, positive or negative, weighs very heavily. Since in most companies clients and profits are the name of the game, a letter from a client is about the best thing you could have in your file. A negative letter, on the other hand, could be one of the worst things. So if a client says to you, "Unless you do X, I'm going to write to your boss and tell him what a bum you are," don't sit up on your high horse and ignore him. Do X, even if you don't think you should do X. Because that's really looking out for #1.

One of the men we questioned was head of the personnel department of a major firm. He said that even though he knew some of the letters he found in resumes were obviously arranged, he admired the people who had brains enough to arrange them and felt very comfortable in suggesting they be promoted.

Another way of drawing attention to your positive achievements is to do something that will catch the boss's attention. If you're a young attorney in an enormous law firm or if you're a young accountant in one of the big accounting firms, there is no way that the senior partners are going to notice you. You're just going to be one of many. You're going to be a number. However, in most companies, the people at the top have outside interests and activities in which you can participate, if you're clever enough to find out what they are. In one company we know, the president was the chief fund raiser for the United Fund. Everyone in that company went to work for the United Fund and attempted to raise as much money as possible. Because that's the one thing he saw them doing, he remembered. One very clever young woman I knew didn't go to work for the United Fund the first year she was there. What she did was go around and contact potential contributors. She spent a great deal of time lining them up, not just the month or two of the campaign but almost the entire year before it. The second year she joined, and with her earlier preparation easily outstripped everyone in the company. She stood out, and the president promoted her because the only thing the president knew about that young woman was that she did a fantastic job when he was watching. If you can become involved in the president's favorite activity—fund raising, charity, local Boys' Club, or anything else—it can be very helpful.

Being seen is very important. But knowing when you're being seen is just as important. In most companies, company meetings and company parties are known as "dog and pony shows." The whole purpose is to show off and to show what you can do. They are times for public display and they are critical to your career. They are often the only time people in charge will get to look at you.

When you attend a company meeting, don't treat it as a casual off-the-cuff thing. Remember, you're on display. Pretend you're at an interview. Dress in the same manner you would for an interview in your company. Conduct yourself as you would in an interview and watch very carefully what you're saying. Casual comments made at company meetings are made by fools. To quote one vice-president, "Anyone who makes a casual comment or a suggestion at a company meeting without several days' homework is probably making a mistake." Listen before you leap. If you talk before the boss has stated his position, you may find yourself in opposition to him which puts you in a no-win position. You either have to back off and look as if you're wishy-washy or you have to continue to oppose him. Opposing the boss is about the stupidest thing you can do.

When we looked at the tapes of company meetings, we discovered that not only did the clever people get on the right side of the boss's position, they also tended to get on the boss's right side. When their direct superior was attending a meeting, they sat as close to his right hand as possible. When he was sitting in the audience with them they sat at his right and when he was running the meeting they tried to sit in the front row to his left. It also became apparent that the people with power and prestige gathered together at meetings. In most cases you could psychologically join a clique by sitting very close to them. People made assumptions about associations that were not necessarily true. We also observed that the winners generally didn't show up late. They usually came in right behind their boss. They followed him to his seat and they sat themselves next to him. The people who popped into meetings at the last minute because they were so busy working and lounged against the back wall were generally losers. The winners planned their positioning.

We found that people who positioned themselves correctly at meetings had a far easier time speaking. The fact that they were sitting next to a man of power made it less likely that anyone would interrupt them. We ran a little test and found that if you spoke while sitting next to the boss, people were four times less likely to interrupt you than if you stood in the back of the room. When you do speak at a meeting, don't let anyone interrupt unless it's the boss. Continue your statement; do not be bulldozed. This is a particularly important rule for women. We found many of the women let themselves be run over at company meetings by men who simply interrupted them and pushed them out of the way verbally.

Remember, at company meetings you want to show

off your best, not your worst. If you have a problem in your department, don't have a public discussion at the company meeting. If possible, discuss your accomplishments. If someone brings up a problem in your department, attempt to have it put off. Suggest that you and he have a private meeting. Tell him you can't discuss it without documentation. Tell him anything, but have it put off. What he's really doing is bringing the problem to public attention and undercutting your image. One of the rules at public meetings is defend your private domain.

If someone brings up a subject that will affect you and the people who work for you, be on your guard. The standard defense is to ask the person who brought it up to put it in writing so that you can give it careful consideration. Never let yourself be forced to make a decision in two seconds. The people who are making the suggestion may have planned it for two months. If you attempt to reply off the top of your head, you're working at a tremendous disadvantage. No matter how simple the suggestion or the comment may seem, ask time to study it. Never let anyone run past you in this way.

And finally, remember company meetings do reflect the attitude and the business philosophy of the men who run them. Some company meetings are debating societies because that's what the boss wants. In other company meetings the boss sets up group A to fight with group B and he sits there making decisions about who's going to win. If that's what he wants, that's what you've got to do. Do not try to change the nature of the meeting. This will get you into serious trouble.

While most people recognize that their performance at company meetings will impact their career, they underestimate the significance of company parties and company outings. These are also dog and pony shows. You're being watched. The first rule of attending business-social affairs is the same as the first rule for attending a meeting. Dress well. Wear your best suit with a new shirt and a new tie to the company party and upper-middle-class sportswear to the company outing. If you intend to play golf or tennis, don't show up in a thrown-together outfit. Invest in a good golf or tennis outfit from the most expensive store in town. More than half the executives we questioned indicated that it was very difficult to tell a person's background in the office. "After all, they all wear suits. But once you see them on the golf course, you really know what they're like." So the company party and the company outings are no place to let your hair down.

Just about every executive we talked to agreed that you don't party at the company party. In fact, after talking to them we were able to come up with a set of rules for attending company parties. Arrive when the winners arrive and leave when the winners leave. At most company parties the executives show up an hour to an hour and a half after the party has begun and they leave an hour or two later. Some even make shorter appearances. They're perfunctory in nature. They will have a private party elsewhere. They're not there to have a good time. They understand the function of a business-social meeting is mainly business. You must understand the same. The time of arrival is not as important as the time of departure. After the executives leave, the party usually deteriorates. It's about that time that the party is dominated by the mailroom or a similar group. Be sure you're not the star of the mailroom party.

When you walk into the room, look for the power groups. In most large rooms, the main power group will be found to your left just past the center of the room. The second power group will usually form a little past the center of the room to the right. If there are four power groups, they will tend to move close to the four corners but not up against them. Naturally, if there are buffet tables or other obstacles, the power groups will move to accommodate their physical surroundings. Take a look at who's talking to whom. Pay careful note of the people who seem to be very friendly, then pick a power

group and join it. If you don't know anyone in one of
the power groups, you have to make it a point to become
well-enough acquainted with at least one person in each
of those groups so that you can use him or her as
leverage to join the conversation at the next party.

I can't emphasize too strongly that you do not go to
office parties to enjoy yourself. You must act as if you're
being watched by someone without a sense of humor,
because you are. Companies have no sense of humor.
Limit yourself to two drinks and don't finish the second
one. If you're a woman, don't finish the first. Remember, you're not there to pick up the person in the next
department. You should not want to be known as the
life of the party, the person who does the soft shoe, or
plays the piano. The only thing you want to be known
as is an executive who showed up, carried on polite
conversation, and left.

If I sound like a wet blanket to the men, I'm sure I
sound even worse to the women. Women, particularly
young women, can damage their business image by
simply joining in what would be considered normal party
activities. I attended a party last Christmas at which a
very talented young woman with a great deal of potential was discoing. The movements she made on the floor
were totally acceptable for anyone who was twenty-four
and at a disco. Unfortunately, the people who observed
her were forty-five and had never been to a disco in
their lives. As a result of her dance, she became known
as the young chick with the build and the moves. When
I asked two women in executive positions how they
thought she impacted her career, one put it beautifully.
She said, "With those moves, she's never going to move
up."

The rules for women at office parties, unfair or not,
are much stricter than they are for men. I interviewed
twenty-six successful women and the majority believe
that office parties, specifically Christmas and New Year's
parties, tend to be traps for women. They agree that

many young women who act sensibly all year long make fools of themselves at these parties. And since it's the only time the people in charge really get a good look at them, they're making a serious mistake.

They also pointed out that this is the time when women executives are particularly vulnerable to traditional male chauvinist put-downs. As one woman said, for 364 days of the year a woman is treated as a competent attorney, topnotch accountant, and an efficient department head. But at the Christmas party, if she lets down even a little, she is apt to become "hi, honey," "a real cutey," "built like a brick house," and "a great dancer with nice moves." The first six women we interviewed were all in the same room at the same time, and every one of them had the same experience. They said that someone had tried the "hi, honey" technique as a put-down at a Christmas party. One told a very funny story. Five years before, she was working at corporate headquarters with six other women and thirty-five men. One of the men gave her a "hi, sweetie" routine at the Christmas party and she found out later that he had tried it with several of the other women. The women got together, discussed it, and decided he was doing a job on them and they wanted to get even. At the next party, they made him their sex symbol. They mentioned how cute he'd become and if he couldn't sell his brain he could sell his body. They kept walking up to him during the party and complimented him on his cute rear end and jabbed him. He left after three quarters of an hour. He knew very well that they were doing to him what he had attempted to do to them.

The rules for attending company outings are similar to those for attending office parties. You're not there to have a good time, even if you won a trip to Bermuda as a reward for being the most productive salesperson in your group. You can enjoy the pool, play golf, and participate in any normal resort activity. However, you can't drink too much, become the life of the party, and make a damn fool of yourself. If you want to use the situation in a positive way, you should attempt to join the power groups. There are power groups wherever business people gather. This time the power group will not be standing talking together, they'll be playing golf or tennis, sailing, or scuba diving. But they will be moving as a group.

Here again our research indicates there is a special set of rules for women. The women we talked to said that the clever ones avoid participating in sports that are male dominated. If they are able to compete in tennis or golf, they will. That someone beat them they thought inconsequential, if they played a halfway decent game. However, the women feel that they are put at a disadvantage when the men start playing softball or football. Most of the men were brought up playing these games and women tend to look inept and clumsy. When the women partook in this type of sports activity, the men relegated them to the position of poor, helpless woman, and that image was carried back to the office where they had to fight it. In the opinion of most of the successful women, it wasn't worth the effort.

The women I spoke to said if they were starting over again, they would learn to play tennis and golf. Several were actually taking lessons when I interviewed them. Two or three disagreed and said that participating in any sport where men had the advantage was stupid.

The final piece of advice offered by both male and female executives is when you lose, get out. They agreed one of the biggest mistakes made by men and women is not realizing that office politics is a deadly game. When you lose in most companies, you're dead and you have to move out in order to move up. They said the main reason for failure is getting in a rut and staying there. I realize at the writing of this book that we have a very tight economy and the nature of things being what they are, the economy may get tighter. When I mentioned this to many executives, they said that being an executive meant taking a gamble. You had to gamble on many things. One of the main things you had to gamble on

was your own ability. They didn't suggest that anyone
quit a job until he had another one, but they thought
that if one out of every three executives started looking,
they'd be improving their chances. Each of them knew
of at least two or three men or women in their company,
not going anywhere, who would have a possibility of
moving up if they started fresh in a new company.

11

THE FRIENDSHIP NETWORK

Whether you get out or hang in you must get along. People who like people are the most successful people in the world.

The overwhelming majority of successful men and women we spoke to had a large network of friends. When we first started conducting these interviews, our main problem was getting suitable subjects. As a result, at the end of the interview we asked people if they knew of anyone else who would be willing to be interviewed and if they would recommend us. We found that when we were dealing with unsuccessful people, they only gave us one or two names and often struggled to find the telephone number or the address. They weren't good record keepers. Successful men and women were totally different. When we asked them if there were other people they could recommend, they buried us in names. They gave us names of other people working in the company and in the industry as well as neighbors, friends, people they had worked with five years ago, childhood friends, school chums, and relatives. Every successful person we asked offered us a shopping list of people from whom we could choose.

Two facts became obvious: one, successful people know a lot more key people; two, they name a lot more people from their past. Apparently, they keep up their contacts over a period of years. This alone would account for the fact that they have a tremendous network of friends. Since the average successful executive we talked to was forty-five and worked in at least five places before he reached his present position, if he made three friends in each place, we're talking about a man with fifteen very solid contacts. If, on the other hand, you move five times and the only people you are in touch with are the people you're presently dealing with, you have three contacts.

We found that in addition to staying in touch with their friends, successful people tended to do small favors for them. One man said that his attorney, his accountant, and his lawyer were all the sons of people he had known for years. It is evident to me that if he wanted a favor from any one of those men, he'd get it. Contrary to the popular myth that when men go up they forget those whom they knew in the past, successful men not only remember their friends from the past but they also take care of them. They do anything they can to help their careers and to put them in their debt.

I'm not suggesting for one second that most of these men and women have a conscious plan for making contacts, although I'm sure some of them did. Whether they were making contacts or friends is like asking which comes first, the chicken or the egg. I'm sure that some of them couldn't tell you because, frankly, successful people are always interested in contacts. Yet they have a real feeling of camaraderie and friendship for the people they work with now and those they worked with in the past. It's even possible they convince themselves that they get along best with those people who can be most helpful to them. But the end result is the same. When they need a favor or they need an edge, they've got it.

I witnessed a classic example of how that edge works at a convention in Chicago two years ago. I was hired by a company that does 20 percent of its sales at conventions to redesign their convention booth and sales presentation. I spent three days at the booth, the first day with three men, a young man of twenty-four and two men in their forties. One of the middle-aged men was the outgoing, gregarious type, the other was quiet and not very friendly. At the end of the first day, although I was more attracted to the outgoing man, if you had asked me I probably would have said the second was more likely to succeed because he spent more time with customers than with his competitors. However, I was sadly mistaken because the next day when I showed up they were all sitting around looking rather glum. They had heard the night before that their company had been bought by a large conglomerate. They were wondering if they were still going to be working at the end of the convention. The twenty-four-year-old took it rather nonchalantly as you'd expect. The two men in their forties were obviously upset. However, their reactions were quite different. The man who was very open and friendly with me apparently had been as open and friendly with other people at the convention and he went around talking to his friends and spent half the day out of the booth. When he came back at the end of the day he told us he had one job, a "maybe" on a second, and half a dozen other people looking for him.

The other gentleman sat there and said that he wished he knew as many people in business as the first. I found out they had both been in the business just about the same amount of time. The only difference is one made friends easily and kept them and the other one didn't.

When I interviewed executives about the friendship network, they agreed that it was important and constructive to have friends and keep them. However, many pointed out that it wasn't necessary to have friends. It wasn't necessary for a person to be your friend to do you good. Having contacts was often more important than having friends. One of the most successful men we interviewed said that in his entire life he had two or three people he could consider friends, but he literally had hundreds of contacts. He considered the contact someone with whom he was fairly well acquainted, someone whom he could call and ask for a small favor, ask for an introduction, or ask for a little piece of business and probably get it. He said that the reason these people were likely to give him something was that he was the kind of fellow who would give them something if the situation were reversed. He said that in his industry having contacts was at least as important as having friends, because he recognized the "know principle." They not only have to know you, they have to know what you do and where you do it. This is why the successful attorneys, accountants, and contractors we interviewed said they went to social affairs partially to make business contacts. They said you always feel more comfortable dealing with people you know, and so does everyone else. The more people who know you, the better.

Most successful people insisted that when they went to a party, they were there to have fun, to dance, to drink, to eat, to do everything everyone else did, but they always had in the back of their minds that they were there to make contacts. They introduced themselves to people and let people know what they did, even bragged a little about how good their firm was.

Frankly, I find myself doing the same thing. I sell what I do all the time. I talk about doing research constantly. I enjoy talking about what I do. I do go to parties to have fun and to enjoy myself and to socialize. And I'm there not necessarily to sell John Molloy's research. However, quite often that's exactly what I do. I believe that it is not a conscious plot as much as it is a by-product of being very interested in what you do and being able to talk and get other people interested in it also.

So, here's another way to give yourself an edge and a pleasant one. Make friends and contacts and keep in touch with both.

12

THE EXECUTIVE SPOUSE

Well-meaning wives kill the careers of more promising executives than booze, bimbos, or social blunders. We came by this information as a result of a survey of 226 American executives. The 192 men and 34 women questioned came from 212 corporations and 23 industries and represent a fair cross section of American executive opinion. All of them were management people with at least five years' experience. As part of their responsibilities, they groomed the future leaders in their corporations and eliminated the losers from any shot at an executive position.

These executives answered a three-part question. First, we asked them why most young men and women in corporations failed to get ahead. They gave all sorts of answers. Poor attitude, lack of intelligence, and lack of formal education led the list. We then asked what types of mistakes were most likely to trip up a hardworking, intelligent employee. Most of the 226 mentioned social blunders of one type or another. When we asked them to cite cases of careers that were short-circuited by a social blunder, of the 611 examples recited, 326 of them dealt not with the young man, but with his wife.

In 231 of the cases the wife was guilty of a sin that theoretically does not exist in our democracy. She was

obviously lower class. Her dress, clothing, and speech
pattern identified her and as such, she eliminated her
husband from a shot at the executive suite. I will be the
first to admit that this is unfair. However, it is nonetheless a fact. But since it is a fact that many women find
understandably difficult to accept, I believe it would be
worthwhile to let the men and women executives who
made the accusations speak for themselves.

"Too much makeup, low-cut dress. You know what I
mean."

"She was gaudy and overdone."

"Her jewelry and her dress look as if they were bought
in the five and ten. Everyone at the table was embarrassed. She sat there in her $39.95 evening gown not
saying a word, trying to be very proper. Of course she
was obviously out of place. She knew it and everyone
else did too."

"I asked my wife if she were wearing a cheap dress.
My wife said no, it just made her look cheap."

"When I saw her coming in the room, she looked fine.
But the minute she opened her mouth, *he* was dead."

"We knew right then and there that he wasn't going
anywhere. Imagine an executive wife with bright-purple
lipstick."

"Now, John, you come from New York and I can tell if
I listen carefully. But my God, her accent was ridiculous! It was right out of a 1920s movie."

"Can you believe it? This fellow's wife was actually
chewing gum and clicking it! I thought the president
was going to fall over."

"She would have been all right if she'd kept her mouth
shut. But when one of the women asked if she'd been to
Bergdorf's lately, she said she didn't know the Bergdorfs
and from there on in it went downhill."

"She's the only woman I ever saw eat with elbows on
the table. It would have been amusing if it weren't so
pathetic."

"They served us Beef Wellington and she used the
knife and fork as if it were still alive."

"Our leading engineer had a problem. He married a woman that looked like a waitress in a cheap restaurant. It was our problem too. He was really a very good man, but we had to replace him."

"She talked so loud that everyone at our table could hear her. The president was so upset that he asked whose wife she was. Since we didn't know who she belonged to, he insisted we find out. The fellow obviously was not going anywhere. At least, he was not going anywhere where he represented our company."

And finally the man who seemed to sum it all up. "Her problem was that she was lower class. She looked it and she acted it. And of course, she didn't fit in."

The statistical fact is that 60 to 70 percent of women, no matter what their backgrounds, try to behave in a way that helps their husbands' careers. Unfortunately, they do just the opposite. It isn't that they don't care. Most of them care a great deal and try very hard. The problem is that they usually don't realize that they're doing anything wrong.

We were able to interview twenty-three women who had been identified as career-killers. Of the twenty-three, only one realized that she was doing her husband's career any damage. She correctly believed that her speech patterns hurt her image and she was taking diction lessons. The twenty-two others, however, had no idea of their harmful impact on their husbands' careers. Even the one woman who recognized her speech problem and was taking great pains to correct it, did not yet realize that the way she dressed was just as harmful to her and his image as her speech.

When wives kill their husbands' careers, it is usually a secret and silent death for a variety of reasons. If a man who repeatedly makes social business blunders is considered worth saving by his boss, depending on the blunder and the boss he will be told in different ways. The boss may come right out and tell him, "Look, fellow, you're wearing the wrong clothing. Get rid of that silly tie," or "You *must* wear a suit, shirt, and tie in this office." If the blunder is somewhat more delicate than a matter of dress, if, for example, he has poor table manners, the boss may tell him indirectly, perhaps through a series of hints. If the boss himself does not have the type of rapport with his employees that makes this possible, he might go to one of the man's co-workers or friends and ask them to bring the blunder to his attention. For the most part, if a valued employee of a major company is making a social blunder, there's a pretty good chance that sooner or later someone will tell him about it, directly or indirectly. Whether he's sophisticated enough to pick up (or accept) the message is another question. But he will be told.

But when a wife's appearance or lack of social poise gets in the way of a husband's career, no one says a word. There is almost a conspiracy of silence. Not one of the 226 executives we interviewed said they would ever think of telling a husband that his wife was preventing his promotion. Most indicated it simply wasn't a polite thing to do. One man admitted frankly that he was afraid he'd get punched in the nose. Another executive told of an employee in his department who was in exactly that position. The man was a good employee and the executive was afraid he'd take offense and quit if his wife's blunders were pointed out. The executive preferred to keep his silence and his employee.

The executives' reasons for not telling their employees are infinite and varied. But the fact remains, they don't tell. Therefore I suspect, and these executives confirmed, that there are thousands of women in America killing their husbands' careers without meaning to and without either of them ever knowing it.

Since no one else is ever going to tell you if you're one of these women, I devised a test that may help. We developed the questions after two sets of interviews. In the first set, we interviewed the wives of executives who had been identified as positive influences on their husbands' careers. We asked them to describe in detail their life-style. From their descriptions we developed twenty-eight questions with yes and no answers.

We then took the twenty-eight questions and combined them with seventy-two other questions that had been developed to identify other aspects of life-style. We gave the questionnaire to sixty-nine women, twenty-three identified as career-killers, twenty-three identified as positive influences on their husbands' careers, and twenty-three identified as women who neither helped nor hurt their husbands' careers.

As a result, we developed a sixteen-question test:

1. I have upper-middle-class speech patterns. (Yes/No). (If you're not sure, check our speech chapter).

2. I usually dress in an upper-middle-class style. (Yes/No). (If you're not sure, answer no.)

3. I am a college graduate. (Yes/No).

4. I regularly meet with other executive wives on social occasions: bridge, golf, tennis, tea, etc. (Yes/No).

5. I come from an upper-middle-class background. (Yes/No). (Upper-middle-class background means that your mother and father's friends were doctors, lawyers, or other executives.)

6. I shop for my clothing in the same stores as the wives of my husband's co-workers. (Yes/No).

7. I have had dinner at the home of at least two of my husband's co-workers within the last year and they have had dinner at my home. (Yes/No).

8. My husband and I belong to the same country club as do most of his co-workers and some of his superiors. (Yes/No).

9. I belong to the same social and charitable organizations as do the wives of other executives in my husband's company. (Yes/No).

10. When I meet a woman for the first time, I can tell immediately whether she is going to fit in with the other executives' wives. (Yes/No).

11. I immediately spot someone who has poor table manners. (Yes/No).

12. Although most of the homes in my area are in the same price category, I can immediately tell when I walk in the door whether the people who live there are professionals and executives. (Yes/No).

13. The women with whom I am most friendly are the wives of men who are executives or professionals. (Yes/No).

14. Although I am not an expert in my husband's field, I can intelligently discuss some of the problems faced by his company and his industry. (Yes/No).

15. Although I don't associate on a regular basis with the wives of the top executives, if I found myself at a party or an office gathering thrown into a group with them, I'd certainly feel at ease. (Yes/No).

16. I am aware of the fact that my background is not perfect for a woman in my position and as a result I've taken a whole series of self-improvement steps and believe that I've overcome my background. (Yes/No).

If you answer every question with no, it does not mean that you have killed or will in the future kill your husband's career. However, there is a definite statistical correlation between the number of negative answers and women who, in the past, have negatively impacted their husbands' careers. We found that the women who were positive influences on their husbands' careers very seldom had more than one or two no answers. We also discovered that those who were thought of as being neuter influences generally had three or four negative answers, but that they could have as many as five or six without greatly affecting their status. Finally, those who were identified as career-killers usually answered no to more than half of the questions. Our research also indicated that negative answers to questions 1 and 2 often put women into the career-killer category. These questions are more important than others because while the others measure life-style, these measure socioeconomic message sending. Therefore, if you answer question 1 no, you must take steps to improve your diction. Without upper-middle-class verbal patterns you will not create the proper impression. If you answer question 2 no, you should buy a copy of my *Woman's Dress for Success Book* and read very carefully the section on cross shopping.

Since we've given this test to several thousand women, I'm well aware that the immediate reaction of women who fail the test is to dismiss it as being inaccurate. They prefer to equate it with those quizzes they get in women's magazines that purport to rank their marriage or their sex life on a scale of 1 to 10. But this test has greater significance. We found that it accurately identified women who were positive influences on their husbands' careers approximately 70 percent of the time, and women who were negative influences on their husbands' careers approximately 60 percent of the time. I say approximately because whether a woman is positively impacting her husband's career is a matter of opinion. Nevertheless, if you answered all the questions positively, you should congratulate yourself. And if you answered more than half negatively, you should at least take a look at your life-style to see if anything needs correcting. It is likely that something does.

You can make negative answers positive if you make up your mind to conduct yourself in a different manner. Those that require some effort and some expertise are covered in other chapters in this book.

The answers to our questions revealed a variety of

ways by which women negatively impacted their husbands' careers. The blunder that cropped up most often was drinking too much. By the way, overdrinking at business or social functions is the main reason husbands kill their own careers. But there is a double standard for men and women. Men can do a lot more drinking than women can. As long as a man doesn't seem to be tipsy, he can usually get by. Women, on the other hand, don't have to get drunk or even tipsy to endanger their own image and their husbands' careers. In most cases, if a woman has more drinks than the man in charge (or his wife) thinks appropriate it will be noted and noted negatively. Our survey of executive men and their wives indicated that in any situation where drinks were served, almost no one thought that having one or two drinks was improper. However, if a woman drank more than two drinks her actions would immediately become suspect. If you ask yourself who's counting, you'd be surprised. If a woman becomes inebriated or simply seems to be, she can kill her husband's career in one night.

The same story was told time and time again, of the boss who had someone in mind for an important slot but canceled his ticket very quickly when he saw the man's wife drinking too much, or even looking as if she might drink too much. There's a particularly ironic story of a man losing his chance at a very important position because his wife entered the room, accepted a drink, said, "My God, I can sure use a martini," and proceeded to down it in two gulps. It so happened that his wife was a surgeon and may have had a very good reason for wanting that martini, but it killed his career nevertheless. After surveying several hundred executives and their wives, I came to the conclusion that the only absolutely safe rule for an executive's wife when it comes to drinking is: Don't do it at all! If you do, keep it to wine and keep it to two (the first one you complete and the second one you don't).

If this seems like too stringent a rule, it's not my rule, it's the rule of the people I've questioned. You must remember that many people were brought up in an environment in which drinking was considered immoral, and still others may have had very negative personal experience with alcohol, either in their family or their business life.

The classic example of a negative experience is the story of Champagne Mary. I was keynote speaker at a sales convention and was sitting at one end of the table with two people I had befriended. Looking down at the other end, I saw that there was a little party going on. Kiddingly, I turned to the couple I was sitting with and said, "Too bad I was stuck down here with the deadheads. I could have been over there partying with the fun group." They both gave me one of those strange knowing looks. After a judicious pause the wife told me that the young woman down at the fun end of the table was drinking with the vice-president's wife, but it was not a party. It was an execution. According to her we were watching yet another victim of Champagne Mary.

The vice-president's wife made it a point of not too gently pushing champagne on wives of the new men in her husband's department. Apparently at her husband's insistence, she tested to see if the young women could be cajoled or even bullied into drinking too much. It seems that several years before, the vice-president had had a chance to move into an executive vice-presidency at corporate headquarters, but his chances were tied up with getting a major account with a foreign country. He was sent to Washington to close the deal, and he took his chief engineer with him. The engineer brought his wife. The scope of the deal was so great that it required government cooperation. On the critical evening, they were invited to the embassy. It was understood that after the party, everyone would sit down and talk turkey.

The engineer's wife, however, dazzled by Washington's diplomatic finery, took a few too many sips of champagne and the engineer had to take her back to the hotel. The vice-president was left to attend his critical meeting without his engineer's technical advice, and consequently (so he believed) lost the contract—as well as his promotion. His wife, in her mind, was simply checking to see that the same thing wasn't going to happen again.

Nevertheless, I thought it was a cheap trick and I said so. But the gentleman I had befriended said, "It *is* a cheap trick. I don't like the man's wife and I don't like him. Neither of them are going anywhere in the company. But don't kid yourself. It's not that uncommon. Companies make a general practice of testing wives." When I started doing this research I found out he was dead right.

The most honest type of test is the invitation to a joint interview. In many cases, when a man is being considered for a position or even a new job with the company, both he and his wife are interviewed or invited for dinner or a weekend where they are closely observed. Frankly, the wife must pass muster with both the executive and his wife because the third most common reason for turning down a man is that his wife doesn't get along with the other women in the group. Many companies refer to themselves and their employees as family and take the description quite literally. These companies arrange it so that not only do their men work together, but they also play together. They believe that this creates loyalty and an esprit de corps. Under such a policy, if the woman does not fit in, her husband will not fit in.

Other companies are not quite as open and some do not even wait until the man is up for promotion before looking at his wife. They may send the couple an invitation to dinner or the club; or if it's out in the field, they may employ a second-rate spying system. It's standard practice for traveling executives to be obliged to visit the homes of their men. Often they will insist on being invited to dinner. If this occurs to anyone reading this book, you are not to assume the man is hungry and simply too cheap to buy a meal. He is probably visiting you because he has been told to check on you. His job is to find out if the husband *and* wife would be acceptable

serving in an executive position. In all probability the
company has been burned in the past when they invited
a man who was an excellent field supervisor to take over
a home office position. When he showed up with his
wife, they wanted to shoot themselves. She was totally
unacceptable, didn't fit in at all, created a lot of problems, and was, in short, a social embarrassment. As a
result they decided that rather than eliminate the field
people from consideration for top slots, they would send
someone out to check on their wives ahead of time.

I know one man who had the job of spy in three
separate companies and he said frankly it was probably
just as easy to fill out a form. I asked him if he'd make
up a form and what he came up with is as follows.

Question 1: "Are Mr. and Mrs. So-and-so gracious
hosts?" This includes the wife's manners, speech patterns, dress, the way she decorates her home, the way
she sets her table, the type of food she serves, the conversation, and so on.

Question 2: "Is Mr. and Mrs. So-and-so's home suitable for entertaining clients?" Again, this is a matter of
personal opinion, but he indicated that almost everyone
agreed that the home must be well decorated, neat, clean,
and located in a fairly decent area.

The tricky part of the form, he said, would be the
point of discussion. He was invariably asked questions
when he returned to the home office about the wife's
attitude toward her husband's moving. Obviously, the
only way he could find this out was to bring it up in a
pseudo-casual way. The answer he was looking for was,
"Of course I'd be willing to move to help my husband's
career! I'd be delighted to do so! Whoopee! I'd be glad to
move." This indicated to him and to the others that at
least she's willing to go along. The one thing they didn't
want to do was move a man to corporate headquarters
only to have his wife hate the move and give him a hard
time at home every evening. This would make the man
miserable and consequently an inefficient, unproductive
worker.

The other subject of conversation that was mandated if his wife worked was "in the case of career conflicts [which the proposed move would incite], who's going to give up theirs?" The answer that the women's magazines offer in light of supposedly liberated company policies is *not* the one the spies are looking for. The answer they're looking for is that the wife is going to sacrifice her career for her husband's. They want wives to say, "Well of course I am interested in my job and I'm very dedicated to it. However, my husband is the main breadwinner and therefore I will go along with whatever furthers his career." In fact the very same companies that encourage career women to have full, meaningful lives and important careers make it a point to be sure that the men working for them are not married to such women—at least not the men who are headed for the top. This attitude is going to have to change. But the fact is that it hasn't happened yet.

The one element that I personally found offensive is the "Are you a dedicated husband and father" question. Our spy said he inevitably asked the wife how she felt about her husband missing birthdays, weekends, and anniversaries because of his work. If she, like a proud wife, indicated that no matter what happened he never missed such occasions, it would be a decided mark against him, because that's not the kind of man the company wants at corporate headquarters. The company wants a man who is willing to sacrifice his family for his career. Although wonderful husbands are to be sought by wives, they're not sought by corporate executives. He admitted, though, that in one case he had disregarded the wife's answer. He knew the fellow was a workaholic and was hardly ever home. He was one of the company's most dependable and hardworking field managers. However, the wife, thinking she was being supportive, declared that her husband was just about perfect and never missed a family gathering. The spy said had he not known the man personally, he might have believed the wife's declaration of her husband's preoccupation with his home and it would have killed the man's career.

However, the question that really threw me was the one about independent income. I have always thought that if I married someone really wealthy it would enhance my chances of working my way up in this world. Apparently that's not true. Companies do not want men whose wives have an independent income. Independent incomes make executives too independent. So if your wife buys a ticket on the sweepstakes and wins, don't let them print your name in the paper.

The final type of checking that my friend the traveling executive did was what he called the friends-and-relatives party. Either he or someone else in the company would strongly suggest that the man and his wife throw a little cocktail party while he was there. They should not go to any special effort, just a friendly gathering. What they really want you to do is invite your friends and neighbors over and bring him along. Let him feel a touch of home in a strange city. After all, he's going to be on the road a long time. If you believe that, you believe in Santa Claus. Actually, what he was doing at that point was not only checking on you but on your friends as well. The advice for this one is obvious. If you have neighbors known as Harry the Lush or Phil the Fighter, or after two drinks, Sarah the Stripper, don't invite them to one of these parties. I would suggest that you cultivate a few doctors and lawyers simply to have them available as potential guests. No two ways about it, this is a show and tell time.

All of these tests for wives are, of course, things that can be handled by any clever woman. She can get through and around them without ever actually believing in them, and many do. We interviewed sixty executive wives over the telephone. Fifty-two of them said they knew that they had been watched by the companies at various points in their husbands' careers; forty-three said they objected to it strenuously. Since there was nothing much they could do at the time, they went along and played the game, but if they ever had a chance to cut that company's throat, they certainly would.

So instead of creating that one big happy family which was the company's original goal, it created a great deal of antagonism in the executives' wives, which I'm sure was reflected in conversations with their husbands and others. I suggest that such companies are making a dreadful mistake by enforcing impractical standards on wives. Most executive wives realize the fact that they're required to entertain and most sensible women realize the fact that if a woman dresses improperly or speaks like a waitress in a bar, she won't fit into her husband's executive social/business environment. But beyond that, most women think that anything else the company requires is a blatant imposition and they resent it.

All of the women we interviewed indicated that they were also aware of one positive element in the scrutiny of their husbands, and that it cheered them in a way. It indicated, after all, that their husbands were being considered for bigger and better positions. They also, it would be of interest to note, pushed their husbands to ask for higher salaries. The general attitude was, "If I'm putting up with that garbage I might as well get paid for it."

When I asked them to give advice to the younger women, it fell into two separate categories. The first is how to beat the game. Most of their advice on that subject is reflected in this chapter. The second is on how to cultivate her image as an executive wife.

Executive wives have several problems. Many of the elements of their younger life-style simply do not suit their new, more affluent and prestigious one. They find that the jewelry, the china, the silver and the crystal, and even the furniture that they have is no longer appropriate to the life-style of a woman who's expected to entertain, if not in a lavish manner, at least in a very sophisticated one. To a young wife whose husband has his goal set on an executive position, the women I interviewed make the following suggestions.

First, instead of buying a complete set of relatively inexpensive china when you're in your twenties, buy one-, two-, or three-place settings of fine china. They suggest you buy open stock from a reliable company in a pattern that is at present selling well. You should take the same step for sterling silver and crystal.

Try to get your crystal first because a good glassware pattern is only on the market for approximately five years. They suggest that you then try to finish your china set because a good china pattern is on the market for ten years, and your silver last, since open stock silver has an average twenty-five-year life-span.

They suggest you buy these things from a good reliable store that has branches across the country and that you keep in contact with that store so that if the pattern is discontinued you will be able to complete your sets at a discount. If you do get a chance to complete a set at discount, they suggest that you buy extra pieces for those that might break or that you might need more of in time (cups, serving dishes, one or two extra-place settings).

They give basically the same advice about jewelry. If your husband gets onto an executive track, it seems that overnight you need a nice fur coat, good jewelry, and new china and crystal, and you just can't buy these things all at once. Instead of having your husband buy you a little ring for Christmas, a necklace for Valentine's Day, and possibly pearl earrings on your birthday, ask him to give you a token gift on two of the occasions and a very nice piece of jewelry on the third. Only by taking this approach over a period of years will you have the type of jewelry you're going to need for the life-style you're going to be required to step into "overnight."

The most productive piece of advice I received was from a woman whose husband had been the president of a very large corporation. She said that although her loyalty should be to the corporation her husband had run for years, it frankly wasn't. Her advice to young women is, "Remember, you spend an average of only twelve to twenty hours a year playing the damned silly games and the rest of the year living off of them." It's not that bad a trade.

While executive wives, at least to a degree, have reconciled themselves to the realities of American business, the same cannot be said of executive husbands. I interviewed several men who are married to successful women and found them to be a most uncomfortable group. Most of these men don't seem to know quite what is expected of them. They feel particularly out of place at their wives' business-related social gatherings. It is a feeling certainly not peculiar to men, but one that men are not used to. All of them, even those who are executives themselves, complained bitterly about the constant rumors indulged in at such gatherings. They complained that when the company people start talking shop, everybody else is out of the conversation. Husbands find themselves standing around like dummies or talking to their drinks. Paradoxically, when they are included in the conversation, they find themselves put on the spot. They're asked what they do for a living, and often they're asked in such a way as to imply that it is assumed they don't do anything at all. One Chicago lawyer has several versions of his own life story. One version gives the impression that his wife's job is a temporary one. In another version, he and his wife come off as equals, while his third version strongly implies he's simply a sex object living off her wages.

But not all of the husbands interviewed saw the possibilities for humor. Several mentioned that they objected to the Mr. Doris Day routine. They found themselves being treated as if they were their wife's property and not individuals. Here again they reflected traditionally female dissatisfactions. Women have been registering the same litany of complaints for decades. Now men are getting their taste of it and they really don't like this bitter sauce for the gander.

Most of these men were understandably interested in

their wives' careers and many of them had taken on such traditionally female duties as housecleaning and child rearing to give their wives the added time needed to pursue their careers. Nevertheless, the same men were so uptight about their positions that they almost always ended the interview when I mentioned the term executive husband. Executive spouse was a much more acceptable term to them. The very idea that their primary identification could be linked with their wives' careers and not their own was obviously too sore a point to even talk about. Even those whose wives gave them an A for attitude were visibly rattled by the suggestion that they spend half their free time being supportive of their wives.

These men were also reluctant to discuss what would happen if careers collided. The stories of talented women leaving the company just before they are to step into executive suites have become part of corporate folklore. Several male and female executives indicated to me that career collisions which often end women's careers are neither inevitable nor are they necessarily accidental.

Two male executives told identical stories about women in their companies. Both men had women employees who were about to be put into top positions. As soon as the promotion became real, both husbands suddenly announced that it was essential to their careers that they move and they handed their wives ultimatums. One husband, an executive in the same industry as his wife, registered a request for transfer when his wife came up for promotion. Then he informed her that he had no choice in the matter. A second was a doctor who gave up a well-established practice and moved to a community that was almost identical to the one he was leaving. What these men had in common was their fear that their wives were about to outrank them.

One of the executives admitted that he now would promote a woman only to her husband's level rather than to the level of her competence. He said that to do otherwise would wreck two careers. When we asked top women executives about this, two attacked the policy ferociously, three said it had some validity, and one admitted it had happened to her.

There were exceptions to the rule. Several men said that they would not promote women because of past negative experience with wives whose careers had come into conflict with their husbands'. But there were several others who said that if the woman was competent, they didn't care if she was married to King Kong. If she was valuable to them, they'd be willing to pay the transport for his cage when she went on business trips.

The real problem with executive husbands, however, is that they haven't got the foggiest idea what's expected of them—and neither do their wives' companies. I cornered twenty executives from eight corporations and asked them to describe the ideal corporate husband. What I got were twenty different descriptions. Of the twenty, nineteen admitted that they had never really thought about the problem before. One woman executive pointed out that it is only another indication that corporations are still not really interested in women executives, which may be the truth.

Of the twenty I questioned, fourteen indicated that while they hadn't given the matter of executive husbands much thought, a woman's mate could and often would be a critical factor in her success. When pressed, the executives questioned came up with a few characteristics that they thought would be essential for a good executive husband.

Generally, they paralleled the requirements of executive wives. All agreed that he should have basic social skills, though they weren't quite as particular about the husband's social skills as they were about the wife's. Also, they weren't as touchy about the husband's drinking at social business functions. More specifically, they thought the husband should be able to carry on intelligent conversation, act as a gracious host, and dress in a suitable manner.

Of the twenty, sixteen indicated that it would be an

advantage to have a prestige job. Further questioning uncovered some rather twisted reasoning. Even though the woman had succeeded on her own, these executives took into account her husband's position when measuring her prestige. The woman executive who was a doctor's wife outranked the woman executive who was a pharmacist's wife. And ironically, women executives who argued that this was unfair and sexist went along with it in practice.

The executives were consistent when I asked them to identify suitable jobs for the husbands of executive women. From the list I gave them, they chose only other professional and executive positions. But they also gave the benediction to out-of-work actors, free-lance writers, and artists. Apparently if you're a woman executive, you can support a guy if he's artsy-craftsy.

All twenty rejected plumbers as well as other well-paid blue-collar workers. However, if the plumber owned his own business, he rated much better. At first they maintained that they were rejecting men in these occupations for lack of social skills, but eighteen of the twenty went on to reject a man we described as a beautifully polished blue-collar worker. One said, "How would it look if our vice-president in charge of marketing was known as the plumber's wife?"

Frankly, all the executives agreed that it was only a matter of time until companies officially or unofficially interviewed executive husbands as they now interview executive wives. And they further agreed that a definition of a suitable executive husband would evolve in the same way it evolved for the suitable executive wife. No one knew what the final definition was going to be, but they were sure there would soon be one. I'm quite certain that not only the companies, but also the executive husbands would be happier once their role and relationship to their wife's company was defined.

Although women may not like the games required of an executive wife, the clever ones understand that it is a game. They can learn what the rules are as well as how to beat them. But executive husbands are in a constant quandary as to how to act, what to do, and what to say. Until their role is finally defined, they will tend literally to be the men in the middle.

13

AT TABLE

Even if Congress kills the business lunch, knowing how to play the restaurant game will be essential to any man or woman who wants to move up in business.

If you think that all tables in restaurants are by the kitchen door or next to the bar, in a draft or out in the middle of the floor, you don't know how to play the restaurant game. As a management consultant who is often forced to come up with a good table on short notice, I've learned a lot through trial and error. But I've also researched the problem for my column. I interviewed several restaurateurs, and executives who entertained regularly, and although the advice the restaurateurs gave did not always square with the advice given by the diners, here are some points that were agreed upon by just about everyone. Frequent at least one good restaurant often enough to be considered a regular. Get to know the names of the maître d' or headwaiter, a good waiter or waitress whose station includes the better tables, the bartender, and the owner. And make sure that they know your name.

This is particularly important if you're a woman. Women do not receive equal treatment in restaurants, not because the people who run them are male chauvinists but because women are notoriously lousy tippers. And since most of the people who work in restaurants earn the majority of their income from tips, they give very poor treatment to those who are known for undertipping. Therefore, if you're a woman, not only must you have a regular restaurant, but you must also show up often enough so that you establish a reputation as a woman who tips.

You must always make your reservation as far in advance as possible and be certain to specify the table or the section you prefer. You can do this not only in a restaurant where you're known, but also in any good restaurant. Even if you don't have a reservation, it's preferable to call a restaurant half an hour in advance of your arrival and ask for a good table. Particularly if you are a woman, you're much more likely to get a better table by telephone than you are in person.

Naturally, you must dress appropriately. Otherwise, even with a reservation you'll find yourself behind a pole or listening to the clatter of dishes. Most of the best restaurants, particularly in large cities, have a minimum dress requirement. They won't admit a man without a shirt and tie and even in those cities where good restaurants do not require shirts and ties, dressing up will help.

When on the island of Maui last year, we conducted a small experiment. We sent six groups of executives to different restaurants on four different nights. Three of the groups wore jackets. Most of them were wearing sports jackets, shirts, and ties, and a few wore suits. The others dressed very casually. The executives who wore jackets and ties found they were given better seats, better treatment, and more attention than the executives dressed in a casual manner. So the rule is, dress for better service.

A final point on which all agreed is timing. It is essential to a last-minute reservation. Keep in mind that most restaurants are packed between 12:15 and 1:15 and again between 7:15 and 8:30. There are obviously some local differences. New York tends to have a later lunch hour; Kansas City has an earlier dinner hour, and in Mexico City the dinner crowd hardly ever arrives before ten. If you avoid peak times in your area you can often get a good table even without a reservation.

One point on which restaurant people and regular diners seem to disagree is when to tip the maître d' or headwaiter. Restaurant people claim that the maître d' should be tipped after the meal, while most experienced diners insist it's more effective if you tip him before service. When we went back to the restaurateurs and repeated what the diners had told us, one of the men who owns a very famous restaurant in New York pointed out that the maître d' cannot seat you at a fine table after you've slipped him money in front of everyone in the restaurant. The other customers who may not be as well located will think this is the only way to get a good table and would take their business elsewhere. I believe the disagreement is not about when to tip, but how to tip. You should take into consideration the politics of the situation and be discreet. The ideal way to tip the person who is to seat you is to do it beforehand but not publicly. If you're unable to arrange that, you can assure him through various not-too-subtle hints that you will tip generously at the end of the meal. The best way, of course, is to show up an hour beforehand or the day before and tell him you need a good table for a specific occasion and slip him an appropriate sum. That way no one's embarrassed and you are guaranteed a good table. When you can't get there ahead of time, there are several ways to let a maître d' know, even in a strange restaurant, that you're used to finer service and you're going to pay for it. The manager of one of New York's restaurants suggests that you order a drink at the bar and tip the bartender a couple of dollars. Treat the bartender like an old friend and ask him confidentially to see what he can do for you. Chances are he will tell the maître d' there's a big spender at the bar who wants a nice table. Another ploy is, if you're waiting in line for a table, ask the waiter to get you a pack of cigarettes and give him a handsome tip for doing it. This will announce your generosity.

Another approach to getting a good table is recommended by a great number of people. It is the method of the masters. They operate on the premise that the headwaiters are there not to be intimidating, but to serve and to be intimidated. Here's the scenario. A master gets the name of the maître d' from the hatcheck girl or bartender. Then he walks up to the maître d' and says, "Charles, I must have a good table tonight." Now Charles knows he can't remember every important customer and this customer looks and acts important. So Charles doesn't dare take a chance of insulting such an impressive character and coughs up a good table. This is the type of advice that's given in most books on how to beat the restaurant game and it has a certain validity. But there's a word of caution that must be added. If you fail to carry it off properly, you will not just be seated next to the kitchen door; the indignant maître d' whose honor and professionalism you've offended will probably seat you in the kitchen next to, or if he can arrange it, in, the oven.

As important as it is to get a good seat in a restaurant, it is equally important to know what to do once you have the table.

As a host you have responsibilities. You should recommend dishes if you know the restaurant. After everyone has his menu you can make your suggestions. If you're new to the restaurant yourself, simply order for yourself and let everyone else do the same. As the host or hostess you will probably be expected to order the wine. If you know something about wines and foods, ordering is a simple matter. If you don't know how to order wine, ask for a wine list which is brought either by a waiter or sommelier. Whoever brings the wine list is expected to know something about the wines. Ask him for his recommendation and take it. This is an easy way out and relieves you of responsibility.

When the wine is served, you will be presented with the cork. It is not necessary to sniff it. Simply touch the part that's been in the bottle with your finger. If it looks undamaged, in all probability air has not seeped in and the wine has not soured. If it looks as if it has been damaged, smell the cork to determine any telltale odor of vinegar. The final test for a wine is in a glass. The waiter will proceed to pour a small portion into your glass. Sip it. If the wine has definitely turned, you can send it back. You should not send back a bottle of wine simply because you do not like it. If you're not used to tasting wine, sending it back is very dangerous. The restaurant may object and they may be correct and make you look like a fool. There are only two reasons for turning wines back: (1) they have turned to vinegar, and (2) the bottle has already been opened in the kitchen.

The rules for eating at a restaurant are almost the same as for eating in someone's home. Of course in a restaurant you have an advantage. The utensils are always set up so that you work your way in from the outside. You don't have to worry, the waiters will guide you. But if you do need that guidance, you're in trouble if you eat at your boss's home or invite him to yours.

Probably the most meaningful thing I can do to impress upon you the importance of table manners is to report a simple survey we conducted. When we looked at the men who were presidents, vice-presidents, and chairmen of the boards of major corporations, we found 80 percent of them had impeccable table manners. Their movements at the table were polished and self-assured. When we looked at people in middle management, the number with such polish dropped to 40 percent. When we looked at young people just out of school, the number slipped to 12 percent.

Even more significant is a survey we did of management people and their reaction to those who displayed poor table manners. We found that top executives considered it an almost immediate turnoff. About 60 percent of them said they would not consider letting an employee represent their company publicly unless that person knew how to handle himself at the table. They made no bones about it. They didn't apologize for it.

Picture 25

Standard place setting.

They simply made a statement. The possession of good table manners is an absolute requirement for any executive position in their corporation.

If you were not brought up in an environment in which your mother or grandmother or someone else taught you which knife and fork to use, I would suggest that you read this chapter very carefully. And when you finish reading it, I would suggest that you practice at every meal for at least two months. If you do not own the proper table settings, go out and purchase them. You have to have all the pieces to play the game.

Since the best place to begin is at the beginning, and each stage of a meal has its own set of rules, we'll start with the obvious. You sit only after the hostess has been seated and put your napkin on your lap after the hostess has put hers on her lap. After she has been served and has picked up her fork, you pick up yours. That is the signal to begin the meal. In short, at the beginning of the meal you play follow the hostess. When you start, the first utensil she picks up is the one that you pick up.

Picture 26

Variation on standard place setting.

After that, however, you may not be able to follow her because she may be doing other things, so you're going to have to know something about place settings. Since in some cases a picture is worth a thousand words, we've shown four place settings. If you look at Picture 25, you'll see the standard place setting for most American meals.

The spoon used in the first course is the soup spoon. The second course is the meat course. In this, as in most settings, you use the largest fork and the largest knife for the meat course.

The third setting is for the salad course. The dessert utensils are usually placed above the plate in the manner shown. There is no number on the butter spreader, as you use it whenever you like. The only thing you must know about the butter spreader is you never use it to cut bread. Its purpose is to spread. Break the bread or the rolls with your hands. The two other utensils at this place setting are a water glass and a wine glass. The water glass is the larger one. There are also individual

Elaborate place setting
with fish course.

2 3 4

4 3 2 1

salt and pepper shakers. At a large table, one set of salt
and pepper shakers is usually placed between two people or one is set at each place setting.

The second illustration (26) shows a variation on the
basic place setting. Here the first setting is for shrimp
cocktail, a traditional appetizer. The fork is known as a
cocktail or oyster fork and it is used to spear things. It
is never used with the fish course. The second knife and
fork are salad settings, placed here before the meat
course because the hostess may choose to alter the order
of courses. The knife is optional and usually used only
if cheese is served with the salad. Next we have the
third course which in this case is the meat course. Again,
the largest knife and the largest fork at the table are
used. Finally, we have a dessert course. All dessert
settings do not necessarily use spoons and forks. You
may also be given a knife, depending on what's being
served.

The third illustration (27) shows a more complicated

Picture 28

Sized place setting.

2 4 3   3 4 2 1

arrangement. This setting includes a fish course. The
first course again is a soup with a soup spoon. The
second course is a fish course. There are two ways to tell
whether the setting is for a fish, dessert, or salad course.
The knife for the fish course often has two little inden-
tations on the blade and is a little bit broader than the one
used for dessert. However, you may not know for sure
until the course is served. In many modern table settings, the utensils used for the fish course are interchangeable with those used for the salad and dessert
courses. If you simply obey the rule of working your way
in from the outside, you're likely to be safe and correct.

Another way of spotting whether there's going to be a
fish course is to notice the number of wine glasses that
are going to be used. If there's a light tulip-shaped wine
glass (number three) and it is a very formal meal, it is
likely that there will be a fish course. The next course is
a meat setting, again using the largest knife and fork.
And lastly, we have the salad setting.

Picture 29

Dessert setting.

Picture 30

Correct use of soup spoon.

The dessert utensils at some very formal affairs where the hostess has an ample amount of help will not be placed on the table, as it would tend to overload it. They will be delivered after the meal as shown in Picture 29.

Picture 31

A. Correct arm and head movement.

B. Incorrect arm and head movement.

Picture 28 shows a type of setting that I think is incorrect, but that you may very well encounter. Any hostess who places her utensils in order of size runs the risk of creating a problem for her guests. Almost any hostess will place the soup spoon or the appetizer fork at the extreme right. After that the settings are lined up: fish, salad, and meat. Whereas the order of the actual courses is: fish, meat, and salad. As you can see,

Picture 32

Serving yourself correctly from the serving plate.

the numbers vary. If you run across this type of setting where the utensils are not laid out in the order in which they are going to be used, don't get flustered. The general rule when dealing with a fish course is to take the smallest knife and fork on the table. If you're not sure which is which, fake it. If it's that confusing, everyone else at the table is probably doing the same.

Picture 29 shows you the dessert plate being delivered with utensils on it. When they are delivered on the plate, simply remove them from the plate and place them in their correct position (spoon on the right, fork on the left) on the table.

Obey the rule of common sense. If the dessert is gooey, use the spoon. Where you need to, use a fork. And naturally, you may use a combination of utensils whenever you find it necessary. If a finger bowl, which is a rarity today, is brought, it will be placed in the upper left of your table area.

Not matter what you are eating, use your utensils in a manner that will reduce the chances of dropping any-

Picture 33

Returning utensils to serving platter.

thing on the tablecloth or on yourself. If you're eating
soup, take the soup spoon the way it is shown in Picture
30, dip it into the soup in a motion away from you, and
then bring it back to your mouth. When you bring it to
your mouth, lean slightly forward. Don't go to extremes
and look as if you're diving into your soup dish.

The general rule when you're eating is not to move
the entire arm. A more sophisticated movement of the
wrist with as little arm movement as possible is very
important. Almost everyone will judge your socioeconomic background on how much you move your arm
when you eat. Very limited, precise movements at the
table are a sign of breeding (Picture 31).

During most formal dinners those serving you will
bring serving dishes to you and you will be expected to
take utensils from the serving dish and use them to
transport portions to your plate. Take moderate portions. Serving platters always should be offered from
the left side. Take the serving fork in your left hand and
the serving spoon in your right. Hold them as shown in

Picture 34

Continental use of fork—left hand, prongs down.

Picture 35

American use of fork—right hand, prongs up.

Picture 36

Correct holding of fish knife.

Picture 32 and move a portion of the meat or fish from the platter to your plate. If you're not sure of yourself, move as small a portion as you can. The smaller the portion, the easier it is to move.

Although the fork is often put underneath the fish or meat to transport it, if the meat or fish is covered by sauce or is juicy by nature, put the spoon underneath and encourage the person serving you to move the platter closer to you to avoid splatters. Return the serving utensils to the serving plate as indicated in Picture 33.

Vegetables should be placed on your plate in a neat, orderly manner. The person serving vegetables may come to you from either side and you should use a spoon with your right hand and a fork with the left. Again, keep your portions small. If the person who is serving you stands too far away, encourage him to move closer, particularly if you are not sure of what you're doing.

The standard American way of handling a knife and fork is to start with the fork in the left hand, prongs down. Use the fork to spear meat, fish, and vegetables so that you may hold them in a steady position while you cut with your knife. When you finish cutting, place the knife diagonally on the upper right-hand area of the plate with the blade facing in and move the fork to the right hand. Eat with the fork in the right hand, the prongs up.

The continental style of eating, which is gaining more favor today, is a far simpler method in which the fork is kept prongs down in the left hand, and the knife is used not only to cut, but to push and shove food onto the fork. The fork is always held in the manner shown in Pictures 34 and 35, never in any other manner. The knife is used to cut meat as shown in Picture 34. Used to cut fish, it is held always as shown in Picture 36. All other variations are incorrect.

Naturally, public or semipublic meals are occasions for social intercourse. During these occasions we are not expected simply to sit, stuff our faces, and leave. Therefore, you must know that when your hostess sets up a seating arrangement such as man/woman, man/woman, she expects the man to turn directly to the woman on his right and start talking. You are certainly not forbidden to talk to the person on your left, but you should be careful not to isolate the woman on your right. It is your social obligation to speak to her unless she is otherwise engaged.

The standard rules for good manners apply at the table as well as everywhere else. Never speak too loudly. You should not be heard by people at both ends of the table. The dinner table is not a lectern and you're not there to give a public speech. You must carry on polite, intimate conversation with the people seated nearby. Naturally, you don't chew with your mouth open or try to eat and talk at the same time.

When you are conversing, you're expected to put the knife and fork on your plate in the manner shown in Picture 37 which indicates that they are in a rest position. Note that the sharp edge of the knife is always pointed toward you and the fork is always placed prongs down. When you are finished, however, you place your knife and fork, again with the blade pointed in and the fork prongs down, in the position shown in Picture 39. This time they are parallel to each other. When you no longer require the fork, leave it on the plate as shown in Picture 38, prongs up. If the meal did not require the use of one of the implements that had been set out, leave that utensil on the table. Do not put it on the plate with the utensils you did use.

The rules for finger foods, which ones are and which aren't and how to deal with them, are very confused and vary from one section of the country to another. For example in the South, although table manners are far more important than they are in the North, there is a great deal more leeway as to which foods are finger foods. While in the North you may pick up such things as asparagus, bacon, the legs of small birds, cakes, celery, olives, and chicken at barbecues with your fingers and be reasonably sure of being correct, the South has a much more sensible rule: if it looks as though you can eat it neatly with your fingers, go right ahead. In the North, if you're not certain, eat the food with a knife and fork to be on the safe side. Asparagus, when it's too long or covered with hollandaise sauce, should be cut with a knife and fork. Cakes, caviar, fish, crepes, and any of the standard meats and vegetables require that you follow the rule of common sense.

Obviously, ice cream has to be eaten with a spoon unless it is so well frozen you can eat it along with your cake. Neatness is the goal. Although you can pick up a sandwich with both hands, it is generally considered more tasteful to cut it in halves or quarters and pick up one piece at a time.

There are a few details that you should keep in mind at all times. Never take anything from a serving plate directly into your mouth, including celery, olives, pickles, and such. Move celery and olives to your butter plate, salt them there, and then eat them. Never do two things at once, such as picking up a water glass to drink

Picture 37

At rest position, knife and fork.

while unfolding your napkin with the other hand. It's always simplest to stop one action before starting another. When you start doing two things at the same time, you're liable to spill something or poke someone.

Common sense also extends to taking things from your mouth as well as putting things in. When you're eating grapes or watermelon, very small seeds can be deposited in the cupped hand. When eating large fruits such as peaches, cherries, and plums, good table manners require you to deposit the pits onto a spoon or fork and move them to your plate in that manner.

Finally, if you're going to eat spaghetti or lobster you should know that each requires particular skills. For spaghetti, twirl it on a fork against a large spoon. Lobster requires that you be deft with a shell cracker and that you eat various sections with your fingers, others with a fork and knife.

When I asked the men who run corporate America why they thought people made mistakes at the dinner table, they surprised me. Most of them said it wasn't

Picture 38

Finished position, fork alone.

Picture 39

Finished position, knife and fork.

that people didn't know what to do. Subordinates often started correctly. They sat down, picked up their napkin, and put it on their lap, carried on polite conversation, and usually got through the first two or three courses successfully. But once the meal got going and they started feeling comfortable, they fell into their normal eating habits and started eating with their mouths open. If you're used to eating in front of television or with a plastic fork, you're going to find it very difficult to conduct yourself properly at a formal dinner. Again, I would suggest that at least two meals a weak be served at home in a very formal manner, if not for your sake, at least for your children's, so that they will have these essential skills as part of their baggage when they enter the outer world where it counts so much.

For those who need them, here is a simple list of don'ts. Don't hold your knife or fork in an improper manner. Don't eat with your mouth open. Don't leave a spoon in your cup or utensils in the dessert dish at the end of the meal; place them on the service dish. Don't put too much in your mouth at once. Don't talk with food in your mouth. Don't slouch in your seat, rock back in your chair, or apologize if you happen to burp or drop something on the floor.

And finally, when you're finished, don't push your plate away, open your vest, loosen your belt, and belch. Simply wait until your hostess has indicated the meal is over and get up when she has given the signal that she is about to leave the table. Never before. Bon Appetit!

14

PRACTICE
FOR SUCCESS

The last chapter in most books announces the beginning of the end; in this book it announces only the beginning. As I told you earlier, I have no formula for easy, instant success, and therefore I think it's inappropriate to end this book with the traditional pep talk that closes most success books. Instead, I am going to invite you to "live for success," to take a realistic look at yourself and to spend weeks, months, possibly even years mastering social, business and personal skills, all of which will increase your chance to succeed in anything you do.

Having given success courses to thousands of men and women, I understand that readers at this point will fall into six basic groups.

Type One, the self-starting perfectionists, have already analyzed their shortcomings, outlined a realistic plan for overcoming them, and have probably begun practicing before reaching this part of the book. If you are one of them, you may not have specific goals and a timetable in your mind at this moment but you will develop them almost by instinct. You are the people who are most likely to succeed. Frankly, you don't need this chapter, but, being Type One, you won't be able to resist reading it. You complete everything you start and you invariably do it well. Obviously, all I can do is wish you luck.

The Type Twos are procrastinators. Their favorite saying is "Not now, I'll get to it later." They really intend to do something about what they've read, they just can't get around to it this week. They hope they may be able to get to it next week or next month but are not quite sure. We know they'll never really get around to it unless we give them a shove and a schedule. I know how procrastinators think. They have a million excuses. Forget them! The trick is to make a definite commitment to start *now, not tomorrow*.

Next we come to the Type Threes, who represent the majority of readers. Their road to hell will be paved with good intentions. They have spotted one or two shortcomings and they are determined to overcome them but their problem is they have no sense of organization or the self-discipline that comes with it. They never bother to figure out exactly what they're going to do. Their plans are too general. They never have a program and therefore they very seldom accomplish much. It is the main reason for their failure. They will find themselves squaring their shoulders and standing a bit more erect for the next few days. They may even begin to listen a bit more carefully to how they speak. But unless they set up a definite program, with a specific set of goals, this book will have little effect on their lives. If you are one of them—and most readers are—I suggest you put the book down now and get a pen, because you're the type who must commit to writing everything you're going to do. The existence of a written document, a black-and-white schedule, acts as an army sergeant. It drills you. You're the typical middle-class soldier: you don't *join* the army but if you're drafted you fight like hell. In the war against failure you must draft yourself.

Type Fours are the professional success-seekers. They read every book with success in the title but they never seem to succeed. They read this book and they weigh it no more heavily than the books written by a million idiots. They're out to get simple success, instant success, and downhill success. They want that secret no one has told them yet and they far prefer authors who promise it to them. The fact that these authors don't deliver doesn't bother them too much. If you are one of these people, I'm going to disappoint you. The one characteristic of people who are successful is they don't believe in instant success. If you believe in instant success, you'll probably never succeed. You must sit down, take a deep breath, and say, "In order to succeed I have to sweat, I have to work, I have to plan, and there's no time like the present to start."

Then, there is the group for whom I have the most sympathy: the Fives. They are overwhelmed by an enormous amount of information. They see so many flaws in themselves, they don't know where to start. They're frankly discouraged by the task that confronts them. This group will find this chapter particularly useful. I will help you set up priorities, goals, and realistic timetables for achieving them and, by doing so, eliminate that sense of being overwhelmed. You can succeed if you try and have a plan.

Finally, there are the Sixes. They are the people who are already successful or well on their way to success, who come to my meetings, read my research reports and buy my books. Their usual comments about my work is, "Of course, of course, oh that's an interesting point." Coming to a success seminar for them is a busman's holiday. They are like opera buffs going to an opera lecture—they may know more than the lecturer, but they come anyway because they enjoy the subject. I am flattered and sometimes astounded by their presence and can state without any hesitation that this chapter is not necessary for them because they run America. They don't need John T. Molloy.

The first step in success training is to identify those areas that need improvement. Most of the time this is simple. You know whether you are unpopular or unable to give orders and we've given you a fair idea of whether you are operating correctly as an office politician or a corporate wife. Most of you will have no trouble listing a half dozen areas in which you would like to improve and listing them in order of importance. Doing so here is the first step in goal setting.

1.

2.

3.

4.

5.

6.

If you had difficulty choosing which areas need improvement or which areas you should work on first, I've developed a little form that may help. The areas in the form are communications skills, power skills, body signals, verbal signals, popularity skills, interview skills, and sales skills. These areas correspond to chapter headings, but you may, of course, substitute any of your own. I've also listed more precise areas of study. If you decide you need to work on power language, or improve your body signals specifically for interviews, you should certainly do so. Finally, I've listed Dressing for Success, which is the subject of my earlier books. There are recognized success skills which are not covered in this book or may be peculiar to a particular industry or geographical location. If you decide you need to work on a social or business skill not included in the chart, do so. It should be part of your personal success-program. Please note that I've left three empty spaces for you to fill in anything you wish. Also, feel free to cross out any

of the sections we've filled in—they are simply guides—
and replace them with your own improvement goals.

The following chart rates each of the areas for improvement on a one-to-ten basis with ten being the highest
score.

If you don't have a good reason for rearranging them,
I suggest you attack one area at a time and start with
the area with the highest score. Since you are your own
teacher, I advise you to rig the course and give yourself
an "A." One of the easiest ways to get students interested is to let them start in an area in which they've
already had some success, in which they're not going to
have too much difficulty and in which their accomplishments will produce an immediate reward. Our experience shows that nothing succeeds like success. When
our students succeed in one area, they quickly go on to
a second and a third area and do just as well.

AREAS FOR IMPROVEMENT	PRESENT ABILITY	EASE OF ACCOMPLISHMENT	ESTIMATED IMPACT WITHIN 1 YEAR	TOTALS
1. Communications				
2. Power Skills				
3. Body Signals				
4. Verbal Messages				
5. Popularity Skills				
6. Interview Skills				
7. Sales Skills				
8. Body Signals for Interviews				

AREAS FOR IMPROVEMENT	PRESENT ABILITY	EASE OF ACCOM- PLISH- MENT	ESTIMATED IMPACT WITHIN 1 YEAR	TOTALS
9. Power Language				
10.				
11.				
12.				

Naturally, the first rule you should apply to any area, including self-improvement, is common sense. If you're presently out of work, or if you're working and looking for a job, it would be silly for you to undertake a major study of communication skills. It would be far more sensible for you to master the interview chapter and overcome shortcomings you have in that area. Obviously, the same is true if you are an executive wife. Although you might be far more interested in developing your power skills than your social skills, it would seem that those social skills that were connected with being an executive wife would be the most sensible projects to undertake first. Being sensible is not enough. You must commit yourself to action. You must choose those areas you wish to improve and the ones you're going to work on immediately.

Areas for Improvement

1.

2.

3.

4.

5.

6.

Now that you have six areas listed in the order in which you are going to attack them, you may find it more efficient to divide some of them into subsections. If you've chosen table manners as your first area, I do not think subsections are necessary. You simply have to memorize the uses of various utensils and practice with them. If, however, you choose to develop your power skills, you will have to decide how much time and effort you're going to give visual power signals, verbal power signals, or power language. You will have to practice each power element independently and then practice them together with either the aid of your family or a mechanical device.

After you've divided your areas of study into subsections, you have to develop a plan of attack. First, write down what you hope to accomplish. Be as specific as possible. We found in our success courses that once students committed themselves to a goal in writing, they felt obliged to reach it. When goals were not put down in black and white, students tended to lower their sights and this became self-defeating. Most of us, unfortunately, are basically lazy and we seek the path of least resistance, if that path is left open. Writing down your goals and being specific closes the path of least resistance and forces you to keep your sights high.

Next you must set up a schedule for reaching goals. Before attempting to do this you have to analyze the type of learning involved in reaching different skills. There are three types. First there are informational skills. If before reading this book you were not able to identify a fish knife and now you can, you have an informational skill. If you are served a fish course you will now be able to choose the right utensil. The second type of learning has to do with use of a fish knife. The fact that you know how to hold a fish knife will do you little good without practice. And, finally, there is habitual knowledge. If you've only used meat knives, it will take practice before you use a fish knife correctly. Habitual knowledge is really the only kind that will give you the self-assurance you need to handle the fish course and conversation with the lady next to you at a formal banquet.

Most of the so-called success books that I've read imply that if you possess information, you automatically have a foot up on the ladder of success. Once you've read those books, you're saved from a life of failure and destined for success. This is just not so. My research shows that information alone is useful in only a small percentage of cases. In most real-life situations, knowledge must become habit before it is truly useful.

If you've read carefully, you know a great deal about success and you have at your fingertips a basis for making judgments. The fact that we know that men from upper-middle-class backgrounds carry their shoulders differently from men from a lower-middle-class background and women from an upper-middle-class background hold their heads differently from women from a lower-middle-class background will be of very little use to you unless you act on the information. If you come from a blue-collar background, you're going to have to practice sitting or standing with your shoulders back or your head erect. My experience in teaching success courses has shown that it would be best if you set up a specific time of day for practicing sitting and standing. I know this may sound silly to people who've never tried it, because their instinct is to say, "I'll do it all the time; everytime it occurs to me I'll stand up straight." But experience shows if you set aside as little as fifteen minutes a day for posture practice your improvement will be two or three times greater than if you spend twenty-four hours a day without a schedule. In addition, sitting every night before a television set will give you a way of measuring your progress. The first night you sit erect for fifteen minutes, you'll be very uncomfortable, but after six or seven weeks you'll be able to sit erect for fifteen minutes and enjoy the television program without even realizing you're doing it.

Now I know there are some of you who want to go one

step farther and set up a six-week course in body language and a three-week course in verbal skills and a four-week course in social skills, but that is really not possible. What you must do is work until you perfect it. There are no C's in success, only A's.

Success does not mean that you cannot fail, it means you cannot accept failure.

LEARN TO SPEAK CORRECTLY AT HOME
IN YOUR SPARE TIME

If, after reading *Live for Success*, you come to the conclusion that you and/or members of your family, particularly your children, need improved verbal patterns, we have very good news for you.

Dr. William Formaad, in addition to being one of the leaders in this field, the head of the speech department of a major university, and the man executives seek when one of their number needs help, has developed a unique method of speech training that is designed to help you self-evaluate, self-motivate, and self-correct your speech patterns. The entire course consists of five forty-minute cassette tapes which you will play over and over as you experiment, practice, and improve this essential image skill. These lessons emphasize crispness and articulation, clarity and projection of tone, esthetic appeal and a reasonable conformity to cultivated usage. The object of this course is to help you develop the speech patterns of well-educated men and women from privileged backgrounds, which is the pattern of successful speech in America.

Mr. John T. Molloy
P.O. Box 526
Washington Bridge Station
New York, N.Y. 10033

Please send me Dr. Formaad's Live for Success Speech Course. Enclosed is my check for $80.00 to cover the complete cost of the program. Outside U.S. add $10.00.

Name_____

Address_____

_____

If you need help choosing proper success clothing, you may in addition use this form to order John T. Molloy's "Dress for Success Computer Printout." Check the appropriate box. Male ☐ Female ☐ And enclose a check for $29.95 for each program.

ABOUT THE AUTHOR

JOHN T. MOLLOY'S two earlier books—*Dress for Success* and *The Woman's Dress for Success Book*—have sold over two million copies and have literally changed the look of corporate America.

These books, along with Molloy's research techniques, are taught in hundreds of universities both here and abroad. He has also been a consultant to over 380 of the *Fortune* 500, to scores of the largest companies in Europe and Japan, and to dozens of governments.

MONEY TALKS!
How to get it and How to keep it!

We Deliver!
And So Do These Bestsellers.

"Cussler twists fact and fiction into a rope of tension that will leave you dangling until the last page."
—*Tulsa World*

A ruthless corporation is about to take control of the seas. For those who oppose them, there is...

WHITE DEATH

This is a mission for Kurt Austin and the NUMA® team.

"SHOULD RISE TO THE TOP LIKE ONE OF CUSSLER'S REAL-LIFE LOST SHIPS."
—*Kirkus Reviews*

In his novels *Serpent*, *Blue Gold*, and *Fire Ice*, #1 bestselling author Clive Cussler chronicled the "wildly entertaining" (*New York Daily News*) missions of Kurt Austin, leader of NUMA's Special Assignment Team and a hero for the new millennium. An instant hit with critics and fans, Austin returns in an "action-fueled, rip-roaring"* adventure as big—and dangerous—as the seven seas . . .

WHITE DEATH

A confrontation with a radical environmentalist group sinks a Danish cruiser off the Faroe Islands—and it's up to Kurt Austin and his colleague Joe Zavala to rescue the men trapped inside. But they soon discover that this was no isolated incident.

A shadowy multinational corporation is attempting to take control of the very seas themselves. Killing anyone who gets in their way, they have made Austin their next target. Now he must evade their brutal tactics, and put a stop to a cataclysmic environmental disaster that has already begun . . .

"A roiling stew of seafaring
adventure [and] cutting-edge science."
—*Publishers Weekly*

continued . . .

WHITE DEATH

A NOVEL FROM THE NUMA® FILES

CLIVE CUSSLER

with PAUL KEMPRECOS

BERKLEY BOOKS, NEW YORK

This is a work of fiction. Names, characters, places, and incidents either are the product of the author's imagination or are used fictitiously, and any resemblance to actual persons, living or dead, business establishments, events, or locales is entirely coincidental.

WHITE DEATH

A Berkley Book / published by arrangement with
Sandecker, RLLLP

PRINTING HISTORY
G. P. Putnam's Sons hardcover edition / June 2003
Berkley mass-market edition / June 2004

Copyright © 2003 by Sandecker, RLLLP.
Cover art and design by Lawrence Ratzkin.

ISBN: 0-425-19545-7

BERKLEY®
Berkley Books are published by The Berkley Publishing Group,
a division of Penguin Group (USA) Inc.,
375 Hudson Street, New York, New York 10014.
BERKLEY and the "B" design
are trademarks belonging to Penguin Group (USA) Inc.

PRINTED IN THE UNITED STATES OF AMERICA

10 9 8 7 6 5 4 3 2 1

WHITE DEATH

PROLOGUE I

West of the British Isles, 1515

DIEGO AGUIRREZ AWOKE from his restless sleep thinking that a rat had scurried across his face. His wide forehead was bathed in a cold sweat, his heart hammered in his chest, and a formless panic gnawed hungrily at his innards. He listened to the muffled snores of his sleeping crewmen and the chuckle and swash of wavelets against the wooden hull. Nothing appeared to be amiss. Yet he couldn't shake the uneasy feeling that an unseen threat lurked in the shadows.

Easing from his hammock, Aguirrez wrapped a thick woolen blanket around his brawny shoulders and climbed a companionway to the fog-shrouded deck. In the muted light of the moon, the solidly built caravel glistened as if it were made of spiderwebs. Aguirrez went over to a form huddled next to the yellow glow of an oil lamp.

"Good evening, Captain," the man said at his approach.

Aguirrez was pleased to see that the watch was awake and alert.

"Good evening," the captain replied. "All goes well?"

"Yes, sir. Still no wind, though."

Aguirrez glanced up at the ghostly masts and sails. "It will come. I can smell it."

"Aye, Captain," the man said, stifling a yawn.

"Go below and get some sleep. I'll relieve you."

"It isn't time yet. My shift's not over for another turn of the glass."

The captain picked up the hourglass next to the lamp and turned it over. "There," he said. *"Now* it's time."

The man grunted his thanks and shuffled off to the crew's quarters while the captain took up a post in the ship's high, squared-off stern castle. He gazed off to the south, staring into the smoky mists that rose like steam from the mirror-flat sea. He was still at his post when the sun rose. His olive-black eyes were red-rimmed, and they ached with weariness. His blanket was soggy with moisture. With typical stubbornness, he ignored the discomforts and paced back and forth like a caged tiger.

The captain was a Basque, an inhabitant of the rugged mountains between Spain and France, and his instincts, honed by years at sea, were not to be taken lightly. The Basques were the best sailors in the world, and men like Aguirrez routinely voyaged to regions that more timid mariners regarded as the realm of sea serpents and giant whirlpools. Like many Basques, he had eyebrows like bramble thickets, large protruding ears, a long, straight nose and a chin like a mountain ledge. In later years, scientists would suggest that the Basques, with their heavy facial features, were the direct descendants of Cro-Magnon man.

The crew emerged yawning and stretching into the gray predawn light and set about their tasks. The captain refused offers to relieve him. His persistence was rewarded near midmorning. His bloodshot eyes glimpsed a shimmering splinter of light through the thick curtain of haze. The quick nervous flicker lasted only an instant, but it filled Aguirrez with an odd combination of relief and dread.

Pulse quickening, Aguirrez raised the brass spyglass that hung by a cord around his neck, snapped the sections to their full length and squinted through the eyepiece. At first he saw only a gray monotone circle of magnification where the fog bank blended with the sea. The captain wiped his eyes with his sleeve, blinked to clear his vision and raised the telescope again. Again he saw nothing. A trick of the light, he thought.

Suddenly, he saw movement through the lens. A sharp prow had emerged from the mists like the probing beak of a raptor. Then the full length of the boat came into view. The slim black-hulled craft shot forward, glided a few seconds, then surged forward again. Two other ships followed in quick succession, scudding over the flat surface like giant water insects. Aguirrez swore softly to himself.

War galleys.

Sunlight reflected off the wet oars that dipped into the sea with a mechanical cadence. With each sweep of the oars, the sleek vessels rapidly closed the gap separating them from the sailing ship.

The captain calmly appraised the fast-approaching ships from stem to stern, taking in the clean, functional lines with the appreciation of a skilled shipbuilder. True greyhounds of the sea, capable of short bursts of high speed, the fighting galleys developed by Venice were used by dozens of European countries.

Each galley was propelled by a hundred-and-fifty oars, three ranks of twenty-five on each side. The low, level profile imparted a streamlined look that was ahead of its time, gracefully curving up at the rear where the captain's house overhung the stern. The prow was elongated, although it no longer functioned as a ram as in times past. The bow had been transformed into an artillery platform.

A small three-sided lateen sail hung from a single mast near the stern, but human muscle power gave the galley its speed and maneuverability. The Spanish penal system provided a steady supply of rowers condemned to die pulling the heavy thirty-foot oars. The *corsia,* a narrow gangway that ran fore and aft, was the realm of hard men who urged the rowers on with threats and whip-lashes.

Aguirrez knew that the firepower arrayed against his ship would be formidable. The galleys were nearly twice the eighty-foot length of his tubby caravel. The fighting galley routinely carried fifty of the single-shot muzzle-loaded smoothbore arquebuses. The heaviest gun, a cast-iron, high-angle mortar called a *bombard*, was mounted on the bow artillery platform. Its position on the right-front side was a holdover from the days when naval strategy centered on ramming the enemy head-on.

While the galley was a throwback to the sturdy Greek craft that carried Odysseus from Circe to Cyclops, the caravel was the wave of the future. Fast and maneuverable for its day, the rugged ship could sail anywhere on the watery surface of the earth. The caravel blended its southern rigging with a tough northern hull of flush-built planking and a hinged, axeled rudder. The easily rigged lateen sails, descended from the Arabic *dhow,* made the ship far superior to any contemporary sailing vessel when sailing close to the wind.

Unfortunately for Aguirrez, those sails, so miraculous in their simple efficiency, now hung limply from the twin masts. With no breeze to stir the canvas, the sails were useless sheets of fabric. The becalmed caravel was glued to the surface of the sea like a ship in a bottle.

Aguirrez glanced at the lifeless canvas and cursed the elements conspiring against him. He seethed at the shortsighted arrogance that had led him to defy his instinct to stay far out to sea. With their low freeboard, the galleys were not designed for open waters and would have had difficulty following the caravel. But he had sailed close to land because the route was more direct. With favorable winds, his ship could outrun any vessel on the sea. He'd never anticipated a dead calm. Nor had he expected the galleys to find him so easily.

He brushed away his self-recriminations and suspicions. Time enough to deal with questions later. Tossing his blanket aside as if it were a matador's cape, he strode the length of the ship bellowing orders. The men came alive as the captain's powerful voice echoed from one end of the ship to the other. Within seconds, the deck resembled a stirred-up anthill.

"Launch the boats!" Aguirrez pointed to the approaching warships. "Look smart, lads, or we'll be keeping the executioners working day and night."

They moved to their tasks with quicksilver speed. Every man on board the caravel knew that the horrors of torture and burning at the stake would be their fate if the galleys captured them. Within minutes, all three of the caravel's boats were in the water, manned by the strongest rowers. The lines attached to the ship went bowstring-taut, but the caravel stubbornly refused to move. Aguirrez yelled at his men to row harder. The air over his head turned blue as he appealed to their Basque manhood with every salty curse he could muster.

"Pull together!" Aguirrez shouted, his dark eyes blazing. "You're rowing like a bunch of Spanish whores."

The oars churned the calm water into a sudsy foam. The ship shuddered and creaked, and finally it began to inch forward. Aguirrez roared his encouragement and dashed back to the stern. He leaned on the rail and put his eye to his spyglass. Through the lens, he saw a tall, thin man in the bow platform of the lead galley looking back at him through a telescope.

Aguirrez's lips tightened in a grim smile. His spyglass had been fashioned by a Basque glassmaker named Diaz, who had discovered the properties of putting lenses in a tube a hundred years before Galileo. These optical instruments were a closely held secret among Basque mariners who used them on their long-distance voyages. The telescopes were fabulously expensive and even a wealthy man like Aguirrez had only two. The one he was using and the other which was stolen from him by the man in the lead galley.

"El Brasero," Aguirrez whispered with unveiled contempt.

Ignatius Martinez saw Aguirrez looking at him and curled his thick voluptuary's lips in a snarl of triumph. His pitiless yellow eyes burned with fanaticism in their deep-set sockets. The long aristocratic nose was lifted in the air as if it had encountered a bad smell.

"Captain Blackthorne," he purred to the red-bearded man at his side, "spread the word among the rowers. Tell them they will be free if we catch our prey."

The captain shrugged and carried out the order, knowing that Martinez had no intention of keeping his promise, that it was merely a cruel deception.

El Brasero was Spanish for brazier. Martinez had earned his nickname for his zeal in roasting heretics at the *auto de fé,* as the public spectacles of punishment were called. He was a familiar figure at the *quemerdo,* or place of burning, where he used every means, including bribery, to make sure that he had the honor of lighting the pyre. Although his official title was Public Prosecutor and Advisor to the Inquisition, he had persuaded his higher-ups to appoint him as the Inquisitor in charge of prosecuting the Basques. The prosecution of the Basques was extremely profitable. The Inquisition immediately confiscated the property of the accused. The stolen wealth of its victims financed the Inquisition's prisons, secret police, torture chambers, army and bureaucracy, and it made rich men of the Inquisitors.

Basques had brought the arts of navigation and shipbuilding to unheard-of levels of expertise. Aguirrez had sailed to the secret fishing grounds across the Western Sea dozens of times on whaling or cod-fishing trips. Basques were natural capitalists, and many, like Aguirrez, had become rich selling whale products and cod. His busy shipyard on the Nervion River built vessels of every type and size. Aguirrez had been aware of the Inquisition and its excesses, but he was too busy running his various enterprises and enjoying the infrequent company of his beautiful wife and two children to give it much thought. It was on his return from one trip that he had learned firsthand that Martinez and the Inquisition were malevolent forces that could not be ignored.

An angry crowd had greeted the fish-laden ships that edged up to the docks to unload their catch. The people had shouted for Aguirrez's attention and pleaded for his help. The Inquisition had arrested a group of local women and charged them with witchcraft. His wife had been among those taken. She and the others had been tried and found guilty and were being moved from prison to the burning place.

Aguirrez calmed the crowd and went directly to the provincial capital. Although he was a man of influence, his pleas to free the prisoners fell on deaf ears. Officials said they could do nothing; this was a church matter, not a civil one. Some whispered that their own lives and property could be placed in jeopardy if they went against the orders of the Holy Office. *"El Brasero,"* they whispered in fear.

Aguirrez had taken matters into his own hands and rounded up a hundred of his men. They'd attacked the convoy taking the accused witches to the stake, and freed the women without firing a shot. Even as he took his wife into his arms, Aguirrez knew that *El Brasero* had engineered the witchcraft arrests and trials to bring the Basque and his property within his greedy grasp.

Aguirrez suspected that there was an even more compelling reason he had come to the Inquisition's attention. The year before, a council of elders had given him stewardship of the most sacred relics of Basqueland. One day they would be used to rally the Basques in a fight for independence against Spain. For now, they were contained in a chest hidden in a secret chamber of Aguirrez's luxurious home. Martinez could have heard of the artifacts. The region was rife with informers. Martinez would know how sacred relics could ignite fanaticism, in much the same way that the Holy Grail had launched the bloody Crusades. Anything that united the Basques would be a threat to the Inquisition.

Martinez did not respond to the freeing of the women. Aguirrez was no fool. Martinez would strike only after he had collected every scrap of incriminating evidence. Aguirrez used this time to prepare. He put the fastest caravel in his fleet up on the ways at San Sebastián, as if it were undergoing repairs. He spread generous amounts of money around to enlist his own army of spies, including some in the prosecutor's entourage, and made it known that the biggest reward would go to the man who warned of his arrest. Then he went about his business as usual and waited, staying close to home, where he surrounded himself with guards, all veterans of combat.

Several months quietly passed. Then one night, one of his spies, a man who worked in the office of the Inquisition itself, galloped breathlessly up to his villa and pounded on his door. Martinez was leading a group of soldiers to arrest him. Aguirrez paid off the grateful spy and put his well-laid plans into effect. He kissed his wife and children good-bye and promised to meet them in Portugal. While his family escaped in a farm wagon with much of their wealth, a decoy was dispatched to lead the arrest party on a merry chase through the countryside. Accompanied by his armed entourage, Aguirrez made his way to the coast. Under cover of darkness, the caravel slid down the ways, unfurled its sails and headed north.

When the sun rose the next day, a fleet of fighting galleys had emerged from the dawn mists in an attempt to cut the caravel off. Using adroit seamanship, Aguirrez had eluded his pursuers, and a steady breeze had sent the ship winging north along the coast of France. He set a course for Denmark, where he would begin the turn west toward Greenland and Iceland, and the Great Land beyond. But then, off the British Isles, the ship's wake petered out along with the wind, and Aguirrez and his men found themselves sitting in a pool of dead air . . .

Now, with the trio of galleys closing in for the kill, Aguirrez was determined to fight to the death if need be, but his strongest instinct was survival. He ordered the gun crew to prepare for battle. In arming the caravel, he had sacrificed armament for speed, firepower for flexibility.

The standard arquebus was a cumbersome muzzle-loaded matchlock gun that was hooked onto a portable stand and needed two men to load and fire. The gunners on the caravel were armed with smaller, lighter versions that could be fired by one man. His crewmen were excellent marksmen who would make every shot count. For heavy artillery, Aguirrez had chosen a pair of bronze cannon that could be moved on wheeled carriages. The gun crews had drilled to the point where they could load, aim and fire with clockwork precision unheard of in most ships.

The rowers were visibly tired, and the ship was like a fly crawling across a bucket of molasses. The galleys were almost within firing range. Their snipers could pick off the rowers with ease. He decided that the men would have to stay at their oars. As long as the ship moved, Aguirrez had a modicum of control. He urged his men to keep pulling, and he was turning back to help the gun crew when his fine-tuned senses detected a shift in temperature, usually the harbinger of a breeze. The smaller lateen sail flapped like the wing of an injured bird. Then it was still.

As the captain scanned the sea for the puckering of the surface that would herald a puff of wind, he heard the unmistakable roar of a bombard. The wide-mouthed mortar was carried in a fixed carriage with no means of training or elevation. The cannonball splashed harmlessly into the sea about a hundred yards off the caravel's stern. Aguirrez laughed, knowing that it was practically impossible to score a direct hit with a bombard, even on a target as slow-moving as the caravel.

The galleys had been moving three-abreast. As a cloud of smoke drifted over the water, the galleys flanking the lead boat shot ahead and came straight in behind the caravel. The maneuver was a feint. Both galleys veered to the left, and one took the lead. Galleys had most of their armament on the right front side. As they passed the slow-moving caravel, they could rake its deck and rigging with small and medium guns.

Anticipating the attack, Aguirrez had placed both cannon close together on the port side and covered their muzzles with a black cloth. The enemy would assume that the caravel also carried the inefficient bombard and that its flanks were virtually unprotected.

The captain scanned the artillery platform through the spyglass and swore as he recognized a former crewman who had sailed with him on many fishing trips. The man knew the route Aguirrez followed to the Western Sea. More than likely, the Inquisition was holding a threat against his family.

Aguirrez checked the elevation of each cannon. He pulled aside the black cloth and sighted through the gun ports on an imaginary circle on the sea. Having encountered no opposition, the first galley came in close to the caravel—and Aguirrez gave the order to fire. Both cannon thundered. One shot was premature and snapped the beak off the galley, but the second cannonball smashed into the artillery platform.

The bow section disintegrated in a burst of fire and smoke. Water poured into the ruptured hull, aided by the galley's forward speed, and the boat slipped below the surface and sank within moments. Aguirrez felt a pang of pity for the rowers, manacled to their oars and unable to escape, but their death would be quick compared to weeks and months of suffering.

The crew of the second galley saw the lead boat's fate, and in a display of the nimbleness the triremes were famous for, it veered sharply away from the caravel, then looped around to rejoin Martinez, who had prudently held his boat back.

Aguirrez guessed that the galleys would split up, come

around both sides of the ship, careful to stay out of cannon range, then circle back and attack the vulnerable rowers. Almost as if Martinez were reading his thoughts, the galleys pulled apart and each began a long swing around the opposite sides of the ship, circling like wary hyenas.

Aguirrez heard a snap above his head, caused by a desultory flap of the mainsail. He held his breath, wondering if it was only an errant puff as before. Then the sail flapped again and filled out, and the masts creaked. He ran to the bow, leaned over the rail and shouted at his deck crew to bring the rowers back on board.

Too late.

The galleys had cut short their long, lazy loop and angled sharply back on a course that brought them directly at the ship. The right-hand galley swung around and presented its long side, and the gunners concentrated their arquebus fire on the defenseless longboat. A withering fusillade raked the rowers.

Emboldened, the second galley tried the same maneuver on the port side. The caravel's marksmen had rallied after being taken by surprise, and they concentrated their fire on the exposed artillery platform where Aguirrez had last seen Martinez. *El Brasero* was undoubtedly hiding behind thick wood, but he would get the message.

The volley hit the platform like a leaden fist. As soon as the marksmen let off one shot, they picked up another weapon and fired again, while crewmen feverishly reloaded the guns. The fusillade was continuous and deadly. Unable to withstand the prolonged hail of fire, the galley veered off, its hull splintered and its oars in fragments.

The caravel's crew rushed to haul in the long boats. The first boat was bathed in blood and half the rowers were dead. Aguirrez yelled orders to his heavy gunners, raced to the helm and grabbed the wheel. Gun crews swarmed around the cannon and muscled the heavy weapons into the bow gunports. Other deckhands adjusted the rigging to wring the most out of the freshening breeze.

As the caravel picked up speed, leaving a growing wake, the captain steered the ship toward the galley that had been raked by fire from his gunners. The galley tried to elude him, but it had lost rowers and was moving erratically. Aguirrez waited until he was within fifty yards. The galley's gunners fired at their pursuer, but the shots had little effect.

The cannon boomed and the balls scored a direct hit on the roofed captain's house on the stern, blasting it to toothpicks. The cannon were speedily reloaded and aimed at the galley's waterline, where they punched massive holes in the hull. Heavy with men and equipment, the galley quickly slipped under the surface, leaving bubbles, shards of wood and a few hapless swimmers to mark its passing.

The captain turned his attention to the third galley.

Seeing the odds change, Martinez was on the run. His galley sped off to the south like a startled hare. The agile caravel turned from its kill and tried to follow. Aguirrez had blood in his eyes as he savored the prospect of dousing *El Brasero*'s fire.

It was not to be. The freshening breeze was still gentle, and the caravel could not match the speed of the fleeing galley, whose rowers were pulling for their lives. Before long, the galley was a dark spot on the ocean.

Aguirrez would have chased Martinez to the ends of the earth, but he saw sails on the horizon and guessed that they might be enemy reinforcements. The Inquisition had a long reach. He remembered his promise to his wife and children and his responsibility to the Basque people. Reluctantly, he swung the ship around and set a course north toward Denmark. Aguirrez had no illusions about his enemy. Martinez might be a coward, but he was patient and persistent.

It would be only a matter of time before they met again.

PROLOGUE II

SHORTLY AFTER MIDNIGHT, the dogs began to howl along a swath of countryside between the city of Hamburg and the North Sea. Terrified canines stared at the black, moonless sky with lolling tongues and shivering haunches. Their keen hearing had picked up what human ears could not: the faint whir of engines from the giant silver-skinned torpedo that slithered through the thick layer of clouds high above.

Four Maybach 12-cylinder engines, a pair on each side, hung in streamlined housings from the bottom of the 800-foot-long airship. Lights glowed in the oversized windows of the control car near the front of the fuselage. The long, narrow control car was organized like a ship's pilothouse, complete with compass and spoked steering wheels for the rudder and elevators.

Standing next to the helmsman, feet wide apart, arms clasped behind his back, was Captain Heinrich Braun, a tall ramrod-straight figure impeccably dressed in a dark-blue uniform and a tall-peaked cap. Cold had seeped into the cabin and overwhelmed its heaters, so he wore a thick turtleneck sweater under his jacket. Braun's haughty profile could have been chiseled from granite. His rigid posture and silver hair, cropped close to his scalp military-style, and the slight elevation to his jutting chin, recalled his days as a Prussian naval officer.

Braun checked the compass heading, then turned to a portly middle-aged man whose bushy, upturned mustache made him resemble a good-natured walrus.

"Well, Herr Lutz, we have successfully completed the first leg of our historic journey." Braun had an elegant, anachronistic way of speaking. "We are maintaining our goal of one hundred twenty kilometers per hour. Even with a slight headwind, fuel consumption is exactly as calculated. My compliments, Herr Professor."

Herman Lutz looked like the bartender in a Munich beer cellar, but he was one of the most highly skilled aeronautical engineers in Europe. After his retirement, Braun had written a book suggesting airship service across the pole to North America. At a lecture promoting his book, he'd met Lutz, who was trying to raise money to fund a polar airship venture. The men were drawn to each other by their firm belief that airships could promote international cooperation.

Lutz's blue eyes danced with excitement. "My congratulations to *you,* Captain Braun. Together we will advance the greater glory of world peace."

"I'm sure you mean the greater glory of *Germany,*" sneered Gerhardt Heinz, a short, slight man who had been standing behind the others, close enough to hear every word. With great ceremony, he lit up a cigarette.

In a steel-tipped voice, Braun said, "Herr Heinz, have you forgotten that above our heads are thousands of cubic feet of highly flammable hydrogen? Smoking is permitted only in the section so designated in the crew's quarters."

Heinz mumbled an answer and snuffed out the cigarette with his fingers. Attempting to gain the edge, he drew himself up like a preening rooster. Heinz had shaved his head to the skin and affected a pince-nez for his nearsighted eyes. The pale-white head was perched on narrow shoulders. While the effect was supposed to be intimidating, it was more grotesque.

Lutz thought that, with his tight black leather overcoat, Heinz looked like a maggot emerging from its pupa, but he wisely kept this thought to himself. Having Heinz on board was the price he and Braun had had to pay to get the airship into the air. That and the aircraft's name: *Nieztsche,* after the German philosopher. Germany was struggling to get out from under the financial and psychological yoke imposed by the Treaty of Versailles. When Lutz had proposed an airship voyage to the North Pole, the public had been eager to contribute funds, but the project had stagnated.

A group of industrialists quietly approached Lutz with a new proposition. With military backing, they would fund an airship to make a secret trip to the North Pole. If the mission succeeded, it would be made public, and the Allies would be presented with a fait accompli that displayed the superiority of German air technology. Failure would be kept a secret to avoid a black mark. The airship was built under cover, Lutz patterning it on the huge airship *Graf Zeppelin.* As part of the deal, he agreed to take Heinz along on the expedition to represent the interests of the industrialists.

"Captain, would you enlighten us as to our progress?" Lutz said.

Braun stepped over to a chart table. "Here is our position. We will follow the course taken by the *Norge* and the *Italia* to the Spitsbergen Islands. From there we make the dash to the pole. I expect the last leg to take about fifteen hours, depending on weather."

"I hope we have better luck than the Italians," Heinz said, unnecessarily reminding the others of previous airship attempts to reach the pole. In 1926, the Norwegian explorer Amundsen and an Italian engineer named Umberto Nobile had successfully reached and circled the pole in an Italian dirigible named the *Norge.* However, Nobile's second expedition in the sister ship known as the *Italia* was supposed to have landed at the pole, but it had crashed. Amundsen had been lost in a rescue attempt. Nobile and some of his men were finally rescued.

"It is not a question of luck," said Lutz. "This airship's design built on the mistakes of others, precisely with this mission in mind. It is stronger and better able to handle rough weather. It has redundant communications systems. The use of Blaugas will allow for greater control because we won't have to vent hydrogen as ballast. We have defrosting ability in our controls. Its machinery is made to operate at subfreezing Arctic temperatures. It is the fastest airship ever built. We have a network of planes and ships in place that will respond immediately if we run into any problems. Our meteorological capacity is second to none."

"I have the utmost confidence in you and the ship," Heinz said with an unctuous smile, as his natural inclination to toady up to others came to the fore.

"Good. I suggest we all get some rest before we reach Spitsbergen. We will refuel there, and proceed to the pole."

The trip to Spitsbergen was uneventful. Contacted by radio, the refueling and resupply crew was ready, and the airship was on its way within hours, heading north, past the Franz Josef archipelago.

The dull gray sea below was speckled with pieces of floating ice. The chunks eventually graduated to large irregular pancakes that joined to form ice broken here and there by dark black veins of open water. Near the pole, the ice became a vast, unbroken expanse. Although the bluish-white surface looked flat from a thousand feet in the air, land explorers had learned the hard way that it was crisscrossed by ridges and hummocks.

"Good news," Braun announced cheerfully. "We are at eighty-five degrees north. We will make the pole soon. The weather conditions are ideal. No wind. Clear skies."

The anticipation grew, and even those who were off-duty crowded into the control cabin and peered out the big windows as if they hoped to see a tall striped shaft marking the spot at 90 degrees north.

One observer called out, "Captain, I think I see something on the ice."

The captain peered through his binoculars at where the crewman was pointing.

"Most interesting." He handed the binoculars to Lutz.

"It's a boat," Lutz said after a moment.

Braun nodded in agreement and directed the helmsman to change course.

"What are you doing?" Heinz said.

Braun handed him the binoculars. "Look," he said, without elaboration.

Heinz fumbled with his pince-nez and squinted through the glasses. "I see nothing," he said flatly.

Braun wasn't surprised at the answer. The man was as blind as a bat. "Nevertheless, there is a boat on the ice."

"What would a *boat* be doing here?" Heinz said, eyes blinking rapidly. "I've heard of no other expeditions to the pole. I order you to return to our course."

"On what grounds, Herr Heinz?" the captain asked, elevating his chin even more. It was apparent from the coldness of his voice that he didn't care what the reply would be.

"Our mission is to go to the North Pole," Heinz said.

Captain Braun glared at Heinz as if he was about to kick the little man out the door and watch his body fall onto the pack ice.

Lutz recognized the dangerous mood the captain was in and intervened. "Herr Heinz, you are right, my friend. But I believe our charge was also to investigate any matter that may be of aid to us or the next expedition."

Braun added, "In addition, we are duty-bound, no less than any ship that sails the sea, to help those who may be in distress."

"If they see us, they will radio someone and jeopardize our mission," Heinz said, trying another tack.

"They would have to be blind and deaf not to have seen or heard us," said Braun. "And if they report our presence, so what? Our ship has no markings except for the name."

Seeing he was defeated, Heinz slowly lit up a cigarette and conspicuously blew smoke in the air, daring the captain to stop him.

The captain ignored the defiant gesture and gave the order to descend. The helmsman adjusted the controls, and the giant airship began its long, sloping glide down to the pack ice.

THE LONE SHIP bearing down on the Faroe Islands looked like the loser in a paintball fight. The hull of the 170-foot *Sea Sentinel* was splashed from stem to stern with an eye-blinding psychedelic potpourri of tie-dye rainbow colors. A piping calliope and a crew of clowns would not have been out of place to complete the carnival atmosphere. The ship's raffish appearance was deceptive. As many had learned to their sorrow, the *Sea Sentinel* was as dangerous in its own way as any vessel in the pages of *Jane's Fighting Ships*.

The *Sea Sentinel* had arrived in Faroe waters after a 180-mile trip from the Shetland Islands off of Scotland. Greeting the vessel was a small flotilla of fishing boats and yachts hired by international press organizations. The Danish cruiser *Leif Eriksson* stood by, and a helicopter circled above in the overcast sky.

It was drizzling, typical summer weather for the Faroes, an archipelago of eighteen specks of rock located in the northeast Atlantic halfway between Denmark and Iceland. The 45,000 human inhabitants of the Faroes are largely descended from the Vikings, who settled there in the ninth century. Although the islands are part of the Kingdom of Denmark, the locals speak a language derived from old Norse. The people are outnumbered by the millions of birds that nest in the towering cliffs that stand like ramparts against the sea.

A tall, ruggedly built man in his forties stood on the ship's foredeck surrounded by reporters and camera technicians. Marcus Ryan, the captain of the *Sea Sentinel,* was conservatively dressed in a black tailored officer's uniform decorated with gold braid on the collar and sleeves. With his movie star profile, tanned skin, the collar-length hair tousled by the breeze and the fringe of ginger-colored beard framing his square jaw, Ryan looked as if he had been cast for the movie role of a dashing sea captain. The image was one he went to great pains to cultivate.

"Congratulations, ladies and gentlemen," Ryan said in a well-modulated voice that carried over the rumble of engines and the swash of water against the hull. "Sorry we couldn't have provided smoother seas. Some of you look a bit green around the gills after our trip from the Shetlands."

The members of the press pool had been chosen by lot to cover the invasion story. After a night spent in cramped bunks as the ship navigated rolling seas, some members of the Fourth Estate were wishing they hadn't been so lucky.

"That's okay," croaked a female reporter from CNN. "Just make sure the story is worth all the damned Dramamine I swallowed."

Ryan flashed his Hollywood smile. "I can almost *guarantee* that you'll see action." He swept his arm theatrically in a wide arc. The cameras dutifully followed his pointing finger to the warship. The cruiser was moving in a wide circle, just fast enough to maintain headway. Fluttering from its main mast was the red-and-white flag of Denmark. "The last time we tried to stop the Faroese from slaughtering pilot whales, that Danish cruiser you see fired a shot across our bow. Small arms fire narrowly missed one of our crew, although the Danes deny they shot at us."

"Did you really slam them with a garbage gun?" asked the CNN reporter.

"We defended ourselves with the materials at hand," Ryan replied with mock seriousness. "Our cook had rigged up a catapult to launch biodegradable garbage bags off the deck. He's a medieval weapons buff, so he developed a gadget similar to a trebuchet that had a surprising range. When the cruiser tried to cut us off, we nailed it with a direct hit, much to our surprise. And *theirs*." He paused and with perfect comic timing said, "There's nothing like being slimed with potato peels, eggshells and coffee grounds to take the wind out of your sails."

Laughter rippled through the group.

The BBC reporter said, "Aren't you worried that antics of that sort add to the reputation given to the Sentinels of the Sea as one of the more radical environmental and animal rights groups? Your organization has freely admitted to scuttling whaling ships, blocking waterways, spray-painting baby seals, harassing sealers, cutting drift nets . . ."

Ryan raised his hand in protest. "Those were *pirate* whale ships, international waters, and the other stuff you mentioned we can document as legal under international agreements. On the other hand, *our* ships have been rammed, our people gassed and shot at and illegal arrests made."

"What do you say to those people who call you a terrorist organization?" a reporter from *The Economist* said.

"I would ask them: What could be more terrifying than the cold-blooded slaughter of fifteen hundred to two thousand defenseless pilot whales each year? And I would remind them that no one has ever been hurt or killed by an SOS intervention." Ryan flashed his smile again. "C'mon, folks, you've met the people on this ship." He gestured toward an attractive young woman who had been standing apart from the others, listening to the discussion. "Tell me honestly, does this lady look scary?"

Therri Weld was in her mid-thirties, of medium height, with a compact, well-proportioned body. The faded jeans and workshirt she wore under her baggy windbreaker did little to disguise her athletic but distinctly feminine figure. An SOS baseball hat covered chestnut hair whose natural curl was made even more pronounced by the damp air, and her gentian eyes were alert and intelligent. She stepped forward and gave the press corps a bright smile.

"I've already met most of you," she said, in a voice that was low but clear. "So you know that when Marcus doesn't have me slaving away as a deckhand, I'm a legal advisor to SOS. As Marcus said, we use direct action as a last resort. We pulled back after our last encounter in these waters to pursue a boycott of Faroe fish."

"But you still haven't stopped the *grinds,*" the BBC reporter said to Ryan.

"The Sentinels have never underestimated how tough it would be to end a tradition that goes back hundreds of years," Ryan answered. "The Faroese have the same stubbornness their Viking forefathers needed to survive. They're not about to give in to a bunch of whale-huggers like us. But while I admire the Faroese, I think the *grindarap* is cruel and barbaric. It's unworthy of the islanders as a people. I know a few of you have been to a *grind* before. Anyone care to sum it up?"

"Damned bloody business," the BBC reporter admitted. "But I don't like foxhunts, either."

"At least the fox has a sporting chance," Ryan said, his jaw hardening. "The *grind* is simply a *massacre.* When someone spots a pod of pilot whales, the siren goes off, and boats herd the whales in to shore. The locals—women and kids sometimes—are waiting on the beach. There's a lot of drinking and it's a big party, for everyone except the whales. The people stick gaffs into the whales' blowholes and drag the animals inshore, where they have their jugular veins cut and they bleed to death. The water turns red from the bloodletting. Sometimes you'll see people sawing the animals' heads off while the whales are still alive!"

A blond female reporter said, "How is a *grind* any different from slaughtering steers for beef?"

"You're asking the wrong person," Ryan said. "I'm a *vegan.*" He waited for the laughter to die down. "Your point is well-taken, though. We may be protecting the Faroese from themselves. Pilot-whale meat is loaded with mercury and cadmium. It's hurting their children."

"But if they want to poison themselves and their kids," the reporter said, "isn't it intolerant of SOS to condemn their traditions?"

"Gladiatorial combat and public executions were traditions

once. Civilization decided these savage spectacles have no place in the modern world. Inflicting unnecessary pain on defenseless animals is the same thing. They say it's tradition. We say it's *murder.* That's why we're back."

"Why not continue with the boycott?" the BBC man asked.

Therri addressed the question. "The boycott was too slow. Hundreds of pilot whales continue to be killed. So we've changed our strategy. The oil industry wants to sink wells in these waters. If we bring enough bad publicity to the hunt, the oil companies might hold back. That would put pressure on the islanders to end their *grinds.*"

"And we've got other business here as well," Ryan added. "There's a multinational fish-processing company that we're going to picket to demonstrate our opposition to the harmful effects of fish-farming."

The Fox News reporter was incredulous. "Is there *anyone* you don't plan to antagonize?"

"Let me know who we've missed," Ryan said to laughter.

The BBC man said, "How far do you intend to push your protest?"

"As far as we can. This hunt is illegal under international law, in our opinion. You people are here as witnesses. Things could get dicey. If anyone wants to leave now, I can arrange a transfer." He scanned the faces surrounding him and smiled. "No one? Good. Well, then, brave souls, into the breach we go. We've been keeping track of several pods of pilot whales. The waters around here fairly teem with them. That young deckhand you see waving wildly may have something to tell us."

A crew member who had been keeping watch trotted over. "A couple of pods are passing by Stremoy," he said. "Our observer on shore says the siren's wailing and the boats are being launched."

Ryan turned back to the reporters. "They'll probably try to drive the whales ashore at the Kvivik killing field. We'll put ourselves between the boats and the whales. If we can't drive the pod away, we'll start cutting the boats off."

The CNN reporter pointed to the cruiser. "Isn't it going to irritate those chaps?"

"I'm *counting* on it," Ryan said, with a ferocious grin.

• • •

High in the bridge of the *Leif Eriksson,* a man in civilian clothes squinted at the *Sea Sentinel* through a powerful pair of binoculars. "My God," Karl Becker murmured to Eric Petersen, the ship's captain, "that ship looks as if it were painted by a *madman.*"

"Ah, so you know Captain Ryan," Petersen replied, with a faint smile.

"Only by reputation. He seems to have what the Americans call a Teflon shield. For all his law-breaking, he has never been convicted on any charge. What do you know of Ryan, Captain?"

"First of all, he is not mad. He is possessed with a near-fanatical determination, but all his actions are measured. Even the gaudy color scheme of his ship is calculated. It lulls unsuspecting opponents into making mistakes—and shows up quite well on television."

"Maybe we could arrest them for visual pollution of the sea, Captain Petersen," said Becker.

"I suspect Ryan would find an expert to say the ship is nothing less than a floating work of art."

"Glad to see that you've maintained your sense of humor despite the humiliation this ship suffered from its last encounter with the Sentinels of the Sea."

"It only took a few minutes of hosing down the deck to get rid of the garbage they threw at us. My predecessor felt that it was necessary to respond to the garbage attack with gunfire."

Becker winced. "Captain Olafsen was still commanding a desk the last time I heard. The publicity was incredibly bad. 'Danish Warship Attacks Unarmed Boat.' Headlines that the crew was drunk. My God, what a disaster!"

"Having served as Olafsen's first officer, I have the greatest respect for his judgment. His problem was that he didn't have clear direction from the bureaucrats in Copenhagen."

"Bureaucrats like me?" Becker said.

The captain responded with a tight smile. "I follow orders. My superiors said that you were coming aboard as a navy-department observer. Here you are."

"I wouldn't want a bureaucrat aboard my ship if I were in

your shoes. But I assure you, I have no authority to supersede your orders. I will, of course, report what I see and hear, but let me remind you that if this mission is a fiasco, both our heads will roll."

The captain hadn't known what to make of Becker when he first welcomed him aboard the *Eriksson*. The official was short and dark, and with his large, moist eyes and long nose, he looked like a despondent cormorant. Petersen, on the other hand, fit the common mold for many Danish men. He was tall, square-jawed and blond.

"I was reluctant to have you aboard," the captain said, "but the hotheads who are involved in this situation could let things get out of control. I welcome the opportunity to consult with someone from the government."

Becker thanked the captain and said, "What do *you* think of this *grindarap* business?"

The captain shrugged. "I have many friends on the island. They would rather die than give up their old customs. They say it's what makes them who they are. I respect their feelings. And you?"

"I'm a Copenhagener. This whale thing seems like a big waste of time to me. But there's a great deal at stake here. The government respects the wishes of the islanders, but the boycott has hurt their fishing. We don't want the Faroes to lose their livelihood so that they become a ward of the state. Too damned expensive. To say nothing of the revenue losses to our country if the oil companies are persuaded to hold back their drilling because of this whale hunt."

"I'm well aware that this situation is something of a morality play. All the actors know their roles exactly. The islanders have planned this *grind* to defy SOS and to make sure Parliament is aware of their concerns. Ryan has been just as vocal in saying he won't allow anything to stand in his way."

"And you, Captain Petersen, do you know your role?"

"Of course. I just don't know how the drama ends."

Becker grunted in answer.

"Let me reassure you," the captain said, "the Faroe Police have been ordered to stay in the background. Under no circumstances am I to use guns. My orders are to protect the islanders from danger. I can use my judgment on how this is to be done. If the *Sea Sentinel* comes close enough to endanger the smaller boats, then I have the authority to *nudge* the SOS ship aside. Please excuse me, Mr. Becker. I see that the curtain is about to go up."

From several harbors, fishing boats were racing to a disturbed area of ocean. They were moving fast, their bows up on plane, bouncing over the low chop. The boats were converging on a spot where the shiny black backs of a pod of pilot whales broke the surface. Fountains of spray exploded from the whales' blowholes.

The *Sea Sentinel* was also moving in on the whales. Petersen gave his helmsman orders. The cruiser broke out of its holding pattern.

Becker had been mulling over Petersen's earlier words.

"Tell me, Captain, when does a 'nudge' become a ram?"

"Whenever I want it to."

"Isn't there a fine line between the two?"

Petersen told his helmsman to increase speed and set a course directly toward the *Sea Sentinel*. Then the captain turned to Becker and gave him a grim smile.

"We're about to find out."

2

RYAN WATCHED THE cruiser break out of its lazy circle and head toward the SOS ship. "Looks like Hamlet finally made a decision," he said to Chuck Mercer, his first mate, who was at the wheel of the *Sea Sentinel.*

The *Sea Sentinel* had been trying to drive the whales out to sea. The pod held about fifty pilot whales, and some of the female whales were holding back to stay with their calves, slowing the rescue attempt. The SOS ship zigzagged like a lone cowpoke trying to corral stray cattle, but the nervous whales made the job almost impossible.

"Like herding cats," Ryan muttered. He went out on the starboard bridge wing to see how close the advancing whaleboats were to the pod. He had never seen so many islanders involved in a *grind.* It seemed as if every harbor in the Faroes had emptied out. Dozens of boats, ranging in size from commercial trawlers to open dories powered by outboard motors, were speeding from several different directions to join the hunt. The dark water was streaked with their wakes.

Therri Weld was already out on the wing, watching the

armada gather. "You've got to admire their stubbornness," she said.

Ryan was equally awestruck. He nodded in agreement. "Now I know how Custer felt. The Faroese are going all out to defend their bloody traditions."

"This is no spontaneous outpouring," Therri said. "From the orderly way they're moving, they've got a plan."

The words had barely left her lips when, as if on signal, the advancing fleet began to split up in a pincer movement. In a classic military flanking maneuver, the boats swept around Ryan's ship so they were on the seaward side of the slow-moving whales. They spread out in a line, facing inshore, with the pilot whales between them and the *Sea Sentinel*. The ends of the line began to curve slowly inward. The whales bunched closer together and moved toward shore.

Ryan was afraid of hurting the panicked whales or breaking up family units if the ship stood in place. Reluctantly, he ordered the helmsman to move the ship out of the path of the hunt.

As the *Sea Sentinel* moved aside, a loud chorus of triumphant cheers went up from the fishermen. The line of boats began to wrap itself around the hapless whales in a deadly embrace. The whaleboats moved forward, tightening up the line to drive their prey to the killing field, where the sharp knives and spears of the executioners awaited.

Ryan ordered Mercer to steer the *Sea Sentinel* out to open water.

"Giving up awfully easy," Mercer said.

"Wait and see," Ryan said, with an enigmatic smile.

The cruiser came up alongside the *Sea Sentinel* like a cop escorting an unruly spectator from a soccer game, but when the ships were about a half mile from the whale hunt, the navy escort began to fall back. Ryan took over the wheel, frequently checking the cruiser's location. When the ships were in what he judged to be the right position, he picked up the phone to the engine room.

"Full speed ahead," he ordered.

The *Sea Sentinel* was a clunky wide-beamed vessel, high at both ends, with a silhouette like an old-fashioned bathtub. The slow-moving research ship was designed mainly as a stable platform from which to launch undersea instrumentation and nets. The first thing Ryan had done after SOS had acquired the ship at auction was to outfit the engine room with powerful diesels that could push her along at a more respectable clip.

Ryan cut the wheel hard left. The ship shivered from the strain as it circled about in a great arcing swash of foam and raced back toward the whale hunt. Caught off-guard, the cruiser attempted to follow, but the warship couldn't match the *Sea Sentinel*'s tight turn and went wide, losing valuable seconds.

The whale hunt had advanced to within a mile of shore when the *Sea Sentinel* caught up with the pod and the line of herdsmen. The SOS ship made a sharp turn that brought it across the wakes of the whaleboats. Ryan stayed at the wheel. He wanted sole responsibility in case something went wrong. His plan to disrupt the hunt required a deft touch on the helm. Too fast or too close, and the whalers would be overturned and thrown into the frigid water. He kept the ship at an even speed, using its broad beam to create a following sea. The wave hit the boats stern-on. Some boats managed to ride the wave that lifted them out of the water. Others lost headway and spun around in a wild attempt to prevent pitchpoling.

The line broke up into a disorganized jumble, leaving large open spaces between the boats, like gaps in a row of teeth. Ryan spun the wheel again and brought the *Sea Sentinel* around in another sharp turn that placed the ship broadside to the advancing whales. The whales fleeing the advancing whalers sensed the presence of the vessel, turned back in the opposite direction and began to break through the openings in the hunt line.

Now it was the turn of the *Sea Sentinel*'s crew to cheer— but their jubilation was short-lived. The faster-moving cruiser had caught up with the SOS ship and was alongside no more than a hundred yards away, matching the *Sea Sentinel*'s speed knot for knot. A voice speaking in English crackled over the radio.

"This is Captain Petersen of the *Leif Eriksson* calling the SOS vessel *Sea Sentinel*."

Ryan snatched up the microphone. "This is Captain Ryan. What can I do for you, Captain Petersen?"

"You are requested to move your ship to open water."

"We are acting in accordance with international law." He gave Therri a crooked grin. "My legal advisor is standing here by my side."

"I don't intend to debate the finer points of the law with you or your advisors, Captain Ryan. You are endangering Danish fishermen. I have the authority to use force. If you don't move immediately, I will blow your ship out of the water."

The gun turret on the frigate's foredeck turned so that the barrel was pointed directly at the *Sea Sentinel.*

"That's a dangerous game you're playing," Ryan said with deliberate calmness. "A bad shot could miss us and sink some of those fishermen you're trying to protect."

Petersen said, "I don't think we would miss at this range, but I want to avoid bloodshed. You've given the TV cameras plenty of footage. Many pilot whales have escaped, and the hunt has been disrupted. You've made your point and are no longer welcome."

Ryan chuckled. "Nice to deal with a reasonable man. Unlike your gun-happy predecessor. Okay, I will pull out of the way, but we're not leaving Faroe waters. We've got other business."

"You are free to do as you please, as long as it doesn't break our laws or endanger our people."

Ryan breathed a sigh of relief, his outward serenity only an act—he was aware of the danger to his crew and the press people. He turned the helm back to his first mate and gave the order to move off slowly. Once beyond the hunt area, the *Sea Sentinel* headed out to sea. Ryan's plan was to anchor the ship a few miles offshore while he prepared for the protest against the fish farm.

Chastened by the *Sea Sentinel*'s earlier move, Petersen made sure the cruiser stayed slightly behind, ready to dart in and cut off the ship if it tried to break away.

Therri broke the tension in the pilothouse. "Captain Petersen doesn't know what a narrow escape he just had," she said, with a grin. "One shot and I would have dragged him into court and slapped a property lien on his ship."

"I think he was more afraid of our garbage gun," Ryan said.

Their mirth was cut short by the sound of Mercer swearing.

Ryan said, "What's wrong, Chuck?"

"*Damnit,* Mark." Mercer was standing with both hands on the wheel. "You must have messed up the steering pushing this ship around like a Jet Ski." He frowned, then stepped back. "Here, you try it."

Ryan tried to turn the wheel. It gave for an inch on either side, but it seemed locked into place. He exerted a slight pressure, then gave up. "The damned thing is locked into place," Ryan said, with a combination of anger and puzzlement.

Ryan picked up the telephone, ordered the engine room to stop and turned his attention back to the wheel. Instead of slowing down, the ship inexplicably picked up speed. Ryan swore and called down to the engine room again.

"What's wrong, Cal?" he barked. "Those engines finally made you deaf? I said *cut* speed, not *increase* it."

Ryan's engineer, Cal Rumson, was a topflight seaman. "Hell, I know what you said," Cal replied. The frustration in his voice was obvious. "I *did* reduce speed. The engines are acting crazy. The controls don't seem to be working."

"Then kill the power," Ryan said.

"I'm trying, but the diesels are working *harder.*"

"Keep trying, Cal."

Ryan slammed the phone in its cradle. This was insanity! The ship seemed to have a mind of her own. Ryan's eyes swept the sea ahead of the ship. Good news. No vessels or landmasses in the way. The worst that could happen would be to run out of fuel in the Atlantic. Ryan picked up the radio microphone to inform the cruiser of their predicament. But he was interrupted by a yell from Mercer.

"The wheel's turning!"

Mercer was trying to hold on to the wheel, which was gradually spinning slowly to the right, bringing the ship around toward the cruiser. Ryan grabbed the rim, then he and Mercer tried to bring the ship back on course. They used every ounce of strength they could muster, but the wheel slipped out of their sweaty hands and the *Sea Sentinel* moved closer to the warship.

The Danish ship had taken notice of the course change. A familiar voice crackled over the radio.

"Come in, *Sea Sentinel.* This is Captain Petersen. What is the intention of your course change?"

"We're having problems with our steering. The wheel is locked and we can't shut down our engines."

"That's impossible," Petersen said.

"Tell that to the *ship!*"

A pause. Then Petersen said, "We'll bear off to give you plenty of sea room. We'll issue a warning as to any ships in your way."

"Thanks. Looks like you'll get your wish about us leaving the Faroes."

The cruiser began to peel away.

But before the Danish ship could veer off, the *Sea Sentinel* made a sharp turn and drove toward the cruiser's exposed side like a waterborne guided missile.

Sailors lined the cruiser's decks and frantically tried to wave off the advancing ship. The cruiser blew short, rapid warning bursts of its horn. Voices squawked over the radio in Danish and English.

Seeing that the ships were within seconds of disaster, the sailors ran for their lives.

In a last desperate attempt to avert a certain collision, Ryan put all his weight into the wheel. He was still hanging on when the ship smashed into the side of the cruiser. The *Sea Sentinel*'s sharp bow penetrated the steel hull plates like a bayonet, then slid off the moving ship in a horrendous shriek of tearing metal.

The *Sea Sentinel* wallowed in the ocean like a dazed boxer who had just taken a hard right to the nose. The cruiser was struggling to keep afloat, as thousands of gallons of water poured in through the gaping hole in the hull. Crewmen scrambled into the lifeboats and prepared to lower them into the cold sea.

Therri had been thrown to her knees by the impact. Ryan helped her to her feet, and he and the others in the pilothouse dashed down to the deck. The panicked TV people, seeing that they were now part of the story rather than covering it, were trying to get someone to tell them what to do. People were bruised and limping.

Someone was screaming for help, and crew and press people were extracting a bloody body from the metal mush that was all that was left of the bow section.

Ryan shouted orders to abandon ship.

With all the yelling and confusion, no one looked up to see the helicopter wheeling high above the ships. The chopper circled a few times like a hungry buzzard, then headed off along the coast.

3

TWELVE HUNDRED MILES southeast of the Faroe Islands, the search-and-survey ship *William Beebe* lay at anchor in the frigid waters of the Barents Sea. The letters *NUMA* were emblazoned on the 250-foot-long turquoise hull. Named after one of the pioneers in deep-sea exploration, the *Beebe* bristled with muscular cranes and winches capable of hoisting entire boats off the ocean floor.

Four crewmen dressed in neoprene wet suits stood on the stern deck, eyes fixed on a patch of ocean where the surface roiled like a bubbling cauldron. The surface grew paler and mounded into a foamy white dome, and the submersible rescue vehicle *Sea Lamprey* burst from the water like a mutant leviathan coming up for air. With the precision of a navy assault team, the ready crew pushed an outboard-powered inflatable down the stern ramp into the water, scrambled aboard and raced toward the wallowing submersible.

The ready team attached a towline to the bright-orange vehicle, and a winch on board the *Beebe* hauled in the submersible until it was under the tall A-frame that angled out over the ship's stern. Kevlar cables were fastened to eyebolts on the submersible's abbreviated deck. The powerful A-frame motor growled, and the submersible was hoisted from the sea. As it dangled from the cables, the *Sea Lamprey* offered a full view of its unlovely cylindrical hull and strangely truncated accordion bow.

The A-frame swung slowly over the deck and lowered the vehicle into a custom-made steel cradle, while the waiting deck crew placed a ladder against the cradle. Then the hatch at the top of the low conning tower opened and clanged back on its hinges. Kurt Austin poked his head out and blinked like a mole. His steel-gray, almost platinum, hair was radiant in the intense metallic light of the overcast sky.

Austin greeted the deck crew with a wave, then squeezed his broad shoulders through the narrow hatchway, climbed out and stood next to the conning tower. Seconds later, his partner, Joe Zavala, stuck his head out into the fresh air and handed his partner a shiny aluminum case.

Austin tossed the case down to a stocky, middle-aged man who stood at the base of the ladder. The man was dressed in a wool turtleneck sweater, yellow rainproof pants and a slicker. Only the high-peaked cap on his head identified him as Russian navy. When he saw the case go airborne, he let out a yell of despair. He caught the container, bobbled it for an instant, then hugged it close to his chest.

As Austin and Zavala descended the ladder, the Russian opened the case and removed a paper-wrapped object cushioned in protective plastic foam, then he unwrapped the paper to reveal a heavy square bottle. Holding it like a newborn, he mumbled in Russian.

Noticing the perplexed looks on the faces of the NUMA men, he said, "Pardon me gentlemen. I was offering a prayer of thanks that the contents of the container were undamaged."

Austin eyed the label and grimaced. "We just dove three hundred feet and cracked into a submarine to retrieve a bottle of *vodka*?"

"Oh *no*," Vlasov replied, digging into the case. "*Three* bottles. The finest vodka made in Russia." He carefully unwrapped the other containers and planted a noisy kiss on each one before laying it back in the case. "Jewel of Russia is one of our finest and Moskovska is superb. Charodei is the best chilled."

Austin wondered if he would ever understand the Russian mind-set. "Of course," he said cheerfully. "Sinking a submarine to keep your booze cool makes perfect sense when you explain it that way."

"The submarine was an old Foxtrot-class boat used for training," Vlasov said. "It hadn't seen service for more than thirty years." He gave Austin a 14-karat-gold smile. "You must admit it was *your* idea to place objects on the sub to test your ability to retrieve them."

"Mea culpa. It didn't seem like a bad idea at the time."

Vlasov closed the cover of the case. "Your dive was a success, then?"

"By and large," Zavala said. "We've got a few technical problems. Nothing major."

"Then we must celebrate with a drink," Vlasov said.

Austin reached over and took the case from the Russian's hand. "No time like the present."

They picked up three plastic cups from the mess hall, then headed for the ready room. Vlasov opened the bottle of Charodei and poured a healthy portion into each cup. He raised his drink in toast. "Here's to the brave young men who died on the *Kursk.*"

Vlasov slugged down the vodka as if he were drinking herbal tea. Austin sipped his drink. He knew from past experience that demons lurked in the potent Russian firewater.

"And here's to something like the *Kursk* never happening again," Austin said.

The *Kursk* sinking had been one of the worst submarine disasters on record. More than a hundred crewmen had died in 2000 when the Oscar II–class cruise missile sub had sunk in the Barents Sea after an explosion in the torpedo compartment.

Vlasov said, "With your submersible, no young man serving his country in any nation need die such a horrible death. Thanks to the ingenuity of NUMA, we have a way to get into a sunken vessel whether the escape hatch is operable or accessible, or not. The innovations you came up with for this vehicle are revolutionary."

"That's kind of you to say, Commander Vlasov. Joe deserves the credit for hammering some odds and ends together and applying good old American common sense."

"Thanks for the praise, but I stole the idea from Mother Nature," Zavala said with typical modesty. A graduate in marine engineering from the New York Maritime College, Zavala possessed a brilliant mechanical mind. He'd been recruited by NUMA Director James Sandecker right out of college, and in addition to his duties on the Special Assignments Team led by Austin, he had designed numerous manned and unmanned underwater vehicles.

"Nonsense!" Vlasov said. "It's a long way from the lamprey eel to your submersible."

"The principle's the same," Zavala said. "Lampreys are superbly engineered creatures. They latch on to a moving fish, sink their ring of teeth into the skin and suck the blood out of it. We use suction and lasers rather than teeth. The main problem was coming up with a flexible watertight seal that would attach to any surface and allow us to make the cut. With the use of space-age materials and computers, we put together a pretty good package."

Vlasov raised his vodka glass again. "I hold the proof of your ingenuity in my hand. When will the *Sea Lamprey* be fully operational?"

"Soon." Zavala said. "I hope."

"The sooner the better. I shudder to think of the potential for disaster. The Soviets built some magnificent boats. But my countrymen have always leaned toward gigantism over quality." Vlasov finished his drink and rose from his chair. "Now I must go back to my cabin to prepare a report for my superiors. They should be very pleased. I'm grateful for all your hard work. I will thank Admiral Sandecker personally."

As Vlasov left, one of the ship's officers came into the room and told Austin he had a telephone call. Austin picked up the telephone, listened a few moments, asked some questions, then said, "Stand by. I'll get right back to you."

He hung up and said, "That was NATO's East Atlantic submarine disaster office. They need our help on a rescue mission."

"Someone's lost a sub?" Zavala said.

"A Danish cruiser went down off the Faroe Islands, and some of the crew were trapped inside. They're still alive, apparently. The Swedes and the Brits are on their way, but the cruiser doesn't have an escape hatch. The Danes need someone who can go directly through the hull and get the guys out. They heard we were out here making test dives."

"How long do we have?"

"A few hours, the way they tell it."

Zavala shook his head. "The Faroes must be more than a thousand miles from here. The *Beebe* is a fast ship for her size, but she'd need wings to get there in time."

Austin thought about it a minute, then said, "You're a genius."

"Glad you finally realized it. Mind telling me how you came to that conclusion? It would make a great pick-up line in a bar."

"First, let me ask: Is the *Sea Lamprey* in any shape to use on a real-life rescue operation? I detected a note of CYA when Vlasov asked when it would be ready."

"We civil service types automatically take Cover Your Ass 101 when we sign on," Zavala said.

"You must have passed the course with flying colors. Well?"

Zavala pondered the question for a moment. "You saw how she handled coming up."

"Sure, like a Brahma bull, but we made it okay. You'd pay big bucks for a ride like that at Disney World."

Zavala slowly shook his head. "You do have a talent for presenting the possibility of a horrible death in a lighthearted way."

"My death wish isn't any stronger than yours. You told me the *Sea Lamprey* is built like a brick outhouse."

"Okay, I was bragging. Structurally, she's extremely sound. Operationally, she could do better."

"On balance, how do the odds of a successful mission stack up?"

"About fifty-fifty. I can jury-rig some repairs to increase the odds slightly in our favor."

"I'm not pushing you, Joe."

"You don't have to. I'd never sleep again if we didn't try to help these guys. But we've still got to get the submersible to that Danish cruiser. You've figured it out, haven't you, you old fox?" Zavala said, noting Austin's grin.

"Maybe," Austin replied. "I've got a few details to work through with Vlasov."

"Since I'm about to risk my life on a typical spur-of-the-moment Austin scheme, I wonder if you could tell me what's cooking under that prematurely silver-gray hair of yours?"

"Not at all," Austin said. "Do you recall what Vlasov said about Soviet gigantism?"

"Yeah, but—"

"Think *big*," Austin said, heading for the door. "Think *real* big."

4

KARL BECKER RESTLESSLY paced the deck of the Danish research vessel *Thor*. Shoulders hunched, hands thrust into the pockets of his greatcoat, the navy bureaucrat looked like a large wingless bird. Becker wore several layers of clothing, yet he shivered as his thoughts went back to the collision. He had been shoved into a lifeboat, only to be thrown into the freezing water when the overloaded craft capsized during launch. If a Faroese trawler had not plucked his semiconscious body to safety, he would have been dead within minutes.

He stopped to light a cigarette, cupping his hands around the flame, and leaned on the rail. As he stared bleakly at the red plastic sphere that marked the grave of the sunken cruiser, he heard his name being called. The *Thor*'s captain, Nils Larsen, was striding across the deck in his direction.

"Where are those damned Americans?" Becker growled.

"Good news. They just called," said the captain. "They expect to be here in five minutes."

"About *time*," Becker said.

Like his colleague on the *Leif Eriksson*, Captain Larsen was tall and blond with a craggy profile. "In all fairness," he said, "it's only been a matter of hours since the cruiser went down. The NATO response team needed a minimum of *seventy-two* hours to place a mother ship, crew and rescue vehicle on site. The NUMA people have lived up to their pledge to get here within eight hours. They deserve some leeway."

"I know, I *know*," Becker said, more in exasperation than anger. "I don't mean to be ungrateful, but every minute counts." He flicked the cigarette butt into the sea and jammed his hands even further into his pockets. "Too bad Denmark no longer has capital punishment," he fumed. "I'd like to see that whole murderous SOS bunch swinging from the end of a rope."

"You're sure they deliberately rammed you?"

"No doubt of it! They changed course and came directly at us. *Bang!* Like a torpedo." He glanced at his watch. "You're sure the Americans said five minutes? I don't see any ships approaching."

"That is puzzling," the captain said. He raised his binoculars and scanned the horizon. "I don't see any vessels, either." Hearing a noise, he pointed the lenses toward the overcast sky. "Wait. There's a helicopter coming this way. It's moving very fast."

The pencil-point speck grew rapidly larger against the slate-gray cloud cover, and before long the *thrump-thrump* of rotors was audible. The aircraft made directly for the *Thor* and buzzed the ship slightly higher than mast-level, then it banked and went into a wide circle around the research vessel. The letters *NUMA* were clearly visible in big bold letters on the side of the turquoise Bell 212.

The ship's first mate trotted across the deck toward the captain and pointed to the circling chopper. "It's the Americans. They're asking permission to land."

The captain replied in the affirmative, and the crewman relayed the okay into a squawking hand radio. The helicopter swooped in, hovered above the stern deck and descended in slow motion, making a gentle landing at the exact center of the white circle that marked the helipad.

The door flew open, and two men emerged under the spinning rotors and made their way across the deck. As a politician, Becker was an acute observer of people. The men moved with the casual easiness that he had seen in other Americans, but their determined stride and the way they carried themselves projected an air of supreme confidence.

The broad-shouldered man leading the way was just over six feet tall and around two hundred pounds, Becker estimated. His hair was gray, but as the man drew near, Becker saw that he was young, probably around forty. His dark-complexioned companion was slightly shorter, younger and slimmer. He walked with the pantherlike grace of a boxer; it would not have surprised Becker if he'd known that the man had financed his way through college fighting as a middleweight. His movements were relaxed, but with the inherent energy of a coiled spring.

The captain stepped forward to greet the Americans. "Welcome to the *Thor*," he said.

"Thanks. I'm Kurt Austin from the National Underwater and Marine Agency," said the husky man, who looked as if he could walk through a wall. "And this is my partner, Joe Zavala." He shook hands with the captain, then Becker, almost bringing tears to the Dane's eyes with a crushing handshake. Zavala pulverized those bones Austin had missed.

"You made good time," the captain said.

"We're a few minutes behind schedule," Austin said. "The logistics were somewhat complicated."

"That's all right. Thank God you came!" Becker said, rubbing his hand. He glanced toward the helicopter. "Where's the rescue team?"

Austin and Zavala exchanged an amused glance. "You're *looking* at it," Austin said.

Becker's astonishment gave way to barely restrained fury. He whirled around to face the captain. "How in God's name are these two . . . *gentlemen* going to rescue Captain Petersen and his men?"

Captain Larsen was wondering the same thing, but was more reserved. "I suggest you ask them," he replied, with obvious embarrassment at Becker's outburst.

"Well?" Becker said, glaring first at Austin, then at Zavala.

Becker could not have known that the two men who had stepped off the helicopter equaled a shipload of rescuers. Born in Seattle, Austin had been raised in and around the sea, which was not surprising, since his father was the owner of a marine salvage company. While studying for his master's degree in systems management at the University of Washington, he'd attended a highly rated Seattle dive school, where he'd attained proficiency in a number of specialized areas. He'd put his expertise to work on North Sea oil rigs, had worked for his father awhile, then had been hired by the CIA to conduct underwater intelligence. When the Cold War ended, he'd been recruited by Sandecker to head the Special Assignments Team.

Zavala was the son of Mexican parents who had waded across the Rio Grande, settling in Santa Fe. His oil-stained mechanical genius was the stuff of legend around the halls of NUMA, and he could repair, modify or restore any kind of engine ever devised. He had spent thousands of hours as a pilot in helicopters and small jet and turboprop craft. His assignment to Austin's team had proved a fortunate pairing. Many of their assignments would never become public knowledge, but their wisecracking camaraderie in the face of danger masked a steely determination and a competence few could rival.

Austin calmly regarded Becker with piercing blue-green eyes the color of coral under water. He was not unsympathetic to Becker's plight, and deflected the Dane's fury with a broad smile. "Sorry for being flip. I should have explained immediately that the rescue vehicle is on its way."

"Should be here in about an hour," Zavala added.

"There's a lot we can do in the meantime," Austin said. He turned to the captain. "I need help unloading a piece of equipment from the chopper. Can you spare a few men with strong backs?"

"Yes, of course." The captain was relieved to be doing something at last. Moving with crisp efficiency, he dispatched his first mate to round up the work detail.

At Austin's direction, the grunting crewmen lifted a large wooden crate from the helicopter's storage compartment and set it down on the deck. Using a crowbar from the helicopter, Austin pried the top off the box and peered inside. After a quick inspection, he said, "Everything looks shipshape. What's the latest on the situation?"

Captain Larsen pointed to the bobbing buoy that marked the sunken cruiser. While Austin and Zavala listened intently, Larsen provided a quick summary of the collision and sinking.

"It doesn't make sense," Austin said. "From what you say, they had plenty of sea room."

"So did the *Andrea Doria* and the *Stockholm*," Zavala said, referring to the disastrous sea collision off Nantucket.

Becker mumbled something about SOS criminals, but Austin ignored him and concentrated on the business at hand. "What makes you so sure the captain and his men are still alive?"

"We were doing a whale population survey not far from here when we got the call for help," Larsen said. "We dropped a hydrophone over the side and picked up the sound of someone tapping an SOS on the hull in Morse code. Unfortunately, we can only receive, not send, messages. However, we determined that there were thirteen men, including Captain Petersen, trapped in a pocket of air in the forward bunkroom. The air is foul, and they were in the early stages of hypothermia."

"When did you last hear from them?"

"About two hours ago. It was essentially the same message, only the tapping has become much fainter. Toward the end, they tapped out the same word over and over."

"What was it?"

"Desperate."

Austin broke the grim silence that followed. "Did you get any other equipment down to the ship?"

"The Faroese Coast Guard called the NATO base on Stremoy. They contacted the NATO submarine rescue network minutes after the cruiser went down. Those ships you see out there are mostly from Scandinavian countries. We've been acting as the interim mother ship. A Swedish vessel should arrive soon with a rescue vehicle, but like the others, it's useless in this situation. It's set up to rescue men through a submarine rescue hatch. We've been able to pinpoint the cruiser's location two-hundred-sixty feet down, but beyond that, for all our technical ability, we're only spectators at a disaster in the making."

"Not necessarily," Austin said.

"Then you think you can help?" Becker said with pleading eyes.

"Maybe," Austin said. "We can say better after we see what we're up against."

Becker apologized for his earlier abruptness. "Sorry I flew off the handle. We're grateful for your offer to help. I owe a special debt to Captain Petersen. After we were hit and there was no doubt the cruiser would sink within minutes, he made sure I had a place in a lifeboat. When he learned others were still below, he rushed off to help them and must have been trapped when the ship sank."

"He's a brave man. All the more reason for saving him and his crew," Austin said. "Do you have any idea of the ship's position on the bottom?"

"Yes, of course. Come with me," the captain said. He led the way to an electronics lab off the main deck. The room was equipped with computer monitors used for remote sensing projects. "This is a high-resolution sonar picture of the *Leif Eriksson*," he said, indicating the image on a large monitor. "As you can see, she is lying at a slight angle on an inclined slope. The crews' quarters are here, one deck below the mess area, a short distance back from the bow. Obviously, air was trapped here." He circled a section of hull with the cursor. "It's a miracle they're still alive."

"It's a miracle they may wish never happened," Becker observed glumly.

"Tell us about the compartment."

"It's quite large. There are bunks for two dozen crewmen. It's reached by a single companionway through the mess hall. There is also an emergency hatch."

"We'll need specific details about the bunkroom, particularly the location of pipes, conduits and structural supports."

The captain handed over a file. "The navy department faxed this material to us in anticipation of the rescue attempt. I think you'll find everything you need. If not, we can get it to you quickly."

Austin and Zavala studied the ship's schematic layouts, then went back to the sonar image. "There's only so much we can learn from pictures," Austin said finally. "Maybe it's time I went for a swim."

"Good thing you brought your swimsuit," Zavala said.

"It's the new Michelin model. Guaranteed to wow the ladies."

Becker and the captain wondered if they had stumbled into

the company of madmen. They exchanged puzzled glances, then hurried to keep up with the NUMA men. While Zavala sketched out their strategy for Captain Larsen and Becker, Austin supervised the four strapping crewmen as they moved the crate until it was under a boom. They unwound cable from the crane, then Austin ran it into the big box and gave the signal to start the hoist.

The bright-yellow figure that rose from the crate was nearly seven feet tall and looked like a robot in a fifties sci-fi film. The cast aluminum arms and legs did indeed bulge like those of the Michelin Man, and the helmet resembled an oversized fishbowl. The arms ended in pincers like those of an insect. Four small fans protected by circular housings projected from the elbows and the back of the arms.

Austin rapped his knuckles against the unit pack attached to the figure's back. "This is the latest in Hardsuit technology. This model can operate at depths of two thousand feet for up to six hours, so I'll have plenty of leeway. Mind if I borrow a short ladder? I'll need an experienced boat crew in the water, too."

The captain dispatched his first mate to carry out the requests. Austin stripped off his windbreaker, pulled a heavy wool sweater over his turtleneck jersey, and yanked a black navy watch cap down over his ears. The suit broke at the waist into two sections. Austin climbed the ladder and eased his body into the bottom pod. Then the top section was attached, the lifting line attached, and the boom slowly lifted him off the deck.

Using the suit's radio, which was the same frequency as the ship's handsets, he called a halt when he was a few feet above the deck. He moved his arms and legs, aided by sixteen hydraulically compensated rotary joints. Then he tried out the manually operated manipulators at the end of each hand pod. Finally, he tried the foot-pad controls and listened to the whirr of the vertical and horizontal thrusters.

"All systems go," Austin said.

The atmospheric diving suit, or ADS, had been developed to protect divers from intense ocean pressures while allowing them to carry out tasks of relative delicacy. Despite its humanoid shape, the Hardsuit was considered a vehicle and the diver referred to as its pilot.

With Zavala supervising the operation, the boom pivoted over the water. Austin swung back and forth like a yo-yo at the end of its swing. Seeing that the launch crew had its boat in the water, he said, "Lower away."

The cable paid out and Austin dropped into the heaving swells. Green froth surged over his helmet. The boat crew detached the cable fastening, and Austin sank like a stone for several fathoms, until he adjusted the suit to neutral buoyancy. Then he played with the thrusters, moving up, down, back and forward, then into a hover. He took a last look at the pale surface glimmering above him, switched on the lights on the chest section, mashed the vertical control pad and began his descent.

5

UNAWARE OF THE events unfolding more than two hundred feet above his head, Captain Petersen lay in his bunk and stared into the darkness, wondering whether he would freeze to death or suffocate first from lack of oxygen. It was purely an intellectual exercise. He was beyond caring how the end came. He only hoped that it arrived soon.

The cold had drained most of his energy. Every labored breath of carbon dioxide that he and his crew exhaled made the air less able to sustain life. The captain was drifting off into the comatose state that comes when the will to live ebbs like the lowering tide. Even thoughts of his wife and children could not pull him back.

He longed to reach the numb stage that might cushion his aches and pains. His body still harbored enough life to sustain his misery. His tortured lungs launched into a coughing fit that triggered a throbbing in his left arm, broken when he'd been thrown against a bulkhead. It was a simple fracture, but it hurt like hell. The groans of his crewmen reminded Petersen that he was not alone in his discomfort.

As he had a dozen times already, the captain ran through the collision in his mind, and wondered if he could have avoided it. All had been going well. A dangerous confrontation had been avoided, and the *Sea Sentinel* was being escorted out to sea. Then without warning, that crazy circus-painted ship had veered toward the cruiser's exposed side.

His frantic order to bear off had come too late. The tortured sound of tearing steel had told him that the wound was fatal. His naval training had quickly come into play. He'd given the order to abandon ship and had been supervising the launch of the lifeboats when a sailor ran up and said that men were injured belowdecks. Petersen hadn't hesitated. He'd left the lifeboat launch in the hands of his first mate and hurried to aid his men.

The night watch had been asleep when the *Leif Eriksson* was hit. The *Sea Sentinel*'s bow had penetrated the hull behind the sleeping quarters, sparing the crew from instant death but injuring some men. Petersen dashed into the mess hall, then half-tumbled down the companionway and saw that the uninjured were tending to their comrades.

"Abandon ship!" he ordered. "Form human stretchers."

The ship was sinking at a stern-down angle from the weight of the sea that poured in through the gaping hole. Water flowed into the mess hall, then down through the open hatch into the bunkroom, cutting off escape. Petersen climbed partway up the ladder, slammed the hatch shut and spun the wheel that locked it tight. Then the ship lurched as he was descending, and he slammed against the bulkhead, losing consciousness.

It was a fortunate accident because he didn't hear the horrible moans and creaks the ship made on its fatal plunge to the bottom. And his limp body wasn't further injured when, moments later, the cruiser slammed into the soft mud. Even so, when the captain awoke in the darkened cabin, it was to an even more terrible sound, the cries of his men. Soon after he regained consciousness, a beam of light had stabbed the darkness and revealed bloodied and pale faces among the jumbled bunks and sea chests. The ship's chef, a short, round man named Lars, called the captain's name.

"Over here," Petersen croaked.

The flickering light came his way. Lars crawled up beside Petersen holding an electric torch.

"Are you all right, Lars?" the captain asked.

"Some bumps and bruises. My fat protected me. How about you, sir?"

Petersen managed a wet laugh. "I'm not so lucky. Broken left arm."

"What happened, Captain? I was sleeping."

"A ship slammed into us."

"Damn," Lars said. "I was having a sweet dream of good things to eat before I got tossed from my bunk. Didn't expect to see you down here, sir."

"One of the crew said you were in trouble. I came to help." He struggled to get up. "I'm not much help sitting here. Can you give me a hand?"

They fashioned an improvised sling from the captain's belt and went around the cabin. With the help of a few men who hadn't been severely injured, they tried to make those less fortunate comfortable. The damp, biting cold was the worst immediate danger. They might be able to buy time, Petersen thought. The bunkroom had a supply of immersion suits used for cold-water protection if the ship went down.

It took awhile to round up the suits, which were scattered throughout the cabin in bags, and to get the injured men into them. They slipped on their gloves and pulled down the hoods. Then they rounded up spare blankets and clothes and wrapped themselves in several layers.

With the cold temporarily held at bay, Petersen turned his efforts to the air problem. One of the aluminum lockers held breathing devices to be used in case of fire or other emergency. These were passed around. They, too, would buy time. Petersen decided to use up their canned air first because it was purer than the air in the cabin, which was making the men sick.

Petersen formed tapping crews for the same reason POW officers allocate duties to maintain morale. The men took turns using a wrench to rap SOS on the hull. As one man after another tired of the job, Petersen continued to tap away, although he wasn't sure why. Bored with the SOS, he began tapping out messages describing their plight. Eventually, he tired and rapped the bulkhead whenever strength allowed, which wasn't often. Then he stopped altogether. His thoughts turned from rescue, he shut his eyes, and once more he began to think of death.

Using the marker buoy line as his guide, Austin sank into the depths feet-first and slightly angled forward, like an old hard-hat diver being lowered at the end of an invisible air hose. Dancing rainbow shafts lanced the water like sunlight streaming through stained-glass windows. As Austin plunged deeper, the water filtered out the colors and the twilight abruptly turned into a violet night.

The powerful halogen lights mounted on the front of the Hardsuit caught snowy motes of marine vegetation and nervous schools of fish in their beams, but before long, Austin was dropping into the benthic levels, where only the hardiest of fish lived. At two hundred feet, his lights pick out the cruiser's masts and antennas, then the ship's ghostly contours materialized.

Austin hit the vertical thrusters and slowed to a stop at deck level. Then the horizontal thrusters whirred, and he cruised along the hull, rounded the stern and came back to the bow. The ship lay as shown in the sonar picture, at a slight angle on the slope, with the bow higher than the stern. He studied the ship with the intensity of a medical examiner inspecting the autopsied body of a murder victim, paying particular attention to the triangular gash in the side. No vessel could have survived the giant bayonet wound.

Seeing only twisted metal beyond the jagged opening, he moved toward the bow again. He approached within inches of the hull, feeling as dwarfed as a fly on a wall, leaned his helmet against the steel plating and listened. The only sounds were the hollow noise of his breathing and the whirr of thrusters as they kept the suit at a hover. Austin pushed off several feet, came around, goosed the horizontal thrusters and let his metal knees slam into the ship.

On the other side of the hull, Petersen's half-closed eyes blinked fully open. He held his breath.

"What was that?" a hoarse voice said in the darkness. Lars had been huddled on the bunk next to the captain's.

"Thank God you heard it, too," Petersen whispered. "I thought I was going mad. Listen."

They strained their ears and heard tapping on the outside of the hull. Morse code. Slow and measured, as if the sender were struggling with each letter. The captain's eyes widened like those of a cartoon character, as he translated the rough taps into letters.

P-E-T-E . . .

Austin was cursing the awkwardness of communicating. At his direction, one of the crew had attached a specially adapted ball-peen hammer to his right hand manipulator. The mechanical arm moved with agonizing slowness, but by concentrating all his resources, he finished tapping out one word in Morse code.

. . . ERSEN

He stopped and put his helmet against the hull. After a moment, he heard dots and dashes clunked out in reply.

YES
STATUS
AIR BAD COLD
HELP SOON
A pause. Then, HURRY
SOON

Petersen called out to his men that rescue was imminent. He felt guilty lying. Their time was about to run out. He was having a problem focusing. It was getting harder to breathe, and soon it would be impossible. The temperature had plunged to below zero, and even the immersion suit couldn't keep out the cold. He had stopped shivering, the first sign of hypothermia.

Lars interrupted Petersen's drifting thoughts. "Captain, can I ask you a question?"

Petersen grunted in the affirmative.

"Why the hell did you come back, sir? You could have saved yourself."

Petersen said, "I heard somewhere a captain is supposed to go down with his ship."

"This is about as far *down* as you can go, Captain."

Petersen made a gargling sound that was as close to laughter as he could muster. Lars did the same, but their strength soon left them. They made themselves as comfortable as they could and waited.

6

THE BOAT CREW was watching for Austin to pop out of the water, and they snagged him like a runaway calf. Within minutes, he was back on the deck, where he spelled out the situation to Becker and Captain Larsen.

"Dear God," Becker said. "What a terrible way to die. My government will spare no expense to retrieve their bodies for the families."

Becker's pessimism was starting to annoy Austin. "Please stop playing the role of the melancholy Dane, Mr. Becker. Your government can hold on to its wallet. Those men aren't dead yet."

"But you said—"

"I *know* what I said. They're in tough shape, but that doesn't mean they're doomed. The *Squalus* submarine rescue took more than a day to accomplish, and thirty-three were saved." Austin paused as his sharp ears picked up a new sound. He stared at the sky and shaded his eyes against the glare of the overcast.

"Looks like the cavalry has arrived."

A gigantic helicopter was bearing down on the ship. Dangling below the helicopter in a sling was a blimp-shaped submarine with a blunt nose.

"That's the largest helicopter I've ever seen," Captain Larsen said.

"Actually, the Mi-26 is the biggest helicopter in the *world*," Austin said. "It's more than a hundred feet long. They call it the flying crane."

Becker smiled for the first time in hours. "Please tell me that strange-looking object hanging below the helicopter is your rescue vehicle."

"The *Sea Lamprey* isn't the prettiest craft in the sea," Zavala said with a shrug. "I sacrificed form for function in designing her."

"To the contrary," Becker said. "She's *beautiful*."

The captain shook his head in wonderment. "How on earth did you get this equipment here so quickly? You were twelve hundred miles away when the rescue call went out."

"We remembered that the Russians like to do things in a *big* way," Austin said. "They jumped at the chance to show the world they're still a first-rate nation."

"But that helicopter couldn't have carried it all that way in such a short time. You gentlemen must be magicians."

"It took a lot of work to pull this rabbit out of a hat," Austin said, as he watched the helicopter maneuver. "The Mi-26 picked up the submersible at sea and transferred it to a land base, where two Antonov N-124 heavy-duty transport planes were waiting. The *Sea Lamprey* went on one plane. The big chopper and the NUMA helicopter were loaded on the other. It was a two-hour flight to the NATO base in the Faroes. While they unloaded the submersible and got it ready to fly, we came out here to prepare the way."

The powerful turboshaft engines drowned out the captain's reply as the aircraft moved closer and hovered. The eight rotor blades and five-bladed tail rotor threshed the air, and the downdraft they created scooped a vast watery crater out of the sea. The submersible was released a few feet above the roiling water, and the helicopter moved off. The *Sea Lamprey* had been fitted out with large air-filled pontoons. It sank beneath the waves, but quickly bobbed back to the surface.

Austin suggested that the captain ready the sick bay to treat extreme hypothermia. Then the boat crew ferried them out to the submersible. The launch crew detached the pontoons. The submersible blew air from its ballast tanks and sank below the blue-black surface.

The *Sea Lamprey* hovered, kept at an even keel by its thrusters. Austin and Zavala sat in the snug cockpit, their faces washed by the blue light from the instrument panel, and ran down the dive checklist. Then Zavala pushed the control stick forward, angled the blunt prow down and blew ballast. He steered the submersible in a descending spiral as casually as if he were taking the family out on a Sunday drive.

Austin peered into the gauzy bluish blackness beyond the range of the lights. "I didn't have time to ask you before we came aboard," he said, almost in afterthought. "Is this thing safe?"

"As a former president once said, 'Depends on your definition of *is*.' "

Austin groaned. "Let me rephrase my question. Are the leaks and the pump fixed?"

"I think I stopped up the leaks, and the ballast pump works well under ideal conditions."

"What about *actual* conditions?"

"Kurt, my father used to quote an old Spanish proverb. 'The closed mouth swallows no flies.' "

"What the hell do flies have to do with our situation?"

"Nothing," Zavala said. "I just thought we should change the subject. Maybe the problem with the ballast control will go away."

The vehicle had been built as a rescue system of last resort. Once its lasers punched a hole in a sunken vessel, water would rush in after the sub disengaged. There was no way to plug the opening. All trapped crewmen had to be evacuated in one trip. This was a prototype, built to carry only eight people plus a pilot and copilot. If all thirteen men and their captain were taken off the cruiser, they'd be over the weight limit by six.

Austin said, "I've been running the figures in my head. Estimate a hundred fifty pounds per man, and we've got more than a ton of weight. There's a safety margin built into the

Lamprey, so it's probably no big whoop, except for the lame ballast tank."

"No problem. We've got a backup pump if the main isn't working." In designing the *Sea Lamprey,* Zavala had followed common practice and built redundant systems. Zavala paused. "Some of the crew might be dead."

"I've been thinking about that," Austin said. "We'd increase our safety margin if we left bodies down there, but I'm not leaving until we've got every man aboard. Dead or alive."

The cockpit grew silent as both men considered the awful possibilities. The only sound was the hum of electric motors as the ungainly craft dropped into the depths. Before long, they were at the side of the cruiser. Austin directed Zavala to the penetration point. Then came a soft clunk as the front end of the submersible bumped the curved steel plates. Electric pump motors hummed, and the submersible stayed where it was, glued to the steel by a vacuum.

The escape tunnel, made of a tough but pliable synthetic material, was extended. Eight vertical and horizontal thrusters kept the vehicle steady under the direction of computers that monitored its movement in relation to the current. The instruments indicated when the seal was complete. Normally, a thin probe would penetrate the hull to look for explosive fumes. Sensors gauged the pressure within the seal and kept the vacuum on place. Given the safe signal to enter, Austin strapped on a small air tank and a scuba regulator and emerged from the air lock. There was some leakage around the seal, but not enough to worry about. He started to crawl through the escape tunnel.

Inside the cruiser, the crew and captain had slipped into a deathlike sleep. Captain Petersen was roused from his cold slumber by the sound of a giant woodpecker. *Damned bird!* While one level of his brain cursed the source of the noise, another was automatically analyzing it, grouping the raps into familiar patterns, each the equivalent of a letter.

HELLO

He flicked the torch on. The chef had heard the noise, and

his eyes were as big as fried eggs. The captain's stiff fingers groped for the wrench by his side and banged it weakly against the hull. Then again, with more force.

The reply was immediate.

MOVE AWAY

More easily said than done, the captain thought. Petersen told the chef to back off from the bulkhead, then followed, rolling out of his bunk. He crawled across the deck and called out to the other men to move. He sat with his back to a locker for what seemed an eternity, not sure what to expect.

Austin crawled back into the *Lamprey*. "Mission accomplished," he said.

"Turning on the can opener," Zavala said. He hit the switch for the ring of cutting lasers. They sliced through the two-inch metal skin as easily as a paring knife through an orange. A monitor showed the penetration and the brilliant red of the lasers. The lasers automatically shut off.

Petersen had been watching as a faint pink circle deepened in color until it was a bright molten reddish-orange. He felt welcome heat against his face. There was a hollow clang as a section of the hull fell into the cabin, and he had to shield his eyes against a bright disk of light.

Steam filled the escape tunnel, and the edges of the opening were still hot from the laser cutters. Austin pushed a specially made ladder over the rim and stuck his head through the opening.

"Any of you gentlemen call a taxi?" he said.

Despite his lighthearted manner, Austin wondered if the rescue was too late. He had never seen such a bedraggled bunch. He called out for Captain Petersen. A grease-covered apparition crawled forward and croaked, "I'm the captain. Who are you?"

Austin climbed into the ship and helped the captain to his feet. "The introductions will have to wait. Please tell your men who can still move to crawl through that hole."

The captain translated the order. Austin threw a couple of soggy blankets onto the rough edges of the opening, then helped those who couldn't make it under their own power. Pe-

tersen collapsed as he was trying to crawl into the submersible, and Austin had to give him a shove, then clambered
in behind him. As he entered the air lock, he saw water trick-
ling in through the rim of the seal where Zavala had done a
hasty patch job.

He quickly closed the hatch behind him. Zavala had put
the controls on auto while he pulled the crew through the air
lock. The bulky survival suits didn't make the task any easier.
It was a miracle that any of the crew was still alive. Amazingly, some had made the trip themselves. The passenger
space consisted of two padded benches running the length of
the sub, separated by a narrow aisle. The survivors crowded
onto the benches or stood in the aisle like commuters on a
Tokyo subway.

"Sorry there's no first-class section," Austin said.

"No complaint," said the captain. "My men will agree that
it is better than our former living arrangements."

With the crew settled, Kurt returned to the cockpit. "We
had a little leakage around the seal," he reported.

Zavala indicated a blinking light on a computer-generated
diagram of the submersible. "More than a little. The O-ring
blew out like a flat tire a second after we closed the air lock."

He retracted the telescopic escape tube, disengaged the
submersible from the dead ship and backed off, clearly revealing in its floodlights the round hole where the lasers had
cut out the escape route. When the sub was clear of the wreck,
he activated the ballast pumps. The electric motors clicked
into action with a low hum, except from the front right pump,
where there was a sound like a fork going down a garbage
disposal. One ballast tank still had water in it, disrupting the
sub's equilibrium as the others filled with compressed air.

The *Sea Lamprey* operated like any other submarine; it
pumped water into its ballast tanks to dive, pumped in air to
ascend. The computer tried to compensate by giving more
power to the vertical thrusters. The submersible lurched into a
nose-down angle, and the smell of hot metal came through the
vents. Zavala pumped water back into the other tanks, and the
Lamprey leveled out, more or less.

Austin stared at the instrument panel. A light was blinking
on a schematic troubleshooting diagram. He ran a check on

the computer that served as the brains of the vehicle. The trouble system indicated that the warning light had been triggered by an actual mechanical problem, the kind of glitch that could show up with new equipment, and was probably easily repairable. But this was not a test run; it was a deep submergence dive to fifty fathoms. Another light started blinking red.

"Both front motors are gone," Austin said. "Better use the backup pumps."

"Those *were* the backup pumps," Zavala said.

"So much for redundant systems. What's the problem?"

"I could tell you in a minute if I had this thing up on a lift."

"I don't see any garages nearby, and in any case, I forgot my credit card."

"As my father used to say, 'All it takes to move a stubborn burro is a stick of dynamite.'" Zavala said.

Around the halls of NUMA, Austin had a well-deserved reputation for having an unflappable stubbornness in the face of adversity. Most men wisely cut and run in the face of sure disaster; Austin faced it with equanimity. The fact that he was still alive and breathing showed that he possessed a remarkable combination of resourcefulness and luck. Those who'd had to tough it out with him found his serendipity frightening. Austin always shrugged off their complaints. But now, Joe was giving him a taste of his own medicine. Austin compressed his lips in a tight smile, laced his fingers behind his head and sat back in his seat.

"You wouldn't be so relaxed if you didn't have a plan," Austin said.

Zavala gave his partner an exaggerated wink and removed the two-pronged key that had been hanging from a chain around his neck. He flipped open a small metal cap in the center of the console and inserted the key. "When I turn this key and flick the little switch next to it, the third redundant system comes into play. Explosive charges will blow off all the ballast tanks, and up we go. Smart, eh?"

"Not if the *Thor* is in the way when we come flying out of the water. We'd sink the ship and us."

"If it makes you feel any better, press that button. It sends up a warning buoy to the surface. Flares, whistles. The whole nine yards."

Austin punched the button. There was a *swoosh* as the buoy was ejected from the sub. He advised their passengers to hold tight.

Zavala jerked his thumb skyward, a boyish grin on his face. "Going *up*!"

He hit the switch and they braced themselves. The only sound was Zavala swearing under his breath in Spanish. "The switch didn't work," he said with a sheepish grin.

"Let's see if I can summarize this. We're three hundred feet down, with overloaded capacity, the cabin full of half-dead sailors, and the panic button doesn't work."

"You have a knack for brevity, Kurt."

"Thanks. I'll expand further. We've got two front tanks full of water, two rear ones empty, and that spells neutral buoyancy. Any way of lightening the *Lamprey*?"

"I can jettison the connector tube. We'll get to the surface, but it won't be pretty."

"Doesn't seem we have much of an alternative. I'll tell our passengers to hold on."

Austin made his announcement, buckled himself into his seat and gave the signal. Zavala crossed his fingers and blew off the rescue tube. It had been made detachable as a precaution, in case the submersible had to extricate itself from a rescue in a hurry. There was a muffled explosion, and the submersible lurched. The *Sea Lamprey* rose a foot, then a yard, then several yards. Their progress was excruciatingly slow at first, but the craft gained more speed the higher it went. Before long, it was speeding to the surface.

The *Sea Lamprey* exploded from the sea stern-first and splashed down in a fountain of white water. The vehicle rolled violently, tossing those inside around like dice in a shaker. Alerted by the warning buoy's sound-and-light show, small boats dashed in and their crews attached pontoons that stabilized the craft in a more or less horizontal position.

The *Thor* got a line on the vehicle and hauled the *Sea Lamprey* close to where a crane could lift it to the deck. Medical personnel swarmed over the submersible the second the hatch was popped, and the survivors were extracted one by one, loaded onto stretchers and hustled onto waiting Medivac helicopters that transferred them to the land hospital. By the time

Austin and Zavala climbed from the submersible, the deck was practically deserted, except for a handful of crew who came over and congratulated them, then quickly left.

Zavala looked around the near-empty deck. "No brass band?"

"Heroism is its own reward," Austin said pontifically. "But I wouldn't turn down a shot of tequila if someone offered it to me."

"What a coincidence. I just happen to have a bottle of blue agave tucked away in my duffel bag. Primo stuff."

"We may have to delay our celebration. Mr. Becker is coming our way."

The Danish bureaucrat was striding across the deck, his face beaming with unmistakable happiness. He pumped their hands, pounded the NUMA men on the back and showered them with effusive praise.

"Gentlemen, I thank you," he said breathlessly. "Denmark thanks you. The *world* thanks you!"

"Our pleasure," Austin said. "Thanks for the opportunity to test the *Sea Lamprey* under actual conditions. The Russian chopper is at the NATO base with the transport planes. We'll give them a call, and we can be out of here in a few hours."

Becker's face reassumed its usual mask of businesslike dourness. "Mr. Zavala is free to go, but I'm afraid you might have to delay your trip. A special investigative court that was formed to look into the cruiser incident is convening a hearing in Tórshavn tomorrow. They would like you to testify."

"Don't see how I can help. I didn't see the actual sinking."

"Yes, but you dove on the *Eriksson* twice. You can describe the damage in detail. It will help make our case." Seeing the doubt in Austin's face, he said, "I'm afraid we'll have to insist that you be our guest in the Islands until the hearing is terminated. Cheer up. The U.S. embassy has been informed of our request and will transmit it to NUMA. I've already arranged lodging for you. We'll be staying in the same hotel, in fact. The Islands are beautiful, and you'll only be delayed a day or two before you can rejoin your ship."

"It's no problem for me, Kurt," Zavala said. "I can get the *Lamprey* back to the *Beebe* and wrap up the tests."

Austin's eyes flashed with anger. He didn't like being told

what to do by an officious little government drone. He made no effort to disguise the annoyance in his voice. "Looks like I'll be your guest, Mr. Becker." He turned to Zavala. "We'll have to put off our celebration. I'll call the NATO base and get things moving."

Before long, the engine roar of the huge Russian helicopter filled the air. The sling was attached under the *Sea Lamprey*'s belly, and the helicopter lifted the vehicle from the ship's deck. Then Zavala took off in the NUMA helicopter and followed the submersible back to the base where the sub would be loaded onto a transport plane for the return trip.

"One other thing," Becker said. "I'd like you to keep that remarkable suit on board in case the court has the need for further evidence. If not, we'll gladly ship it anywhere you wish."

"You want me to make another dive?"

"Possibly. I would clear it with your superiors, of course."

"Of course," Austin said. He was too tired to argue.

The captain came over and announced that the shuttle was ready to take them back to the mainland. Austin wasn't enthusiastic about spending any more time than he had to with the Danish bureaucrat. "I'll come ashore tomorrow if it's all right with you. Captain Larsen wants to show me some of the results of his whale research."

The captain saw the desperation in Austin's eyes and played along. "Oh yes, as I said, you'll find our work fascinating. I'll deliver Mr. Austin to shore in the morning."

Becker shrugged. "Suit yourself. I've spent enough time at sea to last me a lifetime."

Austin watched the shuttle boat head toward land and turned to the captain. "Thanks for rescuing me from Mr. Becker."

Larsen sighed heavily. "I suppose bureaucrats like Becker have a value in the scheme of things."

"So do the stomach bacteria that aid in digestion," Austin said.

The captain laughed and put his hand on Austin's shoulder. "I think a liquid celebration of your successful mission is in order."

"I think you're right," Austin said.

7

AUSTIN RECEIVED VIP treatment aboard the research vessel. After drinks in the captain's cabin, he enjoyed a delicious meal, then he was entertained with incredible underwater footage of the ship's whale research. He was given a comfortable cabin and slept like a log, and the next morning he said his farewell to Captain Larsen.

The captain seemed sorry to see him go. "We're going to be here a few days doing survey work on the cruiser. Let me know if there is anything I can ever do for you or for NUMA."

They shook hands and Austin climbed into the shuttle for the short trip to the Western Harbor. Happy to be on dry land once more after weeks on and under the sea, he made his way along the cobblestone quay past the line of fishing boats. The capital city of the Faroe Islands was named Tórshavn, "Thor's Harbor," after the mightiest of the Scandinavian gods. Despite its thundering namesake, Tórshavn was a quiet settlement located on a headland between two busy boat harbors.

Austin would have preferred to explore the narrow streets that ran between the colorful old houses, but a glance at his watch told him he had better get moving if he wanted to make the hearing. He dropped his duffel bag off at the hotel room that Becker had arranged for him. He figured he wouldn't be in the Faroes more than another day or so, and decided to leave whether Becker wanted him to or not. On his way out, he asked the desk to book him a flight to Copenhagen in two days.

His destination was a short walk up the hill toward Vaglio Square in the heart of the city's commercial center. A few minutes later, he stopped in front of an impressive nineteenth-century building built of dark-hued basalt. The plaque on the exterior identified the structure as the *Raohus,* or Town Hall. He mentally girded his loins for the ordeal ahead. As an employee of a federal agency, Austin was no stranger to the hazards of navigating governmental seas. The rescue of the men trapped in the *Leif Eriksson* might have been the easiest part of his Faroese adventure, he reflected.

The receptionist in the *Raohus* lobby told Austin how to get to the hearing room. He followed a corridor to a door guarded by a burly policeman and identified himself. The officer told him to wait and slipped into the room. He reappeared a moment later with Becker. Taking Austin by the arm, Becker moved out of earshot.

"Good to see you again, Mr. Austin." He glanced at the policeman and lowered his voice. "This matter requires a great deal of delicacy. Do you know anything about the Faroe Islands government?"

"Only that there's an affiliation with Denmark. I don't know the details."

"Correct. The Islands are part of the Kingdom of Denmark, but they have had home rule since 1948. They're quite independent, even keeping their own language. However, when they get into financial trouble, they don't hesitate to ask Copenhagen for money," he said, with a faint smile. "This incident occurred in Faroese waters, but a Danish warship was involved."

"Which means SOS wouldn't win any popularity contests in Denmark."

Becker brushed off his comment with an airy wave. "I've made my feelings clear. Those crazy people should be *hanged* for sinking our ship. But I am a realist. The whole regrettable incident would never have happened if it hadn't been for the Islanders' stubbornness in keeping their old customs."

"You mean the whale hunt?"

"I won't comment on the morality of the *grindarap*. Many in Denmark regard the *grind* as a barbaric and unnecessary ritual. More important are the economic considerations. Companies that might buy Faroese fish or explore for oil don't want the public to think they are doing business with whale murderers. When the Faroese can't pay their bills, Copenhagen must open its pocketbook."

"So much for independence."

Becker smiled again. "The Danish government wants to resolve this case quickly, with the minimum amount of international publicity. We don't want these SOS people seen as courageous martyrs who acted rashly but in defense of helpless creatures."

"What do you want from me?"

"Please go beyond your technical observations in your testimony. We know *what* sank the cruiser. Feel free to emphasize the human suffering you witnessed. Our goal is to convict Ryan in the court of public opinion, then get these reckless hooligans out of our country and make sure they don't come back. We want to make sure that the world sees them as pariahs rather than martyrs. Perhaps then, something like this won't happen again."

"Suppose Ryan is innocent in all this?"

"His innocence or guilt is of no concern to my government. There are greater issues at stake."

"As you say, a matter of great delicacy. I'll tell your people what I saw. That's all I can promise.

Becker nodded. "Fair enough. Shall we go in?"

The policeman opened the door, and Becker and Austin stepped inside the hearing room. Austin's eyes swept around the large dark-paneled chamber and took in the suits, presumably government and legal people, who filled several rows of chairs. He was wearing his usual working gear of jeans, turtleneck and windbreaker, having no need on board ship for dressier outfits. More suits sat behind a long wooden table at the front of the room. Sitting in a chair to the right of the table was a man in a uniform. He was speaking in Danish, his words taken down by a stenographer.

Becker indicated a seat, sat next to Austin, and whispered

in his ear. "That's the representative from the coast guard. You're next."

The coast guard witness concluded a few minutes later, and Austin heard his own name called. Four men and two women sat at the table, with the group evenly divided between Faroese and Danish representatives. The magistrate, an avuncular Dane with a long Viking face, said his name was Lundgren. He explained to Austin that he would ask questions, with the others on the board offering follow-up. This was only an inquiry to collect an informational base, not a trial, he explained, so there would be no cross-examination. He would also translate when necessary.

Austin eased into the chair, and under questioning, offered a straightforward account of the rescue. He didn't have to embellish the suffering or the crew's ordeal in its dark and practically airless tomb. The expression on Becker's face showed that he was pleased with what he heard. Austin stepped down after forty-five minutes, with the thanks of the board. He was anxious to leave, but decided to stay when the court's chairman announced, in Danish and English, that the captain of the *Sea Sentinel* would present his case.

Austin was curious how *anyone* could defend himself against eyewitness accounts. The door opened and two policemen walked in. Between them was a tall and ruggedly built man in his mid-forties. Austin took in the ginger Captain Ahab chin-fringe, the coifed hair and the gilt-trimmed uniform.

The magistrate asked the witness to sit down and introduce himself.

"My name is Marcus Ryan," the man said, his gray eyes making direct contact with those in the audience. "I am the executive director of the Sentinels of the Sea organization and captain of the SOS flagship, the *Sea Sentinel*. For those who don't know us, SOS is an international organization dedicated to the preservation of the sea and the marine life that dwells within it."

"Please give the court an account of the events surrounding your collision with the Danish cruiser *Leif Eriksson*."

Ryan started into a diatribe against the whale hunt. Speaking in a firm voice, the magistrate asked him to keep his remarks confined to the collision. Ryan apologized and described how the *Sea Sentinel* had suddenly veered toward the cruiser, striking it.

"Captain Ryan," Lundgren said with unconcealed amusement. "Do you mean to tell me that your ship *attacked* and *rammed* the *Leif Eriksson* of its own accord?"

For the first time since he'd started testifying, Ryan lost his aplomb. "Uh, no, sir. I'm telling you that the controls of my ship did not respond."

"Let me see if I understand this clearly," said a woman on the board of inquiry. "You are saying that the ship took control of itself and went off on its merry way."

There was a ripple of laughter in the audience.

"It seems so," Ryan conceded.

His admission opened the doors for a round of probing questions. The hearing may not have been adversarial, Austin thought, but the court was nibbling Ryan apart like a flock of hungry ducks. Ryan did his best to parry the questions, but with each reply, his case became weaker. Finally he lifted his hands, as if to say *enough.*

"I realize that my explanation raises more questions than it answers. But let me say this unequivocally, so there is no misunderstanding. We did *not* deliberately ram the Danish ship. I have witnesses who can back me up. You can check with Captain Petersen. He'll tell you that I warned him."

"How long before the collision did this warning occur?" Lundgren asked.

Ryan took a deep breath and let it out. "Less than a minute before we hit."

Lundgren asked no further questions. Ryan was excused, and the female reporter from CNN took the stand. She was calm during her recounting of the collision, but she broke down and glared at Ryan with accusing eyes when she described the death of her cameraman.

Lundgren signaled a court officer to insert a videotape into a TV set that had been set off to one side where everyone had a good view of the screen. The tape began to roll. It showed Ryan standing on the deck of his ship surrounded by reporters and photographers. There was some joking about rough seas, then the reporter's voice saying: "Just make sure the story is worth all the damned Dramamine I swallowed."

The camera executed a close-up of Ryan's grinning face as he replied: "I can almost guarantee that you'll see action." As the camera followed his finger pointing toward the Danish cruiser, there was a muttering in the audience. That's it, Austin thought. Ryan is *toast*.

The tape ended, and Lundgren asked the reporter one question. "Was that your voice on the tape?"

When the reporter replied in the affirmative, Ryan sprang to his feet.

"That's unfair. You're using my comment completely out of context!"

"Please be seated, Mr. Ryan," Lundgren said, a bemused expression on his face.

Ryan realized his outburst would bolster the image of a hothead capable of ramming a ship. He regained his composure. "My apologies, sir. I was not told that the video would be introduced into evidence. I hope I will have the chance to comment on it."

"This is not an American court of law, but you will have every opportunity to make your side known before this hearing is adjourned. The board will hear from Captain Petersen and his crew as soon as they are able. You will remain in protective custody at the police station until then. We will do our best to expedite the process."

Ryan thanked the court. Then, escorted by the policemen, he left the room.

"Is that all?" Austin asked Becker.

"Apparently so. I expected they might ask you back to the stand, but it appears they don't need you anymore. I hope your plans haven't been disrupted."

Austin assured Becker that it was no problem. He sat in his chair as the room began to empty, chewing over Ryan's testimony. Either the man was telling the truth or he was a very good actor. That would be for wiser men to decide. First a good, stiff cup of coffee, then he would check out earlier flights to Copenhagen. From there, he'd fly back to Washington.

"Mr. Austin."

A woman was walking toward him, her face wreathed in a bright smile. Austin noticed her athletic and well-proportioned figure, the chestnut hair that fell to her shoulders, the unblemished skin and alert eyes. She was dressed in a white Icelandic wool jumper known as a *lopapesya*.

They shook hands. "My name is Therri Weld," she said, in a voice that was mellow and warm. "I'm a legal advisor with the SOS organization."

"Nice to meet you, Ms. Weld. What can I do for you?"

Therri had been watching Austin's serious expression as he gave his testimony, and she was unprepared for his devastating smile. With his broad shoulders, burnished features and blue-green eyes, he reminded her of a buccaneer captain in a pirate movie. She almost forgot what she was going to say, but quickly regained her mental footing.

"I wonder if you could spare a few minutes of your time," she said.

"I was about to look for a cup of coffee. You're welcome to join me."

"Thanks. There's a pretty decent café around the corner."

They found a quiet table and ordered two cappuccinos.

"Your testimony was fascinating," she said, as they sipped their coffee.

"Your Captain Ryan was the star of the day. My words paled by comparison with his story."

Therri laughed softly. Her laughter had a musical lilt that Austin liked. "Today wasn't his finest hour, I'm afraid. Usually he can be quite eloquent, particularly on those subjects he's most passionate about."

"Tough trying to explain to a bunch of skeptics that your ship was possessed by evil spirits. The reporter's testimony and the video didn't help."

"I agree, which is why I wanted to meet with you."

Austin gave her his best country-boy grin. "Aw, shucks, I had hoped you found yourself hopelessly attracted by my animal magnetism."

Therri raised a finely arched brow. "That goes without saying," she said. "But the main reason I wanted to talk was to see if you could help SOS."

"To begin with, Ms. Weld—"

"*Therri*. And may I call you Kurt?"

Austin nodded. "I've got a couple of problems right off the bat, Therri. First of all, I don't know how I can help you. And second, I don't know if I *want* to help your organization. I'm not in favor of whale slaughter, but I don't endorse radical nutcases."

Therri skewered Austin with a leveled gaze of her laser-bright eyes. "Henry David Thoreau, John Muir and Edward Abbey were considered radical nutcases in their times. But I concede your point. SOS tends to be too activist for the taste of many. Okay, you say you don't endorse radicals. Do you endorse *injustice,* because that's exactly what's involved here."

"In what way?"

"Marcus did *not* ram that Danish ship on purpose. I was in the pilothouse when it happened. He and the others did everything they could to avoid that collision."

"Have you told this to the Danish authorities?"

"Yes. They said they didn't need me to testify and told me to leave the country."

"Okay," Austin said. "I believe you."

"Just like that? You don't seem like someone who accepts the world at face value."

"I don't know what else to say without offending you."

"*Nothing* you say can offend me."

"Glad to hear that. But what gives you the idea that I would care whether the case against Ryan is just or not?"

"I'm not asking you to *care* about Marcus."

Therri's tone hinted that there was a bit of hard steel behind her soft features. Austin suppressed a smile. "What exactly do you want from me, Therri?"

She brushed a lock of hair out of her face and said, "I'd like you to make a dive on the *Sea Sentinel.*"

"What purpose would a dive serve?"

"It might prove that Marcus is innocent."

"In what way?"

She spread her hands. "I don't know. But you might find *something*; all I know is that Marcus is telling the truth. To be honest, much of his radicalism is hot air. He's really a hard-nosed pragmatist who calculates the odds very carefully. He's not the kind of person who goes around ramming navy ships in a fury. Besides, he *loved* the *Sea Sentinel*. He even picked the ridiculous psychedelic color scheme himself. No one on the ship, including me, intended for anyone to get hurt."

Austin leaned back in his chair, clasped his hands behind his head and stared at Therri's earnest face. He liked the way her perfect lips turned up in a Mona Lisa smile even when she was serious. Her girl-next-door appearance couldn't disguise the sensuous woman who lurked behind remarkable eyes. There were a thousand reasons why he should simply thank her for the coffee, shake her hand and wish her good luck. There were maybe three good reasons why he might consider her request. She was beautiful. She might have a case. And, right or wrong, she was passionate about her cause. His plane flight was two days away. There was no reason his short stay in the Faroes had to be boring.

Intrigued, he sat forward, and ordered another round of coffees.

"Okay, then," Austin said. "Tell me exactly what happened."

8

A FEW HOURS later, Austin was a world away from the warmth of the coffee shop, encased in the bulbous protective armor of his aluminum Hardsuit, sinking once more into the cold Faroese sea. As he dropped into the deep, he smiled as he pictured how Becker would react if he knew that a Danish vessel was being used to help Marcus Ryan and the SOS. It would serve the conniving little bureaucrat right, Austin thought, his chuckle echoing inside the helmet.

After taking leave of Therri Weld, he had gone back to the hotel, called Captain Larsen and asked permission to make another dive from the *Thor*. He said he wanted to shoot pictures of the rescue scene for a report, which was partially true. Larsen didn't hesitate to say yes and even sent a shuttle boat in to bring Austin back to the ship. Since Becker had asked Austin to leave the Hardsuit, it was all ready for him.

Austin's fathometer told him he was nearing bottom. He slowed his descent with short bursts of the vertical thrusters and came to a hummingbird hover about fifty feet above the bow section of the cruiser. The sea had wasted no time gathering the ship to its bosom. A shaggy coat of marine growth covered the hull and superstructure like an alpaca blanket.

Schools of deepwater fish nosed in and out of the portholes, drawn by sea life that had made its home in the shadowed nooks and crannies of the vessel.

Using a digital still camera, Austin shot pictures of the hole that the *Sea Lamprey* had made during the rescue mission and of the three-sided gash where the *Sea Sentinel* had punctured the hull. Austin had quizzed Captain Larsen about the last known position of the *Sea Sentinel,* relative to the cruiser. Using an undersea dead reckoning, he headed in the general area of the sinking.

He used a standard search pattern, running a series of roughly parallel courses until his lights picked out the psychedelic paint job on the ship's hull. Like the cruiser, the SOS ship was already growing a fur coat of marine growth. The combination of sea grass and tie-dye effect was startling. The *Sea Sentinel* had landed right-side-up on the bottom, and except for its smashed pug nose, the ship appeared to be in sound condition.

Austin surveyed the crushed bow and recalled Ryan's testimony. The engines had gone haywire, Ryan said, and failed to respond to controls. There was no way to check out the engines without going inside the wreck, but the steering system might more easily be investigated, because part of it was external. The steering of a modern ship is done with a combination of electronics and hydraulics. But even with computers, GPS positioning and autopilot, the concept is no different than it was when Columbus set sail to look for India. At one end is a wheel or a tiller. At the other is a rudder. Turn the wheel, and the rudder pivots, sending the vessel in the appropriate direction.

Austin soared above the stern, executed a hairpin turn, then dropped several yards until he was facing the man-tall rudder.

Curious.

The rudder was intact, but something was out of sync. Bolted to the rudder were two cables that led forward from the blade to each side of the hull. Austin followed the starboard cable to a steel box about the size of a large suitcase that was welded to the hull. An electrical conduit led from the box through the hull.

Even more curious.

The welds around the boxes and conduit were shiny and looked new. He backed off and followed the cable to an identical box on the other side. He raised the camera and made a couple of shots. A rubber-coated line as thick as a man's thumb connected the two boxes. Another line ran from the port-side box along the curve of the hull to a point that would have been above the waterline when the ship was afloat. At its end was a flat plastic disk about six inches in diameter. The significance of what he was seeing dawned on Austin.

Looks like someone owes you an apology, Mr. Ryan.

Austin took some pictures, then pried the disk off with his manipulators and placed it in a carrying case attached to the outside of the Hardsuit. He stayed down another twenty minutes, exploring every square inch of the hull. Finding nothing more out of the ordinary, he tapped his vertical thruster control and began the trip to the surface. Once out of his Hardsuit, he thanked Captain Larsen for the use of the *Thor* and caught a boat ride into Tórshavn.

Back in his hotel room, he slipped the cassette out of the digital camera and into his laptop computer and brought the underwater pictures onto the screen. He studied the enlarged and enhanced pictures until he practically had them committed to memory, then he called Therri and asked to meet her again at the coffee shop. He got there early and had the computer set up on the table when she arrived a few minutes later.

"Good news or bad?" she said.

"Both." Austin pushed the laptop across the table. "I've solved one mystery, but uncovered another."

She sat down and stared at the picture on the screen. "What exactly am I looking at?"

"I think it's a mechanism to override or bypass the steering controls from the bridge."

"You're *sure* of this?"

"Reasonably certain."

He clicked the computer mouse through a series of pictures that showed the boxes welded to the hull from different angles. "These housings could cover winches that can pull the rudder in either direction or lock it in place. Look here. This electrical connection runs up the side of the ship to a receiver above the waterline. Someone outside the ship could have controlled the steering."

Therri furrowed her brow. "Looks like a little pie plate."

Austin dug into his jacket, pulled out the plastic disk he'd pried off the hull, and dropped it on the table. "No pie in this plate. It's an antenna that could have been used to pick up signals."

Therri glanced at the screen, then picked the disk up and studied it. "This would explain the steering problems Marcus had. What about the engines he couldn't shut down?"

"You've got me there," Austin said. "If you could get into the ship and tear the engine room apart, maybe you'd find a mechanism that would allow the ship's speed to be controlled from the outside as well."

"I knew everyone on the *Sea Sentinel.* They're intensely loyal." She jutted her chin forward as if she expected an argument. "There's no one in that crew who would sabotage the ship."

"I haven't made any accusations."

"Sorry," she said. "I suppose I should keep an open mind about someone from the crew being involved."

"Not necessarily. Let me ask what they say at airport security. Did anyone else pack your baggage or has it been out of your sight?"

"So you *do* think someone from the *outside* could have sabotaged the ship."

Austin nodded. "I found a power source line for the winches leading into the hull to tap the ship's energy supply. Someone would have to get inside the ship to accomplish that."

"Now that you mention it," she said without hesitation, "the ship needed some engine work. It was in dry dock for four days in the Shetland Islands."

"Who did the work?"

"Marcus would know. I'll ask him."

"It could be important." He tapped the screen. "This may be Ryan's ticket out of jail. I'd suggest you get in touch with a guy at my hotel named Becker who seems to be some sort of behind-the-scenes mucky-muck with the Danish navy department. He might be able to help."

"I don't understand. Why would the Danes want to help Marcus after all the awful things they've said about him?"

"That's for public consumption. What they really want is to kick Ryan's butt out of the Faroes and make sure he never shows his face here again. They don't want him to get on his soapbox, because it might scare away companies that are thinking about investing in the Faroes. Sorry if this messes up Ryan's martyrdom plans."

"I won't deny that Marcus was hoping to make this a cause célèbre."

"Isn't that a risky strategy? If he pushes the Danes too far, they may be forced to convict him and toss him into jail. He doesn't strike me as a reckless guy."

"He isn't reckless at all, but Marcus will take a calculated risk if he thinks the stakes are worth it. In this case, he would have weighed going to jail against a chance to stop the *grind*."

Austin extracted the camera cassette from the computer and presented it to Therri. "Tell Becker that I will testify to what I saw and verify that I took these pictures. I'll run a check on the manufacturer of this antenna, but it's possible that it was put together out of standard parts and won't tell us anything."

"I don't know how to thank you," Therri said, rising from her chair.

"My standard fee is acceptance of a dinner invitation."

"I'd be more than pleased to—" She stopped short and glanced across the room past Austin's shoulder. "Kurt, do you know that man? He's been staring at you for some time."

Austin turned, and saw a balding, long-jawed man in his sixties, who was now making his way to the table.

"It's Kurt Austin of NUMA, if I'm not mistaken," the man said in a booming voice.

Austin stood and extended his hand. "Professor Jorgensen, nice to see you. It's been three years since we last saw each other."

"Four, actually, since we worked on that project in the Yucatán. What a wonderful surprise! I saw the news of the miraculous rescue you performed, but assumed you had departed the Faroes."

The professor was tall and narrow-shouldered. The ample tufts of hair flanking his freckled pate resembled swan wings. He spoke English with an Oxford accent, which was not surprising, since he had spent his undergraduate years at the famed English university.

"I stayed on to help Ms. Weld here with a project." Austin introduced Therri, and said, "This is Professor Peter Jorgensen. Dr. Jorgensen is one of the foremost fisheries physiologists in the world."

"Kurt makes it sound far more glamorous than it is. I'm simply a fish physician, so to speak. Well, what brings you to this far-flung outpost of civilization, Ms. Weld?"

"I'm an attorney. I'm studying the Danish legal system."

Austin said, "How about you, Professor? Are you doing some work here in the Faroes?"

"Yes, I've been looking into some peculiar phenomena," he said, without taking his eyes off of Therri. "Maybe I'm being forward, but I have a splendid suggestion. Perhaps we could have dinner together tonight and I could tell you about what I've been doing."

"I'm afraid Ms. Weld and I already have plans."

A pained expression crossed Therri's face. "Oh, Kurt, I'm so sorry. I started to say I'd be pleased to have dinner with you, but not tonight. I'm going to be busy with that legal matter we discussed."

"Hoist by my own petard," Austin said with a shrug. "Looks like you and I have a date, Professor."

"Splendid! I'll see you in the dining room of the Hotel Hania around seven, if that sounds all right." Turning to Therri, he said, "I'm devastated, Ms. Weld. I hope we will meet again." He kissed her hand.

"He's charming," Therri said, after Jorgensen left. "Very courtly in an old-fashioned way."

"I agree," Austin said, "but I'd still rather have you as my dinner partner."

"I'm so sorry. Perhaps when we get back to the States." Her eyes darkened a shade. "I've been thinking about your theory about the possibility that the *Sea Sentinel* was controlled from the outside. What would be the range involved in controlling a ship?"

"It could be done from quite a distance, but whoever did it would stay close by to see if the ship were responding to command. Any ideas?"

"There *were* a number of boats carrying press in the area. Even a helicopter."

"The controls could have been worked from the sea or the air. It wouldn't have required much in the way of equipment. A transmitter with a joystick, maybe, like you see for video games. Assuming we know the *how*, let's talk about the *why*. Who would benefit by neutralizing Ryan?"

"Do you have all day? The list could go on *forever*. Marcus has made enemies all over the world."

"For a start, let's confine ourselves to the Faroe Islands."

"The whalers would top the enemy list. Passions run high over the issue, but they're basically decent people, in spite of their odd customs. I can't see them attacking the navy ship that's been sent to protect them." She paused in thought. "There's another possibility, but it's probably too farfetched to consider."

"Try me."

She furrowed her brow in concentration. "After the *grindarap* operation, Marcus and his crew planned to make a showing at a fish farm owned by the Oceanus Corporation. The Sentinels are also against large-scale aquaculture, because of the harm to the environment."

"What do you know about Oceanus?"

"Not much. It's a multinational distributor of seafood products. Traditionally, they've bought fish from fleets around the world, but in the last few years they've gotten into aquaculture in a huge way. Their fish farms are on the same scale as some of the land farms operated by the agribusiness outfits in the States."

"You think Oceanus could have arranged this whole thing?"

"Oh, I don't know, Kurt. They would have the resources, though. And, just maybe, the motive."

"Where was their fish farm located?"

"Not far from here, near a place called Skaalshavn. Marcus planned to run the *Sea Sentinel* back and forth in front of the farm for the benefit of the cameras." Therri glanced at her watch. "That reminds me . . . I should be going. I've got a lot of work to do."

They shook hands, vowing to get together again. Therri made her way across the dining room and stopped briefly to throw him a coquettish glance over her shoulder. The gesture was probably meant to be reassuring, but it only made Austin sadder.

9

PROFESSOR **J**ORGENSEN **HAD** politely watched for several minutes as Austin tried to navigate his way through the incomprehensible courses listed on the menu, but finally he could bear it no longer. He leaned across the table and said, "If you'd like to try a Faroese specialty, I'd recommend the fried puffin or the pilot-whale steak."

Austin pictured himself gnawing on a drumstick from one of the stubby little birds with the parrot beak and passed on the puffin. After hearing the bloody way in which pilot whales met their demise in the Faroes, he decided he would rather eat shark snout, but he settled for the *skerpikjot,* well-aged mutton. After one bite, he wished he had gone for the puffin.

"How's your mutton?" Jorgensen said.

"Not quite as tough as shoe leather," Austin replied, working his jaw.

"Oh my, I should have advised you to get the *boiled* mutton, as I did. They dry *skerpikjot* in the wind. It's usually prepared at Christmas and served the rest of the year. It's a bit over the hill, as they say." He brightened at a new thought. "The life expectancy in the Faroes is quite high, so it must be good for you."

Austin sawed off a small bite and managed to swallow it. Then he put his knife and fork down while he gave his jaw muscles a rest. "What brings you to the Faroes, Dr. Jorgensen? It can't be the food."

The professor's eyes danced with amusement. "I've been looking into reports of diminishing fish stocks in the islands. It's a real mystery!"

"In what way?"

"I thought at first that the cause of the vanishing fish might be pollution, but the waters are amazingly pure around the Faroes. I can only do so much testing on-site, so I'm heading back to Copenhagen tomorrow to run some water samples through the computer. There may be small traces of chemicals that might have a bearing on the problem."

"Any theories as to the source of the chemicals?"

"It's strange," he said, tugging at one of his tufts of hair. "I'm sure the problem has something to do with a nearby fish farm, but so far there is no discernible link between the two."

Austin had been eyeing the mutton, wondering where he could get a burger, but his ears perked up at the professor's words. "Did you say you were testing the water near a fish farm?"

"Yes. There are several aquaculture facilities in the islands that produce trout, salmon and the like. I collected samples from the waters around a farming operation in Skaalshavn, a few hours' drive up the coast from Tórshavn on Sundini, the long sound that separates Stremoy from the island of Eysturoy. Used to be a whaling station there in the old days. The farm is owned by a big fisheries conglomerate."

Austin took a long shot. "Oceanus?"

"Yes, you've heard of it?"

"Only recently. As I understand what you're saying, Professor, the fish levels near this farm are lower than they should be."

"That's right," Jorgensen replied with furrowed brow. "A real puzzle."

"I've heard fish farms can be harmful to the environment," Austin said, recalling his conversation with Therri Weld.

"True. The waste products from a fish farm can be toxic. They feed the fish a special chemical diet so they'll grow faster, but Oceanus claims it has a state-of-the-art water purification system. So far I haven't found any evidence to dispute that claim."

"Have you visited this fish farm?"

Jorgensen bared his big teeth in a grin. "No visitors allowed. They've got the placed locked up tighter than the crown jewels. I managed to speak off-premises with someone from the law firm that represents the company in Denmark. He assured me that no chemicals were used at the farm and that it has the finest in water-cleaning facilities. Always the skeptical scientist, I rented a little house not far from the Oceanus operation and went as close as I could by boat to take the water samples. As I said, I'm leaving for Copenhagen tomorrow, but you and your young lady friend are welcome to go up to the cottage. It's a pretty ride."

"Thanks, Professor. Unfortunately, Ms. Weld will be busy the next few days."

"That *is* unfortunate."

Austin nodded absentmindedly. He was intrigued by Jorgensen's mention of the tight security at Oceanus. Where some might see this as an obstacle, Austin saw an invitation to probe the connection between Oceanus and the disastrous collision of the SOS ship and the cruiser. "I might take you up on your cottage offer. I'd like to see a little more of the Faroes before I leave."

"Wonderful! Stay as long as you want. The islands are spectacular. I'll call the landlord to say you'll be coming. His name is Gunnar Jepsen, and he lives in a house behind the cottage. You can use my rental car. There's a small boat that goes along with the cottage and plenty to keep you busy. Incredible birding on the cliffs, the hiking is superb, and there are some fascinating archeological ruins nearby."

Austin smiled and said, "I'm sure I'll find something to do."

After dinner, they had a nightcap in the hotel bar, then bid each other good-bye with a promise to hook up in Copenhagen. The professor was staying with a friend that night and would leave the islands in the morning. Austin went up to his hotel room. He wanted to get an early start the next day. He went over to the window and stood awhile in thought as he looked out over the quaint town and harbor, then he snatched up his cell phone and punched out a familiar number.

Gamay Morgan-Trout was in her office at NUMA headquarters in Washington, D.C., staring intently at the computer monitor, when the telephone rang. Without moving her eyes from the screen, she picked up the telephone and mumbled an absentminded hello. At the sound of Austin's voice, she broke into a dazzling smile that was made distinctive by the slight space between her front teeth.

"Kurt!" she said with obvious delight. "It's wonderful to hear from you."

"Same here. How are things back at NUMA?"

Still smiling, Gamay brushed a strand of long, dark-red hair away from her forehead and said, "We've been treading water here since you and Joe left. I'm reading a new abstract on toadfish nerve research that could help cure balance problems in humans. Paul's at his computer working on a model of the Java Trench. I don't know when I've had so much excitement. I feel sorry for you and Joe. That daring rescue must have bored you to tears."

Paul Trout's computer was back-to-back with his wife's. Trout was staring at the screen in typical pose, with head dipped low, partially in thought, but also to accommodate his six-foot-eight height. He had light-brown hair parted down the middle in Jazz Age style and combed back at the temples. As always, he was dressed impeccably, wearing a lightweight olive-tan suit from Italy, and one of the colorful matching bow ties that were his addiction. He peered upward with hazel eyes, as if over glasses, although he wore contacts.

"Please ask our fearless leader when he's coming home," Paul said. "NUMA headquarters has been as quiet as a tomb while he and Joe have been making headlines."

Austin overheard Trout's question. "Tell Paul I'll be back at my desk in a few days. Joe's due later in the week, after he wraps up tests on his latest toy. I wanted to let you know where I'd be. I'm driving up the Faroe coast tomorrow to a little village called Skaalshavn."

"What's going on?" Gamay said.

"I want to look into a fish-farm operation run by a company called Oceanus. There may be a connection between Oceanus and the sinking of those two ships here in the Faroes. While I'm poking around, could you see what you can learn about this outfit? I don't have much to go on. Maybe Hiram can help out." Hiram Yeager was the computer whiz who rode herd on NUMA's vast database.

They chatted a few more minutes, with Austin filling Gamay in on the rescue of the Danish sailors, then hung up, with Gamay promising to get right on the Oceanus request. She related the gist of her conversation with Austin.

"Kurt can whistle up a wind better than anyone I know," Paul said with a chuckle, alluding to the ancient belief that whistling on a ship can attract a storm. "What did he want to know about fish-farming, how to run your tractor underwater?"

"No, a grain binder," Gamay said with exaggerated primness. "How could I forget that you practically grew up on a fishing boat?"

"Just a simple son of a son of a fisherman, as Jimmy Buffett would say." Trout had been born on Cape Cod, into a fishing family. His ancestral path had diverged when, as a youngster, he hung around the Woods Hole Oceanographic Institution. Some of the scientists at the Institution had encouraged him to study oceanography. He'd received his Ph.D. in ocean science at the Scripps Institution of Oceanography, specializing in deep-ocean geology, and was proficient in using computer graphics in his various undersea projects.

"I happen to know that despite your display of ignorance, you know a lot more about aquaculture than you let on."

"Fish-farming is nothing new. Back home, folks have been seeding and harvesting the clam and oyster flats for a hundred years or more."

"Then you know it's essentially the same principle, only extended to fin fish. The fish are bred in tanks and raised in open-net cages that float in the ocean. The farms can produce fish in a fraction of the time it takes to catch them in the wild."

Paul frowned. "With the government clamping down on the wild fishery because of stock depletion, competition like that is the last thing a fisherman needs."

"The fish farmers would disagree. They say aquaculture produces cheaper food, provides employment and pours money into the economy."

"As a marine biologist, where do you stand on the issue?"

Gamay had received a degree in marine archaeology before changing her field of interest and enrolling at Scripps, where she'd attained a doctorate in marine biology, and in the process met and married Paul.

"I guess I stand smack in the middle," she said. "Fish-farming does have benefits, but I'm a little worried that with big companies running the farms, things could get out of control."

"Which way is the wind blowing?"

"Hard to tell, but I can give you an example of what's happening. Imagine you're a politician running for office and the fish-farm industry says it will invest hundreds of millions of dollars in the coastal communities, and that investment will generate jobs and billions of dollars each year in economic activity in your district. Which side would *you* back?"

Trout let out a low whistle. "*Billions?* I had no idea there was that kind of money involved."

"I'm talking about a *fraction* of the world business. There are fish farms all over the world. If you've had salmon or shrimp or scallops lately, the fish you ate could have been raised in Canada or Thailand or Colombia."

"The farms must have incredible capacity to pump out fish in those quantities."

"It's *phenomenal.* In British Columbia, they've got seventy million farm-raised salmon compared to fifty-five thousand wild caught."

"How can the wild fishermen compete with production like that?"

"They *can't,*" Gamay said, with a shrug. "Kurt was interested in a company called Oceanus. Let's see what I can find."

Her hands played over the computer keyboard. "Strange. Usually the biggest problem with the Internet is too *much* information. There's almost nothing on Oceanus. All I could find is this one-paragraph article saying that a salmon-processing plant in Canada had been sold to Oceanus. I'll peck around some more."

It took another fifteen minutes of hunting, and Paul was deep in the Java Trench again, when he heard Gamay finally say, "Aha!"

"Pay dirt?"

Gamay scrolled down. "I found a few sentences about the acquisition buried in an industry newsletter story. Oceanus apparently owns companies around the world that are expected to produce more than five hundred million pounds a year. The merger gives market access in this country through an American subsidiary. The seller figures the U.S. will buy a quarter of what they produce."

"Five hundred million pounds! I'm turning in my fishing rod. I wouldn't mind seeing one of these plants. Where's the nearest one?"

"The Canadian operation I just mentioned. I'd like to see it, too."

"So what's stopping us? We're twiddling our thumbs while Kurt and Joe are away. The world isn't in need of saving, and if it is, Dirk and Al are always available."

She squinted at the screen. "The plant is in Cape Breton, which is more than a skip and a jump from the shores of the Potomac."

"When will you learn to trust my Yankee ingenuity?" Paul said with a fake sigh.

While Gamay watched with a bemused smile, Paul picked up the phone and punched out a number. After a brief conversation, he hung up with a triumphant grin on his boyish face. "That was a pal in NUMA's travel department. There's a NUMA plane leaving for Boston in a few hours. They have two seats available. Maybe you can charm the pilot into an add-on to Cape Breton."

"It's worth a try," Gamay said, pushing the OFF button on her computer.

"What about your toadfish research?" Paul said.

Gamay replied with a bad imitation of a toad's croak. "What about the Java Trench?"

"It's been there for millions of years. I think it can wait a few more days."

His computer monitor went blank as well. Relieved that their boredom, at last, had come to an end, they raced each other to their office door.

10

THE MORNING GLOOM had burned off, and the Faroes were enjoying a rare moment of sunshine that revealed the splendor of the island scenery. The countryside seemed to be covered in bright-green billiard table baize. The rugged terrain was barren of trees, dotted by grass-roofed houses and an occasional church steeple, and laced by crooked stone walls and foot trails.

Austin drove the professor's Volvo along a twisting coastal road that offered inland views of distant mountains. Jagged gray outcroppings rose from the cold blue sea like huge, petrified whale fins. Birds swirled around the lofty vertical cliffs where the sea had sculpted the irregular shoreline.

Around midday, Austin emerged from a mountain tunnel and saw a doll-like village clustered on a gently sloping hill at the edge of a fjord. The serpentine road followed a series of descending switchbacks, dropping thousands of feet in a few miles. The Volvo's wheels skirted the edge of hairpin turns with no guardrails along the berm. Austin was happy when he reached the level road that ran between the foam-flecked surf and the colorfully painted houses built on the slope of the hillside like spectators at an amphitheater.

A woman was planting flowers in front of a tiny church, whose grassy roof was surmounted by a short, rectangular steeple. Austin glanced at his Faroese phrasebook and got out of the car.

He said: *"Orsaka. Hvar er Gunnar Jepsen?"* Excuse me, where could I find Gunnar Jepsen?

She put her trowel down and came over. Austin saw that she was a handsome woman who could have been between fifty and sixty. Her silvery hair was tied in a bun, and she was tanned except for the sun blush on her high cheekbones. Her eyes were as gray as the nearby sea. A bright smile crossed her narrow face, and she pointed toward a side road that led to the outskirts of town.

"Gott taak," he said. Thank you.

"Eingiskt?"

"No, I'm American."

"We don't see many Americans here in Skaalshavn," she said, speaking English with a Scandinavian lilt. "Welcome."

"I hope I'm not the last."

"Gunnar lives up there on the hill. Just follow that little road." She smiled again. "I hope you have a good visit."

Austin thanked her once more, got back in the car and followed a pair of gravel ruts for about a quarter of a mile. The road ended at a large grass-roofed house built of vertical, dark chocolate–colored planking. A pickup truck was parked in the drive. A hundred yards down the slope was a smaller twin of the main house. Austin climbed the porch stairs and knocked.

The man who answered the door was of medium height and slightly on the portly side. He had an apple-round face and cheeks, and thin strands of reddish-blond hair combed over his bald head.

"Ja," he said with a pleasant smile.

"Mr. Jepsen?" Austin said. "My name is Kurt Austin. I'm a friend of Professor Jorgensen's."

"Mr. *Austin.* Come in." He pumped Kurt's hand like a used-car salesman greeting a prospect. Then he ushered him into a rustic living room. "Dr. Jorgensen phoned and said you were coming. It's a long drive from Tórshavn," Jepsen said. "Would you like a drink?"

"Not now, thanks. Maybe later."

Jepsen nodded and said, "You're here to do a little fishing?"

"I've heard you can catch fish on dry land in the Faroes."

"Not quite," Jepsen said with a grin, "but almost as good."

"I was doing some ship salvage work in Tórshavn and thought fishing would be a good way to relax."

"Ship salvage? *Austin.*" He swore in Faroese. "I should have known. You're the American who saved the Danish sailors. I saw it on the television. Miraculous! Wait 'til the people in the village learn I am entertaining a celebrity."

"I was hoping I wouldn't be bothered."

"Of course, but it will be impossible to keep your visit a secret from the townspeople."

"I met one of them outside the church. She seemed nice enough."

"That would be the minister's widow. She's the postmistress and head gossip. *Everyone* will know you're here by now."

"Is that the professor's cottage down the hill?"

"Yes," Jepsen said, removing a key ring from a nail in the wall. "Come, I'll show you." Austin got his duffel from the car. As they walked down the hard-packed path, Jepsen said, "You're a good friend of Dr. Jorgensen?"

"I met him a few years ago. His reputation as a fish scientist is world-known."

"Yes, I know. I was very honored to have him here. Now you."

They stopped in front of the cottage, whose porch offered a view of the harbor, where a picturesque fleet of fishing boats was anchored. "Are you a fisherman, Mr. Jepsen?"

"In a little place like this, you survive by doing many things. I rent out my cottage. My expenses aren't great."

They climbed onto the cottage porch and went inside. The interior was basically one room with a single bed, bathroom, kitchen area, a small table and a couple of chairs, but it looked comfortable.

Jepsen said, "There's fishing gear in the closet. Let me know if you need a guide for fishing or hiking. My roots go back to the Vikings, and no one knows this place better."

"Thanks for your offer, but I've been around a lot of people lately. I'd like to spend some time on my own. I understand that a boat goes with the cottage."

"Third one from the end of the pier," Jepsen said. "A double-ender. The keys are in it."

"Thank you for your help. If you'll excuse me, I'd like to unpack, then I'll go into the village and stretch my legs," Austin said.

Jepsen told Austin to let him know if he needed anything. "Dress warm," he said as he went out the door. "The weather changes quickly around here."

Heeding Jepsen's advice, Austin pulled a windbreaker over his sweater. He went outside and stood on the cottage porch, sucking in the cool air. The land sloped gradually down to the sea. From his vantage, he had a clear view of the harbor, the fish pier and the boats. He walked back up the path to the Volvo and drove into the village.

Austin's first stop was the bustling fish pier, where a procession of trawlers unloaded their catches under an umbrella of squalling seabirds. He found the boat tied up as Jepsen had described. It was a well-built wooden inboard about twenty feet long, turned up dory-fashion at both ends. He checked the motor and found it relatively clean and new. The key was in the ignition, as Jepsen had said. Austin started the engine and listened to it for a few minutes. Satisfied that it was running smoothly, he switched it off and headed back to his car. On the way, he encountered the minister's widow coming out of a loading bay.

"Hallo, American," she said with a friendly grin. "Did you find Gunnar?"

"Yes, thank you."

She was holding a fish wrapped in newspaper. "I came down here to get some supper. My name is Pia Knutsen."

They shook hands. Pia's grip was warm and firm.

"Nice to meet you. I'm Kurt Austin. I've been enjoying the sights. Skaalshavn is a beautiful village. I've been wondering what the name means in English."

"You are talking to the unofficial village historian. Skaalshavn means 'Skull Harbor.' "

Austin glanced out at the water. "Is the bay shaped like a skull?"

"Oh *no*. It goes way back. The Vikings discovered skulls in some caves when they founded the settlement."

"People were here before the *Vikings*?"

"Irish monks, perhaps, or maybe even earlier. The caves were on the other side of the headland at what was the original harbor for the old whaling station. It became too small as fishing grew, so the fishermen moved their boats and settled here."

"I'd like to do some hiking. Would you recommend any routes where I can get a good view of the town and its surroundings?"

"From the bird cliffs, you can see for miles. Take that path behind the village," she said, pointing. "You will go through the moors by some beautiful waterfalls and streams, past a big lake. The trail climbs sharply after you pass the old farm ruins, and you will be at the cliffs. Don't go too close to the edge, especially if it's foggy, unless you have wings. The ledges are nearly five hundred meters tall. Follow the cairns back and keep them on your left. The trail is steep and goes down fast. Don't walk too close to the edge along the sea, because sometimes the waves crash over the rocks and can catch you."

"I'll be careful."

"One more thing. Dress warm. The weather changes quickly sometimes."

"Gunnar gave me the same advice. He seems quite knowledgeable. Is he a native?"

"Gunnar would like people to think he goes back to Erik the Red," she sniffed. "He's from Copenhagen. Moved into the village a year or two ago."

"Do you know him well?"

"Oh, yes," she said, with a roll of her lovely eyes. "Gunnar tried to get me into his bed, but I'm not that hard up."

Pia was a good-looking woman, and Austin wasn't surprised at Jepsen's attempt; but he hadn't driven all this way to tune in on the local romances. "I heard there was a fish operation of some sort up the coast."

"Yes, you'll see it from the cliffs. Ugly concrete and metal buildings. The harbor is full of their fish cages. They raise fish there and ship it out. The local fishermen don't like it. The fishing around the old harbor has gone bad. No one from town works there. Not even Gunnar anymore."

"He worked at the fish farm?"

"In the beginning. Something to do with construction. He used his money to buy his houses and lives off the rentals."

"Do you get many visitors here?" Austin was watching a sleek blue yacht coming into the harbor.

"Bird-watchers and fishermen." She followed Austin's eyes. "Like those men in that pretty boat. It's owned by a rich Spaniard, I hear. They say he came all the way from Spain for the fishing."

Austin turned back to Pia. "You speak English very well."

"We learn it in the schools along with Danish. And my husband and I spent some time in England when we were first married. I don't get much chance to speak it." She lifted the fish under Austin's nose and said, "Would you like to come to my house for dinner? I could practice my English."

"It wouldn't be too much trouble?"

"No, no. Come by after your walk. My house is behind the church."

They agreed to meet in a few hours, and Austin drove to the trailhead. The gravel path climbed gradually through rolling moors splashed with wildflowers, and passed near a small lake, almost perfectly round, that looked as if it were made of cold crystal. About a mile from the lake, he came upon the ruins of an old farm and an ancient graveyard.

The path grew steeper and less visible. As Pia advised, he followed the carefully piled heaps of rock that marked the way. He could see flocks of sheep so far away that they looked like bits of lint. Towering in the distance were layered mountains with cascading wedding-veil waterfalls.

The trail led to the cliffs, where hundreds of seabirds filled the air, balancing delicately on updrafts of air. Tall sea stacks soared from the bay, their flat summits wreathed in fog. Austin chewed on a PowerBar and thought that the Faroes must be the most otherworldly place on the planet.

He kept on going until he stood atop a ridge that gave him a panoramic view of the serrated coast. A rounded headland separated Skaalshavn from a smaller inlet. Clustered along the shore of the old harbor were dozens of neatly arranged buildings. As he surveyed the scene below, he felt a drop of rain on his cheek. Dark billowing clouds were rolling in from the layered mountains to obliterate the sun. He started down from the exposed ridge. Even with switchbacks easing the vertical drop, the going was hard on the steep trail, and he had to move slowly until the ground leveled out again. As he approached sea level, the heavens opened up. He kept heading toward the lights of the town, and before long he was at his car.

Pia took one look at the drenched and bedraggled figure at her door and shook her head.

"You look like you've crawled out of the sea." She pulled Austin in by the sleeve and ordered him to go into the bathroom and strip. Austin was too wet to protest. While he was undressing, she cracked the door open and tossed in a towel and dry clothes.

"I was sure my husband's clothes would fit," she said approvingly, when Austin ventured out in the shirt and pants. "He was a big man like you."

While Pia set the table, Austin spread his clothes out next to a woodstove, then stood practically on top of it, basking in the heat, until she informed him that dinner was ready.

The baked fresh cod melted in his mouth. They washed dinner down with a light homemade white wine. Dessert was a sweet raisin pudding. Over their meal, she talked about her life in the Faroes, and Austin told her a little about his NUMA work. She was fascinated by his travels to exotic places for his NUMA assignments.

"I forgot to ask, did you have a good walk, even with the rain?" Pia said as she cleared the dishes.

"I climbed to the top of the cliffs. The views were incredible. I saw the fish farm you mentioned. Do they allow visitors?"

"Oh *no*," Pia replied, with a shake of her head. "They don't let *any*one in. Like I said before, none of the village men work there. There's a road along the shore that they used when they were building, but it's blocked off with a high fence. Everything comes and goes by sea. They say it's like a separate town out there."

"Sounds interesting. Too bad no one can get in."

Pia refilled Austin's glass and gave him a sly look. "I could get in in a *minute* if I wanted to, through the Mermaid's Gate."

He shook his head, unsure he had heard her correctly. "The Mermaid's Gate?"

"That's what my father used to call the natural arch at the edge of the old harbor. He used to take me out sometimes in his boat, and we'd go there. He never took me in. It's dangerous because of the currents and rocks. Some men have drowned trying to go through the gate, so the fishermen stay away. They say it's haunted by the souls of the dead. You can hear them moaning, but it's only the way the wind blows through the caves."

"It sounds as if your father wasn't afraid of ghosts."

"He wasn't afraid of *any*thing."

"What do these caves have to do with the fish farm?"

"It's a way to go in. One cave joins others that lead to the old harbor. My father said there are paintings on the walls. Wait, I'll show you."

She went to a bookcase and took out an old family album. Tucked between pages of photos was a sheet of paper, which she unfolded and spread on the table. Drawn on the paper were rough sketches of bison and deer. More interesting to Austin were depictions of long graceful boats powered by sail and oar.

"These are very old drawings," Austin said, although he was unable to place them in time. "Did your father show them to anyone else?"

"Not outside the family. He wanted the caves kept a secret because he was afraid they would get ruined if people knew about them."

"Then the caves can't be entered from the land side?"

"There was a way, but it was blocked with boulders. My father said it would be no problem to move them. He wanted to get some scientists in from the university so it would be done right, but he died in a storm."

"I'm sorry."

Pia smiled. "Like I said, he wasn't afraid of anything. Anyhow, after he died, my mother moved the family away to live with relatives. I came back here with my husband. I was too busy raising kids to worry about the caves. Then the fish company bought the land and the old whaling station, and no one could get out there."

"Are there more pictures?"

She shook her head. "Poppa tried to make a map of the

caves, but I don't know what happened to it. He said the people who made the paintings were smart. They used pictures of fish and birds like signs. As long as you follow the right fish, you won't get lost. Some of the caves lead to blind alleys."

They talked into the night. Austin finally looked at his watch and said that he had to go. Pia wouldn't let him leave until he agreed to return for dinner the next evening. He drove along the deserted road in the dusky light that passes for night in northern climes.

A light was on at the main house, but he saw no sign of Jepsen, and guessed he had gone to bed. The rain had ended. He went out on the porch and stood there awhile, looking down on the quiet village and harbor, then went back inside the cottage and got ready to sack out. Although the remote village seemed peaceful, he couldn't shake the uneasy feeling that Skaalshavn was a place of dark secrets. Before he turned in, he made sure that the door and windows were locked.

11

PAUL TROUT THREADED the wide-beamed Humvee through the heavy Washington traffic like a runner going for a touchdown at the Super Bowl. Although he and Gamay often took the Hummer on four-wheeling family trips in the Virginia countryside, nothing they encountered off-road could compare with the challenges of driving in the nation's capital. They made good time, though, as Gamay called out openings in the traffic and Paul spun the wheel over without looking. Their ability to work together like a well-oiled machine had been crucial on countless NUMA assignments and was a tribute to the acumen of Admiral Sandecker, who had hired them together.

Paul turned down a narrow Georgetown street and tucked the Humvee into the parking space behind their brick town house, and they bolted for the door. Minutes later, they were jumping into a taxi, their hastily packed overnight bags in hand. The NUMA executive jet was waiting at the airport with its engines warming up. The pilot, who was flying a contingent of scientists to Boston, knew the Trouts from past missions with the Special Assignments Team. She had gotten the okay from NUMA to add the extra leg to her trip and filed a new flight plan.

After dropping off the scientists at Logan Airport, the plane continued up the Atlantic coast. With a cruising speed of nearly five hundred miles an hour, the Cessna Citation had the Trouts in Halifax, Nova Scotia, in time for a late dinner. They stayed overnight at a hotel near the airport and caught an Air Canada flight to Cape Breton early the next morning, then rented a car at the Sydney airport and drove out of the city up the rocky coast to look for the processing plant that Oceanus had acquired. Gamay had picked up a travel guide at the airport. The travel writer who'd written the section describing this part of the remote coast must have been desperate, because he had listed the fish-processing plant as a tourist attraction.

After not seeing any signs of civilization for many miles, they came upon a combination general store, coffee shop and service station. Gamay, who was taking her turn at the wheel, pulled alongside the battered pickup trucks lined up in front of the ramshackle false-front building.

Paul looked up from the map he was studying. "Charming, but we've got another few miles before we get to the center of town."

"We have to stop for gas anyhow," Gamay said, tapping the fuel gauge. "While you pump the pump, I'll pump the locals for gossip."

Tucking the guidebook under her arm, Gamay stepped over the mangy black Labrador retriever stretched out in a deathlike sleep on the rickety front porch and pushed the door open. Her nostrils were greeted by a pleasant fragrance of pipe tobacco, bacon and coffee. The store, which occupied one half of the room, was crammed with every sort of item, from beef jerky to rifle ammunition. The coffee shop took up the other side of the store.

A dozen or so men and women sat at round Formica-and-chrome tables. All eyes turned to Gamay. At five-ten and a hundred-thirty-five pounds, Gamay's slim-hipped figure and unusual red hair would have attracted attention at a Malibu beach party. The curious stares followed her every move as she poured two plastic cups full of coffee from a self-service dispenser.

Gamay went to pay, and the plump young woman at the cash register greeted her with a friendly smile. "Passing through?" she said, as if she couldn't imagine any traveler staying in town longer than it took to fill a coffee cup.

Gamay nodded. "My husband and I are taking a drive along the coast."

"Don't blame you for not staying," the woman said with resignation. "Not much to see around here."

Despite her striking sophistication, Gamay's Midwestern roots had given her a down-home earthiness that was hard to resist. "We think it's *beautiful* country," she said, with an engaging smile. "We'd stay longer if we had time." She opened the guidebook to the folded-over page. "It says here that there's a pretty little fishing harbor and a fish-processing plant nearby."

"It *does*?" the cashier said with disbelief.

The other people in the room had been listening to every word. A spindly white-haired woman cackled like a hen. "Fishing ain't what it used to be. Plant sold out. Some big outfit bought the business. Fired all the folks working there. Nobody knows what they're doing. People who work there never come into town. Sometimes we see the Eskimos driving around in their big black trucks."

Gamay glanced into the guidebook, looking for something she missed. "Did you say *Eskimos*? I didn't think we were that far north."

Her innocent question started a table debate. Some of the locals contended that Eskimos guarded the plant. Others said that the men driving the SUVs were Indians or maybe Mongolians. Gamay wondered if she had stumbled into the local insane asylum, a thought that was reinforced when the cashier mumbled something about "aliens."

"Aliens?" Gamay said.

The cashier blinked through thick, round-framed glasses, her eyes growing wider. "It's like that secret UFO place in the States, Area Fifty-one, like they show on *The X-Files*."

"I seen a UFO once when I was hunting near the old

plant," interjected a man who could have been a hundred years old. "Big silver thing all lit up."

"Hell, Joe," said the skinny woman, "I've seen *you* so lit up you've probably seen purple elephants."

"Yup," the man said with a gap-toothed grin. "Seen them, too."

The restaurant filled with laughter.

Gamay smiled sweetly and said to the cashier, "We'd love to tell our friends back home that we saw a UFO base. Is it far from here?"

"Maybe twenty miles," the cashier said. She gave Gamay directions to the plant. Gamay thanked the young woman, put a ten-dollar bill in the empty tip jar, scooped up the coffees and headed out the door.

Paul was leaning against the car, his arms folded across his chest. He took the coffee she offered him. "Any luck?"

Gamay glanced back at the store. "I'm not sure. I seem to have run into the cast of *Twin Peaks*. In the last few minutes, I've learned that this part of the world is home to Eskimos who drive big black SUVs, a UFO base and purple elephants."

"That explains it," he said with mock seriousness. "While you were inside, a bunch of big critters the color of plums came thundering by here."

"After what I heard, I'm not surprised," she said, slipping behind the wheel.

"Think the locals were having a little fun at the expense of a tourist?" Paul said, getting into the passenger side.

"I'll let you know after we find big silver things around Area Fifty-one." Seeing the quizzical expression on her husband's face, she laughed and said, "I'll explain on the way."

They drove past the turnoff that led to the town center and harbor, into an area of heavy pine forest. Even with the cashier's detailed directions, which included every stump and stone for miles, they almost missed the turnoff. There was no sign marking the entrance. Only the hard-packed ruts showing fairly recent use distinguished the way from any of the other fire roads that cut into the thick woods.

About a half mile from the main road, they pulled over. The cashier had advised Gamay to park at a clearing near a big glacial boulder and to walk through the woods. A few townspeople who had driven close to the plant's gates had been intercepted and rudely turned away. The Eskimos or whatever they were probably had hidden cameras.

Gamay and Paul left the car and made their way through the woods parallel to the road for about an eighth of a mile, until they could see the sun glinting off a high chain-link fence. A black cable ran along the top of the fence, indicating that the razor wire was electrified. No cameras were visible, although it was possible that they were disguised.

"What now?" Gamay said.

"We can fish or cut bait," Paul replied.

"I never liked cutting bait."

"Me, neither. Let's fish."

Paul stepped out of the woods into the cleared grassy swath around the fence. His sharp eye noticed a thin, almost-invisible wire at ankle height. He pointed to the ground. Trip wire. He snapped a dead branch off a nearby tree and dropped it on the wire, then he slipped back into the woods. He and Gamay flattened out belly-first on the pine needle carpeting.

Soon they heard the sound of a motor, and a black SUV lumbered to a stop on the other side of the fence. The door opened, and fierce-looking pure white Samoyeds as big as lions lunged out and ran up to the fence. The snuffling dogs were followed a moment later by a swarthy, round-faced guard in a black uniform. He cradled a leveled assault rifle in his hands.

While the dogs dashed back and forth along the fence, the guard suspiciously eyed the woods. He saw the branch lying on the trip wire. In an unintelligible language, he mumbled into a hand radio, then he moved on. The dogs may have sensed the two human beings in the woods. They growled and stood stiff-legged, staring at the trees that hid the Trouts. The guard yelled at them, and they jumped back into the SUV. Then he drove off.

"Not bad time," Paul said, checking his watch. "Ninety seconds."

"Maybe it's time we got out of here," Gamay said. "They'll be sending someone to clear away that branch."

The Trouts melted back into the woods. Walking and trotting, they returned to their rental car. Minutes later, they were on the main road.

Gamay shook her head in wonderment. "That guard, did he look like an Eskimo to you?"

"Yeah, kinda, I guess. Never ran into many Eskimos back on old Cape Cod."

"What's an Eskimo doing this far south, selling Eskimo Pies?"

"The only thing that guy and his puppy dogs were selling was a quick trip to the morgue. Let's see what's going on in the big city."

Gamay nodded, and a few minutes later she was taking the turnoff that led to town. The village was hardly quaint, and she could see why it was only a footnote in the travel guide. The houses were protected against the weather by asphalt shingles of drab green and faded maroon, and the roofs were covered with aluminum to allow the snow to slide off. There were few people or cars around. Some of the shops in the minuscule business section posted signs that said they were closed until further notice, and the town had an abandoned look. The harbor was picturesque, as the tour book said, but it was empty of boats, adding to the town's forlorn aspect.

The fish pier was deserted except for a ragged flock of sleeping gulls. Gamay spotted a restaurant/bar neon sign in a small square building overlooking the harbor. Paul suggested that she grab a table and order him fish and chips while he meandered around and tried to find someone who could tell him about the Oceanus plant.

Gamay stepped into the yeasty atmosphere of the restaurant and saw that the place was vacant except for a heavyset bartender and one customer. She took a table with a view of the harbor. The bartender came over for her order. Like the people she'd met in the general store, he proved to be a friendly type. He apologized for not having fish and chips, but said the grilled ham and cheese sandwich was pretty good. Gamay said that would be fine and ordered two sandwiches along with a Molson. She liked the Canadian beer because it was stronger than the American brew.

Gamay was sipping her beer, admiring the fly-specked ceiling, the torn-fishnet-and-weathered-lobster-buoy decorations on the wall, when the man sitting at the bar slid off his stool. Apparently, he had taken the sight of an attractive woman drinking alone in a bar at midday as an invitation. He sidled over with a beer bottle in his hand and ran his eyes over Gamay's red hair and lithe, athletic body. Unable to see her wedding ring because her left hand was resting on her knee, he figured Gamay was fair game.

"Good mornin'," he said, with an amiable smile. "Mind if I join you?"

Gamay wasn't put off by the direct approach. She moved well among men because she had a talent for thinking like they did. With her tall, slim figure and long, swirled-up hair, it was hard to believe that Gamay had been a tomboy, running with a gang of boys, building tree houses, playing baseball in the streets of Racine. She was an expert marksman as well, thanks to her father, who'd taught her to shoot skeet.

"Be my guest," Gamay said casually, and waved him into a chair.

"My name's Mike Neal," he said. Neal was in his forties. He was dressed in work clothes and wore shin-high black rubber boots. With his dark, rugged profile and thick, black hair, Neal would have had classic good looks if not for a weakness around the mouth and a ruby nose colored by too much booze. "You sound American."

"I am." She extended her hand and introduced herself.

"Pretty name," Neal said, impressed by the firmness of Gamay's grip. Like the general store cashier, he said, "Just passing through?"

Gamay nodded. "I've always wanted to see the Maritime Provinces. Are you a fisherman?"

"Yep." He pointed out the window and, with unrestrained pride, said, "That's my beauty over there at the boatyard dock. The *Tiffany*. Named her after my old girlfriend. We broke up last year, but it's bad luck to change the name of a boat."

"Are you taking a day off from fishing?"

"Not exactly. Boat shop did some work on my engine. They won't release *Tiffany* until I pay them. Afraid I'd take off without paying."

"Would you?"

He smirked. "I stung them for a few bucks before."

"Still, that seems shortsighted on their part. With your boat, you could go fishing and earn the money to pay them back."

Neal's smile dissolved into a frown. "I could if there were fish to sell."

"Someone at the general store mentioned that the fishing was bad."

"*Worse* than bad. Rest of the fleet has moved up the coast. Some of the guys come home between trips to see family."

"How long has this been going on?"

" 'Bout six months."

"Any idea what's causing the drought?"

He shrugged. "When we talked to the provincial fisheries people, they said the fish musta moved off, looking for better feeding. They didn't even send someone like we asked. Don't want to get their feet wet, I guess. The marine biologists all must be busy sitting on their fat asses looking at their computers."

"Do you agree with what they said about the fish moving off?"

He grinned. "For a tourist, you've got lots of questions."

"When I'm not a tourist, I'm a marine biologist."

Neal blushed. "Sorry. I wasn't talking about your fat ass. Oh, hell—"

Gamay laughed. "I know exactly what you mean about computer biologists who never leave their lab. I think fishermen have more practical knowledge of the sea than any scientist. At the same time, professional expertise doesn't hurt. Maybe I can help you figure out why there are no fish to catch."

A cloud passed over Neal's features. "I didn't say there are *no* fish. There are fish all right."

"Then what's the problem?"

"These aren't like any fish I've seen in all my years of fishing."

"I don't understand."

Neal shrugged. Apparently this was one subject he didn't want to talk about.

"I've studied fish in and out of the water all over the world," Gamay said. "There isn't much that would surprise me."

"Bet this would."

Gamay stuck her hand out. "Okay, it's a bet. How much is your engine repair bill?"

"Seven hundred fifty dollars, Canadian."

"I'll pay that if you show me what you're talking about. Let me buy you a beer to seal the deal."

Neal's unshaven jaw dropped open. "You're serious?"

"*Very*. Look, Mike, there are no fences in the ocean. Fish go pretty much where they please. There may be something harmful in these waters that could affect American fishermen as well."

"Okay," he said, shaking her hand. "When can you go?"

"How about today?"

Neal grinned like a Cheshire cat. The source of his happiness wasn't hard to figure out. A nice-looking and friendly American woman was paying his boatyard bill and going out on his boat, alone, where he could turn on his rugged charm. Just then, Paul Trout walked into the bar and came over to the table.

"Sorry I took so long," Paul said. "Harbor's pretty deserted."

"This is Mike Neal," Gamay said. "Mike, I'd like you to meet my husband."

Neal glanced up at Trout's nearly seven-foot-tall figure, and his fantasies about Gamay evaporated. But he was a practical man—a deal was a deal. "Pleased to meet you," he said. They shook hands.

"Mike here has agreed to take us out on his boat to show us some unusual fish," Gamay said.

"We can leave in an hour," Neal said. "That'll give you time to eat your lunch. See you over at the boat." He rose from his chair and started to leave.

"Do we need to bring anything?" Paul asked.

"Naw," Neal said. He stopped and said: "Elephant gun, maybe?" He roared with laughter at the Trouts' puzzled expressions. They could still hear him laughing after he passed through the door.

12

WITH HIS LONG-STEMMED pipe, teeth like a broken picket fence and storm-beaten face, Old Eric
looked like a grizzled character out of *Captains Courageous*.
Pia said that the retired fisherman spoke English and knew
the local waters better than the fish. Now too old to go fishing, he did odd jobs around the pier. Despite his fierce expression, he was more than obliging when Austin mentioned
Pia's name.

Austin had arrived at the fish pier early, looking for advice
about local weather and sea conditions. A purple-blue pall
from the throaty exhausts of the Skaalshavn fishing fleet hung
in the damp air. Fishermen decked out in foul-weather gear
and boots slogged through the drizzle as they loaded bait
buckets and tubs of coiled trawl line on their boats in preparation for a day at sea. He told the old salt he was taking Professor Jorgensen's boat out to go fishing.

Old Eric squinted at the scudding gray clouds and pursed
his lips in thought. "Rain should stop, and the fog will burn
off soon." He pointed to a tall pillar of rock guarding the harbor entrance. "Go to the starboard of that sea stack. You'll find
good fishing after a mile. Wind comes up around midday, but

the professor's boat is weatherly. I should know," he said with a gap-toothed grin. "I built her. She'll get you home in one piece."

"How's the fishing the other way along the coast?"

The old fisherman wrinkled his nose. "Stinks around the fish farm. A wet ride, too, coming back with a following sea."

Austin thanked Eric for his advice, stowed his day pack and fishing gear in the boat, checked the fuel level and ventilated the bilge. The inboard engine started right away and soon settled down to a smooth rumble. Austin cast off the lines, pushed away from the dock and pointed the bow toward the two-hundred-foot-high chimney-shaped rock formation that stood like a stone waterspout at the harbor entrance. He went to the left rather than to the right of the lofty column, hoping Old Eric wouldn't see him.

Soon, the boat was cruising past towering cliffs where thousands of nesting seabirds soared like windblown confetti. The motor purred like a milk-fed kitten. There was a slight chop to the water, but the double-ender sliced rather than slapped its way through the waves. Spray occasionally splashed over the bow. Austin stayed warm and dry in the yellow foul-weather gear and boots he'd found in the boat's storage compartment.

The high ramparts along the coast dissolved into a series of craggy bluffs that dropped down to low hills and finally dipped to sea level as he neared the old harbor. He saw no other boats. The local fishermen were working more productive grounds in the other direction. Only when he rounded a point of land did he discover that he was not alone.

The blue-hulled Spanish yacht he had seen entering the harbor the day before lay at anchor in the inlet about a half mile from shore. The sleek boat was more than two hundred feet long. Its low, clean lines suggested that the yacht was built for speed as well as comfort. The name on the stern was *Navarra*. The decks were deserted. No one came out to wave, as was customary when one boat encountered another, particularly in such remote waters. Austin felt unseen eyes watching him from behind the dark-tinted windows as he continued past the yacht toward land. Sunlight shining through the clouds reflected dully off the distant metal rooftops he had glimpsed from the high ridge the day before.

A dot rose in the sky from the general vicinity of the buildings. The speck rapidly grew in size and became a black helicopter with no markings. The chopper came in low and buzzed the boat like an angry hornet, circled twice, then hovered, facing Austin, a few hundred yards away. Rocket pods hung from the fuselage. More company was on its way. A boat was bearing down on his position. It was moving fast, throwing up fountains of spray as it skimmed the wave-tops. The craft ate up the distance, and Austin saw that it was a low-slung Cigarette boat like the souped-up models favored by Florida drug smugglers.

The boat slowed and made a broadside pass close enough for Austin to get a good look at the three men on board. They were short and stocky and had round faces and swarthy complexions. Their black hair was cut in bangs over their almost Asian eyes. One man stayed at the wheel, while the others watched Austin with an unhealthy interest, their rifles raised to their shoulders.

The boat cut engines and slowed to a stop, and the man at the wheel raised an electronic bullhorn to his lips. He yelled something in what sounded like Faroese. Austin responded with a goofy smile and threw up his hands in the universal gesture of ignorance. The man tried again in Danish, then in English.

"Private property! Keep away."

Still playing Mickey the Dunce, Austin maintained the goofy grin. He held his fishing pole over his head and pointed at it. The unsmiling riflemen did the same thing with their weapons. Austin waved as if to say he understood the silent message. He replaced the fishing pole in its rack, then he gunned the motor, waved a friendly good-bye and aimed the boat out of the harbor.

Glancing over his shoulder a minute later, Austin saw the Cigarette boat speeding back toward land. The helicopter sheared off and rapidly outpaced the boat. He passed the yacht again. The decks were still deserted. He continued along the coast toward a headland shaped like a parrot's beak. A few minutes later, he sighted the Mermaid's Gate at the bottom of a vertical cliff. It was amazingly symmetrical for a natural arch. The opening was about twenty feet high and slightly narrower in width. It looked like a mouse hole compared to the overpowering wall of rough, brownish-black rock.

Despite its lyrical name, the Mermaid's Gate was far from welcoming. The sea was relatively calm, but waves pounded the fang-shaped rocks on either side and in front of the arch. Spray flew high in the air. The water in front of the opening boiled and swirled with vicious crosscurrents, like a giant washing machine. Over the crash of the sea, Austin heard a hollow soughing issuing from the opening. The hair rose on the back of his neck. The mournful dirge was what he imagined the moans of drowned sailors would sound like. Regretfully, he didn't see a single mermaid.

Austin halted the boat a respectable distance from the gate. Any attempt to pass through now would be like trying to thread a needle in a jostling crowd. Austin checked his watch and settled back and munched on the bread and cheese Pia had thoughtfully packed for him. He was finishing his breakfast when he sensed a change in the sea conditions. It was as if King Neptune had waved his trident. While the water in the immediate vicinity was still restless, the waves no longer exploded against the archway with artillery force. Pia had said that the gate was safely navigable only on either side of a slack current.

He secured all loose objects on the boat, donned his life jacket, spread his legs wide for stability, throttled up and pointed the boat at the gate. Even at slack current, the water around the opening was dimpled by swirling vortexes. He clenched his teeth and prayed that Pia's childhood memory of her father's words was accurate. When he was only yards away from the lethal reach of the rocks, he gunned the throttle, aiming slightly to the right, as instructed, although it was dangerously close to the rocks. With inches to spare, the boat slithered through the tight opening as easily as an eel.

Making a quick left-hand turn in the domed chamber, he headed toward a narrow cleft in the rocks and entered a canal inches wider than the double-ender. The boat banged against the kelp-covered ledges as it followed the channel in a rough S-course that widened into a circular lagoon the size of a backyard pool. The water's surface was black with seaweed, and the smell of the ocean was almost overpowering in the confined space.

Austin pulled the double-ender alongside a ledge and wrapped the mooring line around a rocky knob. He slipped off his life jacket and foul-weather gear, climbed a short flight of natural steps and stepped into an opening shaped like an upside-down keyhole. He was immediately buffeted by a musty wind. The air was amplified like a trumpeter's breath as it flowed from the cleft, producing the haunting moan of the dead mariners.

He clicked his flashlight on and followed a tunnel that eventually widened into a large cave. Three smaller caverns branched off from the main chamber. Painted on the wall next to each opening was a picture of a fish. Remembering Pia's instructions, he entered the cave marked by a sea bream. He soon found himself in a bewildering maze of caves and tunnels. Without the crude markers, he would have become hopelessly lost. After walking a few minutes, he entered a high-ceilinged chamber whose walls had been smoothed down and were covered with colorful renderings. He recognized the bison and deer from the drawings Pia's father had made. The ochre and red colors were still vibrant.

The pictures unfolded into a hunting scene that included antelope, wild horses and even a woolly mammoth. Hunters dressed in short kilts were shown attacking their prey with spears and bows and arrows. The mural encompassed vignettes of everyday life. There were scenes with people regally dressed in flowing robes, sleek sailing ships, two- and three-story houses of sophisticated architecture. The depiction of mammoths suggested that the drawings went back to Neolithic times, but this was a civilization of the highest order.

Austin followed the sea bream into a series of smaller caves and saw the remains of old fire-pits. He was more concerned with evidence of recent human occupation. The murmur of voices came from just ahead. He edged cautiously forward with his back plastered against a wall and peered around a corner into a cave the size of a small warehouse. The space looked like a natural cavern that had been expanded with the help of explosives and jackhammers. Floodlights hanging from the high ceiling illuminated hundreds of plastic cartons stacked high on wooden pallets.

From the shadows, Austin watched a work crew of a dozen men dressed in black coveralls unload boxes from a forklift and place them on a conveyor belt. The workers were swarthy and dark-skinned, like the men he had seen in the patrol boat. They had straight, jet-black hair cut in bangs, high cheekbones and almond-shaped eyes. They were finishing their task, and after a while, half the work crew drifted out the door and the rest remained a few minutes to clean up. At a word from a man whose air of authority tabbed him as the boss, they, too, straggled out through a door.

Austin stepped from his hiding place and inspected the writing on the boxes. The words stenciled in several languages identified the contents as refined fish food. He continued past a large freight door set into one wall, probably used to bring the fish food into the warehouse, and made his way toward the door that the work crew had gone through.

The next room was a nexus for dozens of pipes and pumps that extended from a huge, round bin. Chutes ran up the side of the container. Austin concluded that the food was poured into chutes, mixed in the tank and conveyed throughout the fish farm by the network of pipes.

He borrowed a pry bar from a tool room next to the mixing area. He hefted the flat metal bar in his hand, thinking it would be about as effective as a feather against automatic weapons, but tucked it in his belt anyhow. Then he followed the feed pipes from the mixing area. The pipes ran through a passageway and ended at a wall with a door in it. Austin cracked open the door, and cold air blew against his face. He listened. Hearing nothing, he stepped into the open. The fresh air felt good after the mustiness of the caverns.

After exiting through the other side of the wall, the pipes continued and ran down a broad, white, gravel-covered alley that separated two rows of buildings placed parallel to each other. Smaller pipes branched out from the main conduit into the buildings. The one-story structures were built of cinder block and had roofs of corrugated steel. The air was heavy with the smell of fish, and the low hum of machinery came from every direction.

Austin went over to the nearest building and found the steel door unlocked. Oceanus probably didn't expect prowlers to get past its boats and helicopter. The interior, lit by low-level ceiling lights, was in semidarkness. The hum he had heard came from electrical motors powering the pumps that circulated water in rows of large blue plastic tanks. They were lined up on either side of a center aisle that ran the length of the building. The tanks were serviced by water mains, feed pipes, pumps, valves and electrical connections. Austin climbed a metal ladder up the side of one tank. The beam from his flashlight stirred up hundreds of startled fish, each no bigger than a finger.

He climbed down, slipped out of the fish nursery and worked his way from building to building. The structures were identical except for differences in the size and species of the fish they housed. He recognized salmon, cod and other familiar types in the holding tanks. A centrally located smaller building housed a central computer center. It was unoccupied. He watched the blinking dials and gauges on the central panel and realized why he had seen few people in his travels. The fish farm was almost totally automated.

As he was emerging from the computer center, he heard the crunch of boots. He dodged around a corner as two guards strolled by. The men had their weapons slung on their shoulders, and they were laughing at some shared joke, never suspecting that an intruder lurked in their midst.

After the guards had passed, Austin made his way to the harbor. A pier that was long enough to accommodate large ships extended from the rocky shoreline. Tied up to the dock was the patrol boat that had intercepted him earlier. There was no sign of the helicopter. The tops of hundreds of fish cages were visible along the harbor's edge. Men in open boats were tending the fish cages under a cloud of noisy gulls. More guards lolled on the dock, idly watching the action.

Austin checked his watch. He had to leave right away if he expected to get back to the Mermaid's Gate before the end of slack current. He circled around the complex and came upon a building similar to the others except that it was set off by itself. Warning signs were posted on the outside. He bypassed a main door and found a secondary entrance on the other side.

Unlike the doors to the other fish nurseries, this one was locked.

Using the pry bar, Austin sprung the lock as quietly as possible and pushed the door open. In the dim interior light, he saw that the tanks were twice the size of those he'd seen earlier, and there were half as many. Something about the place bothered him, but he couldn't put his finger on it. For the first time since he'd begun his explorations, his skin began to crawl.

He wasn't alone in the building. A single guard was strolling around the perimeter of the tanks. He timed the guard, waited until he was at the far end of his patrol, then set the pry bar down, climbed a ladder up the side of the nearest tank and peered over the edge.

The smell of fish was even stronger than the odor emanating from the smaller tanks in the other buildings. He leaned over and heard the soft swish of swirling water. The tank was occupied. He pointed the flashlight to see what was inside, and the water exploded. There was a blurry flash of white and a gaping mouth lined with sharp teeth. Austin jerked back in reflex. Something wet and slimy grazed his head. He lost his hold and fell off the ladder. His flailing hands grabbed a section of plastic hose, breaking it, and he crashed to the concrete floor. Water poured from the broken hose. He scrambled to his feet, and through dazed eyes he saw a red light flashing above the tank. He swore to himself. The systems failure had set off an alarm.

The guard had heard the ruckus and was running his way. Austin ducked into a space between two tanks, nearly tripping on a stack of metal pipe. The guard ran past Austin and stopped when he saw the gushing water. Austin picked up a short length of metal pipe and stepped out behind the guard. The man must have sensed Austin's presence. He half-turned and went to unsling his rifle, but the pipe came down on his head and he crumpled to the floor.

With the immediate threat disposed of, Austin's first instinct was to cut and run, but he decided to create a diversion first. Wielding the pipe as a sledgehammer, he methodically smashed several plastic pipe assemblies. Red alarm lights blinked over several tanks now, and water from the damaged pipes poured onto the floor and created a river.

Austin splashed through the puddles toward the door. The rush of water had drowned out other sounds, and he didn't hear the pounding footsteps of a second man. They met at an intersection between two lines of tanks, almost crashing into each other like a couple of circus clowns. The comic aspect was intensified when they both slipped and went down. But Austin had no reason to laugh when the man sprang to his feet and yanked a pistol from a holster at his belt.

Austin swung the pipe as he rose to a standing position, and the pistol went flying. The man's eyes widened with surprise at Austin's quickness. He reached under the shirt of his black uniform and pulled out a knife with a long blade made from a hard white material. He stepped back, taking up a defensive position. In that second instant, Austin had a chance to study his opponent.

The man was about a head shorter than Austin. His head seemed to sit directly on muscular shoulders that hinted at the power in the squat body. Like the guards, he had a wide, round face with bangs, and almond-shaped eyes that were as black and hard as obsidian. Vertical tattoos decorated his high cheekbones. Beneath the flat nose were wide, fleshy lips. He spread that mouth in a toothy smile, but there was no mirth in it, only cruelty.

Austin was in no mood for a smiling contest. Time was not on his side. More guards could show up at any second. He couldn't retreat. He had to dispatch this obstacle and pray there weren't others. His hands tightened on the pipe. His eyes must have given away his intentions, because the man lunged without warning. He moved with scorpion-speed despite his thickset body. Austin felt a stinging pain on the left side of his rib cage. He had been holding the pipe like a Louisville Slugger, and the knife had slipped inside his guard. Austin felt a wetness where the blade had sliced through his sweater and shirt.

The man's smile grew wider, and the blood-tipped knife was poised for another slashing attack. He feinted to his left. Austin reacted with pure reflex and swung the pipe as if he were hitting a home run. There was a sickening scrunch sound as the pipe connected with the man's nose, crushing bone and cartilage. Blood sprayed as if from a fountain. Austin couldn't believe it! After a blow that would have felled a steer, the man was still on his feet. A dazed look came into the man's eyes, and a second later, the knife fell from his limp fingers and he collapsed to the floor.

Austin began sprinting for the exit, but he heard shouts and ducked behind a fish tank. Several guards burst through the door and ran toward the blinking red lights. Austin stuck his head out and heard excited voices coming from the direction of the harbor. He stepped out into the open, sprinted around the side of the building and returned to the main complex of fish nurseries. With most of the attention focused on the damage he had left behind him, Austin was able to make his way to the fish-food warehouse.

Austin was relieved to see that the warehouse was still deserted. Soon he could lose himself in the labyrinth of caves. He had his hand tight against his chest, but he couldn't stanch the bleeding completely. Even worse, he was leaving a trail of blood droplets. A siren wailed in the distance. He was trotting past the forklift when a thought struck him. He was making it too easy for these guys.

He slid into the forklift seat, started the motor, aimed the tines at a tall stack of food cartons and nailed the accelerator. The vehicle lurched forward and smashed into the boxes with enough force to topple them. The boxes crashed onto the conveyor belt and blocked the opening. He knocked over a couple more piles in front of the access and freight doors. As a finishing touch, he jammed a tine into the control box for the conveyor belt.

Moments later, he was hurrying through the caverns. He paused in the main picture gallery and listened. He could hear yells over his own heavy breathing. An even worse sound was the barking of dogs. His crude barricade had been breached. He continued at a measured trot, following the bobbing bull's-eye of the flashlight. In his haste, he mistook one fish marker for another and lost precious moments finding his way back. The shouts and barks were louder now, and he could see the phantasmagoric glow of lights behind him. The caves amplified and echoed the voices, creating the impression that a whole army was after him.

The stutter of an automatic weapon echoed throughout the caves. Austin dove for the floor, and a hail of bullets splattered harmlessly against the walls. He tried to ignore the searing pain of his chest wound and scrambled to his feet. Another fusillade raked the passageway, but by then he was around a curve and the angled wall protected him. Seconds later, he was squeezing through the last narrow passageway, then he was out and climbing down the natural staircase to the boat.

When he tried to start the engine, it coughed. He reached down into the cold water with his right hand, cleaned the seaweed that had tangled the propeller and tried the starter again. This time, the motor responded. As he pulled away and pointed the boat toward the canal that would take him back to the Mermaid's Gate, two black-clad figures climbed down to the edge of the pool. The beams from their flashlights caught him, but they also illuminated the canal opening.

Austin aimed for the cleft and slammed against the sides of the canal, tearing off hunks of wood. He saw gray daylight ahead, and then the boat burst into the Mermaid's Gate. He snapped the wheel over. The boat made a sharp right turn toward the opening, but the slack current was ending and the devilish confluence of tides and currents had returned. The boat slid sideways down the side of a wave and headed for a wood-splintering collision with the far wall, only to be saved when another billow pitched it back toward the canal opening.

Austin gunned the throttle, trying to gain control. The boat skidded as if it were riding on banana peels. He gave the wheel a quick jerk to avoid crashing into a jagged outcropping that would have sliced the boat in two. The propeller tinged against an underwater ledge. He brought the boat around again, but the waves caught him in another game of Frisbee toss. The double-ender lost headway and was pushed backward into the grotto. Austin gauged the ebb and flow of the circulating water and in desperation aimed for a V that marked a calmer area between currents.

As the boat fishtailed toward the opening, Austin saw that he had company. His pursuers had made their way along the ledges that bordered the canal. They stood on the rocks only yards away from where he was about to pass.

One of the men aimed his rifle at Austin, who was an easy target, but his companion pushed the barrel down. He unclipped a hand grenade from his belt, tossed it lightly in the air a few times like a baseball pitcher warming up, then as Austin passed, the man pulled the pin, holding down on the lever. Austin's eyes glanced from the grenade and into the merciless face of the man who had stabbed him. His nose was a bloody pulp and streams of blood had caked on his cheeks. He must have been in terrible pain, but the face broadened into a wide grin as he leisurely lofted the grenade into Austin's boat. Then he and the other man ducked behind an outcropping of rocks and covered their ears.

The arcing grenade clunked into the boat, landing practically at Austin's feet. Austin wrung the last bit of torque out of the engine. The boat planed at a sharp angle, and the grenade rolled down the deck until it lodged against the narrow transom.

The boat burst through the arch into the open water. Choosing between the devil and the deep blue sea, Austin instinctively chose the latter: A part of his brain made the choice between being blown to bits instantaneously and freezing to death in a few minutes. He launched his body off the boat.

He plunged into the frigid water, and, a second later, heard the muffled thud of the grenade, then the fuel tanks erupted in a secondary explosion. Austin stayed under as long as he could and surfaced under a rainfall of wood splinters. The boat was gone, and he dove again to avoid the burning fuel that floated on the water's surface. When he came up a second time, he was numb with cold, but the survival instinct burned in his chest. He started to swim in the direction of land, but he had taken only a few more strokes before his joints felt as if someone had poured liquid oxygen into them.

Over the wave-tops, he caught a blurred glimpse of a boat speeding his way: His pursuers were no doubt coming to finish off the job. A gurgled laugh escaped from his throat. By the time they arrived, he'd be nothing but a giant Slurpee.

13

SECONDS BEFORE HE slipped below the surface, how-ever, Austin's one-way trip to Davey Jones's locker was cut short. A hand reached over the side of the launch and grabbed him by the hair. His teeth clacked like a pair of cas-tanets, and his scalp felt as if it were being pulled out by the roots. Then other hands were grabbing him by the armpits and collar, and he was hauled from the sea, sputtering and cough-ing, like a kitten in a well.

His legs were still dangling in the water when the motor launch took off and raced over the waves with a roar of jet propulsion engines, its bow high in the air. Through blurred vi-sion, Austin saw, to his surprise, that they were swinging alongside the blue yacht. Semiconscious, he was passed up to the deck and carried to what must be the sick bay, where he was relieved of his soggy clothes, wrapped in warm towels and examined by a frowning man with a stethoscope. Then he was thrust into a sauna, where, eventually, he could move his fin-gers and toes. He was examined a second time and given a blue fleece sweat suit to wear. Apparently, he was going to live.

His transition from near-death to near-life was accomplished under the watchful eye of two men, built like professional wrestlers, who spoke to each other in Spanish. The same guard dogs escorted him as he walked on rubber legs to a luxurious stateroom. They settled him into a comfortable reclining chair, covered him with a soft blanket and left him to rest.

Austin fell into an exhausted sleep. When he awakened, he saw that he was under scrutiny by a pair of dark eyes. A man sat in an armchair, watching him from a few feet away, as if he were a specimen on a lab slide.

The man grinned when he saw Austin's eyelids flutter. "Good. You're awake," he said. His voice was deep and resonant, and he spoke American English with only a hint of an accent.

The man reached over to a side table for a silver-plated flask and poured Austin a drink. With shaking fingers, Austin swirled the greenish-yellow amber liquor around in the bottom of the brandy snifter, breathed in the heavy fumes and took a deep sip. The fiery herbal liquor trickled down his throat, and its warmth spread throughout his body.

Austin glanced at the flask. "This tastes too good to be antifreeze, but the effect is the same."

The man chuckled and took a swig from the flask. "Green Izarra is one hundred proof," he said, wiping his mouth with the back of his hand. "It's usually served in glasses hardly bigger than your thumb. I thought a little extra might be of benefit in your case. How is your wound?"

Austin's hand reached down and touched his ribs. He could feel the stiffness of a bandage under his shirt, but there was no pain, even when he pressed with his fingers. He remembered the flash of white as the ivory knife slashed his flesh.

"How bad was it?"

"Another half-inch deeper and we would have been burying you at sea." The grim assessment was accompanied by a grin.

"It feels okay."

"My ship's doctor is an expert in treating trauma. He sewed you up and froze the wound."

Austin glanced around at his surroundings, his memories returning. "Ship's doctor? This is the blue yacht, isn't it?"

"That's right. My name is Balthazar Aguirrez. This is my boat."

With his barrel chest and large hands, Aguirrez looked more like a longshoreman than the owner of a yacht that was probably worth several million dollars. He had a broad forehead and thick black eyebrows over a strong nose, a wide mouth that curved upward in a natural grin, and a chin like a granite ledge. His eyes were the purple-black of ripe olives. He wore a light-blue sweat suit identical to the one on loan to Austin. A black beret was perched at a jaunty angle on his thick pepper-and-salt hair.

"Pleased to meet you, Mr. Aguirrez. My name is Kurt Austin. Thanks for your hospitality."

Aguirrez extended his hand in a bone-crunching grip.

"Think nothing of it, Mr. Austin. We like to entertain guests." His dark eyes danced with amusement. "Most arrive on board in a more conventional manner, however. May I pour you another Izarra?"

Austin waved it off. He wanted to keep a clear head.

"Perhaps after you have some food. Are you hungry?"

Austin had worked up an appetite since the bread and cheese he'd eaten for brunch. "Yes, now that you mention it. I wouldn't mind a sandwich."

"I would be a poor host if I could not do better than a sandwich. If you feel well enough, I'd like you to join me for a light meal in the salon."

Austin levered himself out of the chair and stood, somewhat shakily. "I'll be fine."

Aguirrez said, "Splendid. I'll give you a few minutes. Come when you're ready." He rose and left the cabin. Austin stared at the closed door and shook his head. His brain still felt waterlogged. He was weak from blood loss. He went into the bathroom and looked in the mirror. He looked like a commercial for ghoul makeup. Not surprising after being stabbed, shot at and blown out of the water. He washed his face with cold, then hot, water. Noticing an electric shaver, he removed the stubble on his chin. When he stepped back into the stateroom, he saw he had company.

The tough-faced stewards who had escorted him earlier

were waiting. One opened the door and led the way, while the other man took up the rear. The walk gave Austin ample opportunity to exercise, and he felt his legs grow stronger with every step. They came to the main deck salon, and one of the men motioned for Austin to enter. Then he and the other man left him alone.

Austin stepped into the salon and raised his eyebrows. He had been on dozens of yachts and had found the décor to be similar. Chrome and leather and clean contemporary lines were the norm. But the *Navarra's* salon resembled the interior of a southern European farmhouse.

The eggshell-white walls and ceiling were of stucco, inlaid with rough-hewn beams, and the floor was a red tile. A fire was crackling in a large, stone fireplace that had been built into one wall. Over the mantle was a painting of men playing a game Austin recognized as jai alai. He went up to a still-life painting of assorted fruit and was examining the signature when a deep voice said, "Interested in art, Mr. Austin?"

Aguirrez had come up from behind without making a sound. Austin said, "I collect dueling pistols, which I think of as a form of art."

"Without question! Deadly art is still art. I picked up that Cézanne for my little collection last year. The other pieces I found at auction or acquired from private sources."

Austin strolled past the Gauguins, a Degas, Manets and Monets. The "little collection" was more extensive than that found in many museums. He moved to another wall that was covered with large photographs.

"These are originals, too?"

"A few of my holdings," Aguirrez said, with a shrug. "Shipbuilding yards, steel mills and so forth." He sounded like a jaded waiter rattling off items on a menu. "But enough of business." He took Austin by the arm. "Dinner is ready."

He led the way through sliding doors into an elegant dining room. At the center of the room was an oval mahogany table set for twelve. Aguirrez removed his beret and, with a snap of his wrist and great accuracy, flung it to a chair across the room. He gestured grandly toward the two opposite chairs at one end of the table. As the two men took their seats, a waiter appeared from nowhere and poured their tall goblets full of wine.

"I think you will like this sturdy Spanish Rioja," Aguirrez said. He raised his glass. "To art."

"To the master and crew of the *Navarra*."

"You're very gracious," Aguirrez said with obvious approval. "Ah good," he said, his eyes lighting up. "I see that our feast is about to begin."

There were no appetizers, and they dug right into the main course, a hearty bean, pepper and pork-rib dish served with cabbage. Austin complimented the chef and asked what the dish was.

"This is called *alubias de tolosa*," Aguirrez said, downing his food with gusto. "We Basques treat it with an almost mystical reverence."

"*Basque*. Of course. *Navarra* is a Basque province. Then there's the jai alai painting. And the black beret."

"I'm impressed, Mr. Austin! You seem to know a great deal about my people."

"Anyone interested in the sea knows that the Basques were the greatest explorers, sailors and shipbuilders in the world."

Aguirrez clapped his hands. "Bravo." He refilled Austin's wineglass and leaned forward. "Tell me, what is *your* interest in the sea?" He maintained his ferocious grin, but pinioned Austin with a penetrating gaze.

Austin admired the way Aguirrez had subtly managed the conversational shift. Until he knew his host better and learned why the blue yacht was hanging out near the Oceanus fish farm, Austin planned to play his cards close to his vest.

"I'm a salvage specialist," he said. "I've been working on a project in the Faroes. I came to Skaalshavn to do some fishing."

Aguirrez sat back and roared with laughter. "Excuse my bad manners," he said with tears in his eyes. "But it was *my* men who fished *you* from the sea."

Austin's mouth widened in a sheepish grin. "A cold swim wasn't in my plans."

Aguirrez became serious again. "From what we saw, there was an explosion on your boat."

"The ventilation for the engine compartment was insufficient, and gasoline vapors collected. It happens sometimes with inboards," Austin said.

Aguirrez nodded. "Strange. In my experience, explosions of that type usually happen when a boat has been sitting at the dock. And your wound undoubtedly was caused by flying metal."

"Undoubtedly," Austin said with a poker face, knowing full well that the ship's doctor would have seen that there were no burn marks on his skin and his wound was too neat to be from a jagged hunk of metal. Austin didn't know why Aguirrez was playing verbal cat-and-mouse, but he went along with the game. "I was lucky you were nearby."

Nodding soberly, Aguirrez said, "We watched your earlier encounter with the patrol boat and saw you head along the coast. When we rounded the point later, you had vanished. Not long after that, you burst from that sea cave like a man shot from a cannon." He clapped his big hands together. "*Boom!* Your boat was in pieces and you were in the water."

"That about sums it up," Austin said, with a faint smile.

After offering Austin a short, thick cigar, which he refused, Aguirrez lit up a dark stogie that smelled like a toxic waste site. "*So* my friend," he said, blowing smoke through his nostrils. "Did you get into the caves?"

"Caves?" Austin feigned innocence.

"For God's sakes, man, that's why I'm here, to find the caves. Surely you must have wondered what my boat is doing in this godforsaken place."

"It had occurred to me."

"Then allow me to explain. I have done very well with my businesses."

"An understatement. You're very fortunate. Congratulations."

"Thank you. My wealth gives me the means and the time to do whatever I like. Some men choose to spend their fortune on beautiful young women. I choose to be an amateur archaeologist."

"Ambitious hobbies in either case."

"I still enjoy the company of beautiful women, especially if they are intelligent. But with me, the past is *more* than a hobby." He looked as if he were about to spring from his chair.

"It is my *passion*. As you said earlier, the Basques were great men of the sea. They pioneered the cod and whale fisheries off North America decades before Columbus. An ancestor of mine, Diego Aguirrez, profited from this trade."

"He would be proud to see his descendant has carried on his legacy."

"You're more than kind, Mr. Austin. He was a man of great courage and unyielding principle, qualities that got him in trouble with the Spanish Inquisition. He angered one of the more ruthless Inquisitors."

"Then he was executed?"

Aguirrez smiled. "He was resourceful, as well. Diego saw his wife and children to safety. I am a direct descendant of his eldest son. Family tradition says he escaped in one of his ships, but his fate is a mystery."

"The sea is full of unsolved puzzles."

Aguirrez nodded. "Nevertheless, he left tantalizing clues that show he intended to put himself far beyond the reach of the Inquisition. The traditional North American route for the Basques included a stopover here in the Faroes. So I began to explore that link. You know the origins of the name Skaalshavn?"

"I've been told it means 'Skull Harbor.' "

Aguirrez smiled and rose from the table to extract an ornately carved wooden box from a cabinet. He unlatched the top and pulled out a skull, cradling it in one hand like Hamlet contemplating Yorick. "This is from one of those caves. I've had it looked at by experts. It has distinct Basque characteristics." He tossed the skull to Austin as if it were a ball, probably hoping to shock him.

Austin caught the skull neatly and spun it in his hand like a geographer studying a globe of the world. "Maybe it's your ancestor Diego." He tossed the skull back.

"I wondered the same thing and had it tested for DNA. This gentleman and I are not related, I'm sad to say." Aguirrez put the skull back into the box and rejoined Austin at the table. "This is my second visit here. The first time, I expected that the caves would be accessible from land. I was dismayed to learn that the harbor and cave area had been purchased for use as a fish farm. I located a man who had worked in demolition when the farm was set up. He said that when the owners were blasting out rock to create storage space, they broke through to the caves. I tried to persuade the owners to let me conduct archaeological explorations, but they refused. I pulled every string I could think of, but even with my connections, Oceanus wouldn't budge. So I came back for another look."

"You're very persistent."

"This has become a quest. Which is why I'm interested in your adventure. I suspected the natural arch might provide entry into the caves, but the waters around them were too dangerous for our launches. Apparently, you found a way to get in."

"Dumb luck," Austin said briefly.

Aguirrez chuckled. "I think it was more than luck. Please, tell me what you saw. I will bribe you with more wine."

He snapped his fingers. The waiter brought a new bottle, opened it and refilled their glasses.

"No bribe is necessary," Austin said. "Consider it partial repayment for your hospitality and the fine meal." He sipped from his glass, enjoying the buildup of suspense. "You're right, there is a way into the caves through the arch. The locals call it the 'Mermaid's Gate.' The cave network is quite extensive. I only saw part of it."

Austin went into detail about the cave art, saying nothing about his side trip into the fish farm. Aguirrez hung on every word.

"Similar Paleolithic paintings dating back twelve thousand years have been found on the walls of caves in Basque country," he murmured at one point. "The other drawings indicate that an advanced civilization must have used the caves."

"That was my impression. Supposedly, the Faroes were uninhabited before the Irish monks and the Vikings settled here. Maybe the historians were wrong."

"I wouldn't be surprised. The scholars have no idea where my people came from. Our language has no antecedents in Europe or Asia. Basques have the highest percentage of RH-negative blood type in the world, leading some to speculate that we go directly back to Cro-Magnon man." He banged his fist lightly on the table. "I'd give anything to get into those caves."

"You saw the warm reception I got."

"You seem to have stirred up a hornet's nest. While you slept, the patrol boats came out from shore and demanded permission to come aboard. We refused, of course."

"The boat I saw had a couple of men with automatic rifles."

Aguirrez waved toward the art hanging on the wall. "When they saw that my men outgunned and outnumbered them, they quickly left."

"They had a helicopter, too. It was armed with rockets."

"Oh yes, that," he said, as if he were talking about a pesky gnat. "I had my men brandish their handheld surface-to-air missiles, and the helicopter stopped bothering us."

Missiles and automatic weapons. The *Navarra* was armed like a warship.

Aguirrez read Austin's mind. "Wealthy men can be a target for kidnappers. The *Navarra* would be fair game for pirates, so I have made sure it is not exactly toothless. Of necessity, I have surrounded myself with loyal and well-armed men."

"Why do you suppose Oceanus is so prickly about people poking into its business?" Austin said. "We're talking about a fish farm, not diamond mines."

"I asked myself the same question," Aguirrez said, with a shrug.

One of the men who had kept watch over Austin came into the dining room. He handed Aguirrez a plastic bag and whispered into his ear.

Aguirrez nodded and said, "Thank you for being so forthcoming about your visit to the caves, Mr. Austin. Is there anything more I can do for you?"

"I wouldn't mind a lift back to the village."

"*Done.* My man has informed me that we are passing the sea stack and should be anchoring in a few minutes." He handed the plastic bag over. "Your clothes and personal effects have been drying out."

Austin was ushered back to his cabin so he could change. The bag also held his wallet, which contained his NUMA photo ID card prominently displayed in its plastic window. Aguirrez was a cool one. He would have known that Austin's story about being in marine salvage was made out of whole cloth, yet he'd never let on. Inside the bag was a business card with his host's name and a telephone number. Austin tucked the card into his wallet.

Aguirrez was waiting on deck to say good-bye.

"I appreciate your hospitality," Austin said, shaking hands with his host. "I hope I'm not being rude having to eat and run."

"Not at all," Aguirrez said, with an enigmatic smile. "I wouldn't be surprised if our paths crossed again."

"Stranger things have happened," Austin said, with a grin.

Moments later, Austin was in the launch heading across the quiet harbor.

14

TWO THOUSAND FEET above Skaalshavn harbor, the
Bell 206 Jet Ranger helicopter that had been tracking the
yacht along the coast came to a hover and focused its Wescam
high-resolution surveillance camera on the launch making its
way to shore. The man in the pilot's seat stared at a video monitor, watching as a lone passenger disembarked from the boat.

The helicopter pilot had a pie-shaped face with high
cheekbones marked with vertical tattoo lines. His coal-black
hair was cut in bangs over his low forehead, characteristics
that might lead a casual observer to take him for a native of the
northern tundra. But the features normally associated with the
Eskimo were distorted. In place of a pleasant smile was a
cruel, leering expression. Eyes that should have twinkled with
innocent good humor were as hard as black diamonds. The
brownish-red skin was pockmarked, as if the corruption
within had seeped through the pores. The hastily applied
bandage taped across the man's crushed nose intensified the
grotesque image.

"We have the target in view," he said with a nasal snarl,
speaking in an ancient language that had its origins under the
aurora borealis.

The electronic signal from the camera, which was housed in a pod beneath the cockpit, was converted into microwaves and transmitted instantaneously to the other side of the globe to a darkened room, where pale-gray eyes watched the same picture seen from the helicopter.

"I can see him quite clearly," the gray-eyed man said. His silky voice was quiet and cultured, but it had the sullen menace of a rattlesnake. "Who is this person who violated our security so easily?"

"His name is Kurt Austin."

A pause. "The same Austin who rescued the Danish sailors from their sunken ship?"

"Yes, great Toonook. He is a marine engineer with the National Underwater and Marine Agency."

"Are you *certain*? A mere engineer wouldn't have been so bold or resourceful as to penetrate our facility. And why would NUMA be interested in our operation?"

"I don't know, but our watcher has verified his identity."

"And the yacht that picked him up and drove off your men. Is it a NUMA vessel?"

"As far as we know, it is private, of Spanish registry. We're checking on the ownership through our sources in Madrid."

"See that it is done speedily. What is the latest damage report at our facility?"

"One guard dead. We were able to repair the damaged pipes and save the prime specimens."

"The guard deserved to die for being careless. I want the specimens moved to Canada immediately. Our experiments are too vital to be jeopardized."

"Yes, great Toonook."

"An idiot can see what has happened. Mr. Austin has somehow drawn a connection between Oceanus and the collision we so conveniently arranged."

"That's impossible—"

"The evidence is in front of your eyes, Umealiq. Don't argue with it. You must *deal* with the situation!"

The pilot tightened his grip on the controls, ready to send the helicopter swooping down like an eagle. The cruel eyes watching the monitor screen followed the figure making its way from the fish pier to the parked car. Within seconds, he could launch his rockets or spray the target with flesh-shredding machine-gun fire and obliterate the life of a bother-some man. The thin lips widened in a cruel smile.

"Should we kill Austin while we have him in our sights?"

"Do I detect a yearning to avenge the damage to your precious nose?" The voice had a mocking tone to it. Without waiting for an answer, he said, "I *should* kill him for the trouble he has caused me. Had he allowed the Danish sailors to die, the revulsion of the world would be directed at SOS and the attention of the press diverted away from Oceanus."

"I will do it now—"

"*No!* Don't be impatient. We must not attract any more attention to his demise than necessary."

"He is staying at an isolated cottage. It would be the perfect place. We could drop his body off a cliff."

"Then *see* to it. But make it look like an accident. Austin must not be allowed to broadcast his findings to the world. Our plans are at a critical stage."

"I will return to the base and organize our men. I will see that Austin enjoys a lingering death, that he experiences fear and pain as the life drains from his body, that—"

"No. Have someone else do it. I have other plans for you. You must leave for Canada immediately to make sure the specimens get there safely, then you are to go to Washington and eliminate that Senator who opposes our legislation. I have arranged cover for you and your men."

The pilot glanced with fierce longing at the monitor and touched the tender mush that was his nose. "As you wish," he said with reluctance.

His hands played over the cyclic pitch control, and a moment later the hovering helicopter darted off in the direction of the old harbor.

Unaware how close he had come to a violent end, Austin sat behind the steering wheel of Professor Jorgensen's Volvo, contemplating his next move. He was wary of the remote location of the cottage. He gazed at the warm lights of the town, then grabbed his duffel and left the car. He walked into the village without encountering a soul and went up to the house behind the church.

Pia beamed when she opened the door at his knock and invited him inside. The exertions of the day must have been apparent in his face. When he stepped into the light, her smile disappeared. "Are you all right?" she said, with concern in her voice.

"Nothing a glass of *akavit* couldn't help."

Clucking like a mother hen, she ushered him to the kitchen table, poured him a tall glass of *akavit,* then watched as he drank. "Well?" she said finally. "Did you catch many fish?"

"No, but I went to visit the mermaids."

Pia let out a whooping laugh, clapped her hands and poured him a couple more fingers of liquor. "I *knew* it!" she said, with excitement in her voice. "And were the caves as wonderful as my father said?"

She listened like a child as Austin described his entry through the Mermaid's Gate at slack tide and his journey into the cave network. He told her that he would have stayed longer but men with guns chased him away. Cursing impressively in Faroese, she said, "You can't go back to the cottage tonight. Gunnar says he doesn't work for those people, but I think he does."

"I was wondering the same thing. I left the car at the fish pier. Maybe I should leave town."

"God, no! You'll drive off the road into the sea. No, you will stay here tonight and leave early tomorrow."

"Are you sure you want a gentleman staying the night? People will talk," Austin said with a broad smile.

She grinned back, eyes sparkling with childlike mischief. "I *hope* so."

Shortly before dawn, Austin awakened and got up from the sofa. Pia heard him stir and rose to make him a breakfast. She cooked an industrial-sized potato omelet with smoked fish and pastry on the side. Then she packed him a lunch of cold cuts, cheese and apple and sent him on his way, first eliciting a promise to return.

The town was coming alive as he made his way in the damp morning air to the fish pier. A couple of fishermen on their way to work waved at him from their trucks as he was opening the car door. The keys slipped from his fingers as he waved back—and when he bent to pick them up, his nostrils picked up a chemical smell, and he detected a soft *splat-splat* sound. He got down on his knees and peered under the car, where the odor was even stronger. Fluid dripped where the brake hoses had been cleanly cut. Austin grunted to himself softly, then he went over to the fish pier and asked around for a good mechanic. The harbormaster said he would call, and before long a lanky, middle-aged man showed up.

After inspecting the damage, the mechanic stood and handed Austin a section of the hose. "Somebody don't like you."

"No chance it was an accident?"

The taciturn Faroese pointed to where the road out of town skirted a cliff, and he shook his head. "I figure you'd be flying with the birds up there on the first curve. No problem to fix, though."

The mechanic repaired the brakes in short order. When Austin went to pay him, he waved away the money. "That's okay, you're a friend of Pia's."

Austin said, "The people who did this might know I was at Pia's. I wonder if I should talk to the police."

"No such thing here. Don't worry, the whole town will keep close watch on her."

Austin thanked him again, and minutes later he was driving out of town. As he surveyed the sea stack in his rearview mirror, he mentally ticked off the events of his short stay in Skaalshavn. He was leaving town with more questions than answers. Look on the bright side, he told himself with a grin. He had made some terrific new friends.

15

PAUL TROUT STEPPED onto the deck of Neal's wooden-hulled trawler and appraised the boat with an expert eye. What he found surprised him. Neal was a charming conniver and a drunk, but he was a no-nonsense fisherman who took pride in his boat. The signs of tender care were everywhere. Woodwork gleamed with fresh paint. The deck was scrubbed clean of oil stains. Rust was kept under control. The pilothouse had the latest in fish-finding and navigational equipment.

When Trout complimented Neal on the condition of his boat, the fisherman beamed like a father who'd been told his firstborn was his spitting image. Soon he and Neal were swapping sea stories. At one point, when Neal was out of hearing, Gamay raised an eyebrow and said, "You and Mike appear to be getting along swimmingly. I suppose you'll be trading recipes before long."

"He's an interesting guy. Look at this boat. It's as well-found as anything I've ever been on."

"Glad to hear you say that. NUMA now owns a piece of *Tiffany*."

The ransom to spring the trawler from the boatyard had

been closer to a thousand dollars than to seven hundred fifty. After a quick fuel-tank fill-up, which Gamay also paid for, Neal set the trawler on a course that would take it into the open sea.

"Fishin' ground's not far," Neal yelled over the throb of the engine. " 'Bout seven miles. Ten fathoms. Bottom's smooth as a baby's behind. Prime for trawling. Be there shortly."

After a while, Neal checked his GPS position, cut the throttle to an idle and lowered the net—a conical mesh bag, around a hundred-and-fifty-feet long, designed to be dragged along the sea bottom. The boat made two sets and caught lots of seaweed, but no fish.

"This is very strange," Trout said, inspecting the cod end, the narrow pouch at the end of the net where harvested fish are concentrated. "I can understand hauling in a poor catch, but it's highly unusual to bring in *nothing*. Not even trash fish. The net's absolutely empty."

A knowing grin crossed Neal's face. "You may wish it *stayed* empty."

The net was lowered again, pulled along the bottom and slowly winched back onto the boat. A boom was used to hoist the cod end over the deck where any catch could be emptied out. This time, something was thrashing wildly in the net. Flashes of silvery-white scales were visible through the tangle of mesh, as a large fish fiercely struggled to free itself. Neal yelled out a warning as he prepared to empty the contents of the net onto the deck.

"Stand way back, folks, we've got a live one!"

The big fish landed on the deck with a squishy thud. Freed from the net, it became even more ferocious in its exertions, skittering across the deck as it arched and snapped its long body, round eyes staring with an unfishlike malevolence, mouth wide and snapping at air. The creature slammed into the fish hold, a raised box built into the deck. Far from slowing it down, the impact seemed to make it angrier. The convulsions became more violent, and it scudded back across the slippery deck.

"Wha-hoo!" Neal yelled, quickly stepping out of the way of the biting jaws. He lowered a gaff handle near the fish's head. In a snapping blur, the fish bit the handle in two.

Paul watched, spellbound, from the raised safety of a pile of netting. Gamay had taken out a video camera and was busy filming. "That's the biggest salmon I've ever seen!" Paul said. The fish was about five feet long.

"This is crazy," Gamay said, holding the camera steady. "Salmon don't act like this when they're caught. They've got weak teeth that would break if they tried to do anything like that."

"Tell that to the damned *fish*," Neal said, holding up the jagged end of the gaff handle. He tossed it aside and grabbed a pitchfork, speared the fish behind the gills and pinned it to the deck. The fish continued to struggle. Neal produced an old Louisville Slugger and whacked the fish on the head. It was stunned for a second, then started snapping again, although less violently.

"Sometimes you have to slam them a few more times before they quiet down," Neal explained.

Moving with great caution, he managed to loop a line around the tail. Then he fed the line into an overhanging pulley, pulled the pitchfork out, lifted the fish and swung it over the open fish hold, still careful to stay clear of the jaws. When the fish was positioned over the hold, he took a filleting knife and cut the line. The fish fell into the hold where it could be heard banging against the sides.

"That was the meanest fish I've ever seen," Paul said, with a wondering shake of his head. "It behaved more like a barracuda than a salmon."

"It looked like an Atlantic salmon, but I'm not sure *what* it was. Those strange white scales. It was almost albino." Gamay shut off the camera and peered into the dimness of the fish hold. "Listen! It's far too big and aggressive to be a normal fish. It's almost as if it were some sort of mutant." She turned to Neal. "When did you first start catching these things?"

Neal took the cigar stub from between his teeth and spit over the side. "First boats started bringing them up in the nets around six months ago. The guys called them 'devilfish.' They tore the hell out of the nets, but they were big so we cut them up and sent them off to market. Guess the meat was okay, because nobody died," he said with a smirk. "Pretty soon that's all we were catching. The smaller fish just disappeared." He gestured to the fish hold with his cigar. "That's the reason why."

"Did you contact any fishery scientists and tell them what you were catching?"

"Oh yeah. We got in touch with the fisheries people. They didn't send anyone down."

"Why not?"

"Short-staffed, they said. Guess you got to look at it their way. You're a marine biologist. Would *you* move out of your lab if someone called and said big ol' devilfish was eating your stock?"

"Yes, I would have been here in a minute."

"You're different from the others. They wanted us to ship one of these babies up for them to look at."

"Why didn't you do it?"

"We were going to, but after what happened to Charlie Marstons, the fishermen got scared and said to hell with it and moved on."

"Who was Charlie Marstons?" Paul said.

"Charlie was an old-timer. Fished these waters for years even after it got hard for him to get around because of a bad leg. He was a stubborn old coot, though, and liked to go out alone. They found him—or what was left of him—coupla miles east of here. From the looks of it, he caught a bunch of these lunkers, got too close and maybe his bum leg gave out. Hardly enough left to bury."

"You're saying the fish killed him?"

"No other explanation. That's when the boys started leaving. I would have gone with them if I had my boat. Funny," he said with a grin, "one of those babies is my ticket out of here."

Gamay was already thinking ahead. "I want to bring it back to the lab for analysis."

"Suits me fine," Neal said. "We'll box it up as soon as it's safe."

He pointed the *Tiffany* back to land. By the time they pulled up to the dock, the fish was practically dead, but it managed a few spasmodic snaps, enough to warrant keeping it on board awhile longer. Neal recommended a boardinghouse where they could stay the night. Gamay gave him a hundred-dollar bonus, and they agreed to meet the next morning.

• • •

A pleasant middle-aged couple warmly welcomed them at the boardinghouse, a Victorian structure at the edge of town. From the enthusiasm with which they were greeted, Paul and Gamay figured that the B and B didn't get much business. The room was cheap and clean, and the couple cooked them a hearty dinner. They had a good night's sleep, and the next morning, after a huge breakfast, they set out to find Neal and reclaim their fish.

The pier was deserted. More worrisome, there was no sign of Neal or the *Tiffany*. They asked at the boatyard, but nobody had seen him since the day before when he'd paid for his engine work. A few men were idling around the waterfront because they had nothing better to do. No one had seen Neal that morning. The bartender they'd met the day before strolled by on his way to open up the restaurant. They asked if he had any idea where Neal might be.

"Probably nursing a hangover about now," the bartender said. "He came in last night with a hundred bucks. Used most of it up buying drinks for himself and the regulars. He was pretty tanked when he left. He's done it before, so I didn't worry about him. Neal navigates better drunk than some men sober. He took off around eleven, and that was the last I saw of him. He's been living on his boat, even when the boatyard had it."

"Any idea why the *Tiffany* isn't here?" Paul asked.

The bartender scanned the harbor and swore under his breath. "Damned idiot, he was in no shape to run a boat."

"Would any of the other people who were in the bar know where he is?"

"Naw, they were even drunker than he was. Only one not drinking was Fred Grogan, and he left before Mike."

Trout's analytical ear was listening for inconsistencies. "Who is Grogan?" Paul asked.

"Nobody you'd want to know," the bartender said with contempt. "Lives in the woods near the old plant. He's the only local guy the new owners kept on when they bought in. Pretty surprising, because Fred is such a shady character. He pretty much keeps to himself. Sometimes he sneaks into town, driving one of the big black SUVs you see around the plant."

The bartender paused and looked across the water, shading his eyes. A small boat had entered the harbor and was moving toward the pier at great speed. "That's Fitzy coming in. He's the lighthouse keeper. Looks like he's in a big hurry."

The outboard-powered skiff skidded up to the dock, and the white-bearded man in the boat tossed a line ashore. He was clearly excited and didn't even wait to climb out of the boat before he started to babble almost incoherently.

"Calm down, Fitzy," the bartender said. "Can't understand a word."

The bearded man caught his breath and said, "I heard a big boom late last night. Rattled my windows. Figured it might be a jet flying real low. Went out this morning to take a look. Pieces of wood all over the place. Look at this." He whipped back a tarpaulin, pulled out a jagged plank and held it over his head. The painted letters *Tif* were clearly visible.

The bartender's lips tightened. He went into his bar and called the police. While he waited for the law to arrive, he made several more phone calls. Pickup trucks began to arrive, and a motley fleet of search boats was organized. With Fitzy in the lead, the flotilla had already set out when the police chief arrived. The chief talked to the bartender and got his story. By then, some of the boats were returning. They had more scraps of wood that identified the boat, but no sign of Neal.

The sheriff put in a call to the coast guard, which said it would send in a helicopter, but the consensus seemed to be that Neal had gotten drunk, decided to go for a joyride and probably hit a rock near the point and sank. The Trouts did not comment on the explanation, but as they drove back to the rooming house, their conversation dwelt on more sinister possibilities.

Gamay put it bluntly. "I think Mike was murdered."

"Guess I wasn't the only one who saw the charring around the wood. I'd guess his boat was set on fire or simply blown up. Neal's bragging about the fish he caught could have got him killed."

"Is *that* what it is all about?" Gamay said, her eyes flashing with anger. "Neal was killed over a *fish*?"

"Maybe."

She shook her head "Poor guy. I can't help thinking that we're somehow responsible—"

"The only ones responsible are the guys who killed him."

"And I'm betting that Oceanus had a big hand in this."

"If you're right, they may come after us next."

"Then I'd suggest that we pack our gear and get out of town."

Paul pulled the rental car in front of the guest house, and they went inside, paid their bill and grabbed their bags. The owners were obviously sorry to see them go, and followed them out to the car. As they chattered on about how it was a shame that they were leaving, Gamay tugged Paul's sleeve and steered him to the driver's side. She got in and waved farewell.

"Sorry to spoil our send-off party. While we were talking, I saw a black Tahoe pass by."

"Looks like the wolves are gathering," Paul said. He turned onto the road that would take them out of town and glanced in the mirror. "No one on our tail."

Except for a few vehicles, they saw little traffic, and once they had gone beyond the town's outskirts, the road was empty. The two-lane road wound through thick pine woods, gradually ascending so they were driving high above the sea. On one side of the road was forest, and on the other a sheer drop-off for hundreds of feet.

They were about two miles from the village when Gamay turned to look at the road behind them and said, "Uh-oh."

Paul glanced in the rearview mirror and saw a black Tahoe bearing down on them. "They must have been waiting down a side road for us to pass."

Gamay tightened her seat belt. "Okay, then, show them what you can do."

Paul gave her an incredulous look. "You realize we are driving a six-cylinder family sedan that is probably half the size and weight of that black behemoth behind us."

"Damnit, Paul, don't be so analytical. You're a crazy Massachusetts driver. Just put the pedal to the metal."

Trout rolled his eyes. "Yes ma'am," he said.

He punched the gas pedal with his foot. The car accelerated to a respectable eighty miles per hour. Easily matching their speed, the Tahoe continued to gain. Paul managed to wring another ten miles per hour out of the engine, but the SUV moved closer.

The road began to go into a series of curves that matched the contour of the coastal hills. The rental vehicle was no sports car, but it held the road better on the turns than the big SUV, which leaned heavily as the curves became sharper. Trout had to hit the brakes to keep from going off the road, but the SUV was even less maneuverable.

Slowed by the serpentine curves, the SUV lost ground. Trout curbed his elation. He kept his eyes glued to the road, hands firmly gripping the steering wheel, pushing his car to just under the speed at which it could go out of control and overshoot a curve. He knew that one lapse—a patch of sandy highway, an errant boulder or an error of judgment—could get them both killed in a fiery crash.

Gamay kept tabs on their pursuer and maintained a running commentary. The car's wheels squealed with each change in direction. Trout held it steady. He was running between sixty and seventy miles per hour, and was heading down a long, gradual slope in the road, when an unbelievable sight met his eyes.

Ahead of them, a black Tahoe had pulled out onto the road from behind a huge boulder. For a second, he thought the SUV behind him had used a shortcut.

Then Gamay shouted, "There are *two* SUVs. They're trying to sandwich us in."

The vehicle in front of the Trouts' car slowed to block the road, and the other SUV quickly caught up from behind. Trout tried to go around, but each time he poked the rental car's nose into the oncoming lane, the SUV pulled in front of him. He touched the brakes to avoid a rear-end collision. The following SUV crashed into his rear bumper, crushing it into the trunk and sending the car into a neck-jolting wild fishtail.

Paul fought the wheel and managed to keep the car from going into a spin. The Tahoe slammed into the car again. The smell of gas from a ruptured tank filled the car. The Tahoe made another lunge, but this time Gamay saw it coming and yelled, "Right!"

Trout spun the wheel to the right and the Tahoe only clipped the bumper. Gamay glanced at the SUVs, which had pulled away.

"They're holding back for some reason."

"That won't last," Paul said.

"Then we'd better do something soon. The rental agency is going to wonder why their car is only two feet long. Damn, he's coming in again. Left!"

Trout jerked the wheel. The car moved into the passing lane, and Trout saw something that made his hair stand up on edge. The road curved sharply to the right. The Tahoes could keep them boxed in until the last minute. The SUV in front would screen the curve from view. Then it would slow to make the turn, and the one behind would knock them off the cliff like a cue stick tapping a billiard ball.

Paul yelled at Gamay to hold tight, and he gripped the wheel even tighter with his sweaty palms. He tried to remove all thought from his mind, relying only on instinct, keeping sharp watch in the rearview mirror. Timing would be crucial.

The vehicle on their tail began to accelerate. Trout made his move. When the SUV came within a few feet of the car's bumper, he jerked the wheel to the right.

The car hit the soft, sandy berm along the side of the road and drove up on the inclined shoulder like a race car on the angled track of a speedway. It crashed through bushes and small trees. Wood shrieked against metal.

He saw a flash of black as the Tahoe flew by him on the left. Then came a horrendous screech of brakes and a crash. The SUV that had been on his tail had slammed into the rear of the vehicle in front, locking bumpers. The lead vehicle tried to slow and turn, but the weight of the attached SUV made any turn impossible, and they were locked together. Both vehicles shot off the cliff like projectiles from a slingshot and plunged hundreds of feet in a fiery tandem death trap.

Trout was having his own problems. The banking had followed the contour of the road, and now it curved while the car maintained a straight trajectory. He lost all control as the car was airborne. Centrifugal force kept him pressed into the driver's door. The car landed at an angle, collapsing the wheels, with a sound like a junkyard symphony. He tried to glance over at Gamay, but the airbags deployed and all he could see was exploding white plastic.

Then only blackness.

16

WELCOME BACK TO Tórshavn, Mr. Austin," said the friendly desk clerk at the Hotel Hania. "Your fishing trip up the coast went well, I trust."

"Yes, thanks. I ran into some very unusual fish."

The efficient desk clerk handed Austin an envelope along with his room key. "This came in earlier today."

Austin opened the envelope and read the message neatly printed on hotel letterhead: *I'm in Copenhagen. Staying at the Palace. Dinner offer still good? Therri.*

Austin smiled as he thought of Therri's incredible eyes and her dulcet voice. He must remember to play the lottery. Maybe the winds of good fortune were blowing in his direction. On a clean sheet of stationery, he wrote a reply: *Tonight at the Tivoli?* He folded the paper, gave it to the desk clerk and asked him to send the message.

"Would you try to reserve a room for tonight at the Palace Hotel?" he said.

"I'd be happy to, Mr. Austin. I'll ready your bill for checkout."

Austin went up to his room, where he took a shower and shaved. The phone rang as he was toweling himself dry. The desk clerk said that his room at the Palace was all set and that he had taken the liberty of canceling the previous reservation at an airport hotel. Austin packed his bag and called Professor Jorgensen. The professor was in class, so Austin left a message saying he would like to see him later in the day if possible. He said he would be en route to Copenhagen and suggested that Jorgensen leave a reply at the Palace Hotel front desk.

Austin gave the desk clerk a generous tip, then he caught the helicopter shuttle from Tórshavn to Vagar Airport and took the Atlantic Airways flight to Copenhagen. Later that day, the airport taxi dropped him off at Radhuspladen, the city's main square. He made his way past the statue of Hans Christian Andersen and the spouting dragon water fountains to the stately old Palace Hotel overlooking the busy square. Two messages waited for him. One was from Therri: *Tivoli it is! See you at six.* The other note was from Professor Jorgensen, saying he would be in his office all afternoon.

Austin dropped his duffel bag off in his room and called the professor to tell him he was on his way. As Austin was leaving the hotel, it occurred to him that jeans and turtleneck were hardly appropriate for a night out with a beautiful woman. He stopped at a men's clothing shop in the concourse and, with the help of a knowledgeable salesman, quickly picked out what he wanted. A hefty bribe to the salesman and tailor insured that the clothes would be ready for him at five.

The University of Copenhagen campus was a short cab ride from the central square. The Marine Biological Laboratory was part of the Zoological Institute. Park lawns surrounded the two-story brick building. The professor's cubicle had exactly enough room to accommodate a desk and computer and two chairs and a clutter limit that the professor had far exceeded. Graphs and charts covered the walls, and folders were piled everywhere.

"Pardon the mess," he apologized. "My main office is at the Helsingor campus. I use this closet when I'm teaching classes here." He removed a pile of papers from a chair to make room for Austin. Nonplussed at what to do with the mess, he placed it precariously atop a teetering stack of other papers on his desk. "Wonderful to see you again, Kurt," he said with his big-toothed grin. "I'm so glad you were able to make it to our beautiful city."

"It's always a pleasure to visit Copenhagen. Unfortunately, my flight back to the States leaves tomorrow, so I only have one night here."

"Better than nothing at all," Jorgensen said, settling into the cramped area behind his desk. "Tell me, did you ever hear anything further from that lovely woman, the attorney who was having coffee with you in Tórshavn?"

"Therri Weld? As a matter of fact, I'm having dinner with her tonight."

"Lucky man! I'm sure she'll be a more enjoyable companion than I was," Jorgensen said with a chuckle. "Well, did you enjoy Skaalshavn?"

"*Enjoy* isn't the word for it. Skaalshavn is a surprising place. Thanks for letting me use your cottage and your boat."

"My pleasure. It's *incredible* country, isn't it?"

Austin nodded. "Speaking of Skaalshavn, I was wondering how your lab tests turned out."

The professor rummaged through the Mt. Everest of papers on his desk. Miraculously, he found the file he was looking for. He took his glasses off and replaced them. "I don't know if you're acquainted with my main areas of expertise. I specialize in the effects of hypoxia. I study how oxygen deficiency and temperature change affect fish populations. I don't claim to be an expert in every area, so I've run my findings by various colleagues in bacterial viruses. We have tested dozens of water samples and fish taken at various locations near the Oceanus operation for signs of anomalies. We wondered if there was a parasite. Nothing."

"What about your original theory that there might be trace chemicals in the water?"

"No, to the contrary. The Oceanus people weren't exaggerating when they bragged their filtration system was state-of-the-art. The water is absolutely *pure*. The other fish farms I tested produced waste from feed and so on. In short, I found nothing that would affect the Skaalshavn stocks."

"Which begs the question, what is decimating the fish population?"

Jorgensen pushed his glasses up on his forehead. "There

could be other reasons we haven't touched. Predators, habitat degradation, a disruption of the food supply."

"Have you ruled out a link to the fish farm completely?"

"No, I haven't, which is why I'm returning to Skaalshavn to make more tests."

"That might be a problem," Austin said in an understatement. He proceeded to give the professor a condensed version of his exploration of the fish farm, his narrow escape and rescue. "I'll be glad to pay you for the loss of the boat," he added.

"The boat is the *least* of my concerns. You could have been *killed*." Jorgensen was flabbergasted. "I ran into patrol boats when I was making my tests. They looked intimidating, but they never attacked or threatened me."

"Maybe they didn't like my face. I *know* I didn't like theirs."

"You may have noticed I am not exactly a movie star," the professor said. "No one tried to kill me."

"It's possible that they knew your tests would come up negative. In that case, there was no reason to scare you off. Did you discuss your work with Gunnar?"

"Yes, he was always there when I returned from my field tests and seemed very interested in what I was doing." A light dawned in the professor's eyes. "I see! You think he was an informant for Oceanus?"

"I don't know for certain, but I was told that he worked for Oceanus during the construction of the fish farm. It's certainly possible that he continued to be employed by the company after the plant was built."

Jorgensen frowned. "Have you mentioned this episode to the police?"

"Not just yet. Technically speaking, I was trespassing on private property."

"But you don't try to *kill* somebody simply for being nosy!"

"That does seem like an overreaction. However, I can't see the Faroe police department pushing the matter. Oceanus would deny that our little dust-off ever took place. The way they reacted to a little harmless snooping tells me they must have something to hide. I'd like to poke around quietly, and the police would simply stir things up."

"As you wish. I know little about intrigue. My realm is science." His brow wrinkled in thought. "That creature in the tank that scared the devil out of you. You don't think it was a shark?"

"All I know is that it was big and hungry and as pale as a ghost."

"A *ghost* fish. Interesting. I'll have to think about it. In the meantime, I'll prepare for my return trip to the Faroes."

"Are you sure you want to go? It might be dangerous after my encounter."

"This time, I'm going in a research vessel. Besides safety in numbers, it will provide access to a full range of research gear. I'd love to bring along an archaeologist to research those caves."

"Not a great idea, Professor, but there's someone in town who might be helpful in that area. Her father visited the caves, and she told me how to gain entry. Her name is Pia."

"The minister's widow?"

"Yes, you've met her? She's quite a woman."

"*I'll* say," Jorgensen said, before catching himself. The blush staining his cheeks told the whole story. "We've met a few times around the village. She's impossible to avoid. Can you change your plans and return to Skaalshavn with me?"

Austin shook his head. "Thanks for the offer. But I've got to get back to my duties at NUMA. I'm leaving Joe to wrap up the tests on the *Sea Lamprey*. Please keep me apprised of your findings."

"I will, of course." Jorgensen cradled his chin in his hand, and a faraway look came to his eyes.

"My scientific training abhors the whole idea of portents. I am trained to draw no conclusion unless I have the facts to back it up. There's something terribly wrong here, Kurt. I can feel it in my bones. Something *unholy*."

"If it's any consolation, I've had the same feeling. It goes beyond a bunch of guys running around with guns." He leaned forward with a level gaze in his blue-green eyes. "I'd like you to promise me something when you go back to Skaalshavn."

"Of course, my boy. Anything you say."

"Take care, Professor," Austin said, in a firm manner that left no room for misunderstanding. "Take *great* care."

17

THE SENSE OF foreboding continued to haunt Austin even after he stepped outside Jorgensen's office building into the bright Danish sunlight. Several times during the cab ride back to the hotel, he found himself glancing through the rear window. He gave up finally and sat back to enjoy the ride. If danger were stalking him, he would never see it with all the traffic.

Austin stopped at the clothing store to pick up his purchases. He carried the neatly tied boxes to his room and called Therri. It was 5:30. "I have a room one floor below yours. I think I can hear you singing in joyful anticipation of our dinner."

"Then you must have also heard me *dancing* as well."

"It's amazing how my charm affects women," Austin said. "I'll meet you in the lobby. We could make believe that we're old lovers encountering each other by chance."

"You're a surprising romantic, Mr. Austin."

"I've been called worse things. You'll know me by the red carnation in my lapel."

When the elevator doors opened, Therri stepped out as if she were on stage and immediately caught the attention of every male in the vicinity, including Austin. He couldn't take his eyes off her as she glided across the lobby. Therri's chestnut hair tumbled down to the thin straps of her white ankle-length lace dress that clung to her slim waist and thighs.

Her warm smile showed that Therri approved of her date as well. She surveyed the European-styled single-breasted jacket of dove gray whose slightly pinched waist emphasized Austin's shoulders like a military uniform. The blue shirt and white silk tie set off his deep tan, coral-colored eyes and pale hair. Pinned to his lapel was a red carnation.

She extended her hand, which Austin kissed lightly. "What a lovely surprise," she said in an upper-class British accent. "I haven't seen you since—"

"Biarritz. Or was it Casablanca?"

Therri put her wrist to her forehead. "Oh, who can say? One place blends with the other over time, don't you agree?"

Austin leaned close to her ear and whispered, "We'll always have Marrakech."

Then he hooked her arm in his, and they strolled out the door as if they had known each other for ages. They walked across the busy square toward Tivoli, the famed nineteenth-century amusement park known for its rides and entertainment. The lively park was ablaze with neon and filled with visitors taking in the theater, dance and symphony music. They stopped to watch a folk-dance troupe for a few minutes. Therri suggested that they have dinner at a restaurant with an outdoor terrace, and they were seated at a table that had a view of the Ferris wheel.

Austin picked up the menu. "Since you chose the restaurant, I'll make the dinner selections, if you don't mind."

"Not at all. I've been subsisting on *smorrebrod* sandwiches."

When the waiter came over, Austin ordered tiny fjord shrimps as an appetizer. For the main course, he ordered *flaekesteg,* roast pork served with crackling and cabbage, for himself, and *morbradbof,* small pork fillets in mushroom sauce, for Therri. Then for drinks, he picked Carlsberg pilsner beer rather than wine.

"You placed that order rather deftly," Therri said admiringly.

"I cheated. I came to this same restaurant the last time I was in Copenhagen on a NUMA assignment."

"Great minds, as they say."

They toasted each other with their foamy glasses and sipped the cool, crisp beer. The shrimp came. Therri closed her eyes with pleasure after the first bite. "This is *wonderful.*"

"The secret of cooking fish is to never let the flavoring drown out the subtle taste. This is flavored with lime and spiced with fresh pepper."

"One more thing to add to my thank-you list."

"Your good mood seems to go beyond the food. Your meeting with Becker went well, I take it."

"Your friend Mr. Becker was actually quite charming. He can't speak highly enough of you and was very impressed with the photos you took of the *Sea Sentinel*. At my urging, they checked out the *Sentinel* for themselves and found it had been sabotaged exactly as you described. We came to terms. They agreed to drop the charges against Marcus."

"Congratulations. No strings attached?"

"A whole ball of twine. Marcus and anyone associated with SOS, including yours truly, must be out of Denmark within the next forty-eight hours. We're booked to fly home on the Concorde tomorrow."

"The *Concorde*? SOS doesn't stint when it comes to travel, does it?"

She shrugged. "The people who contribute millions to SOS don't seem to mind it, as long as the oceans are protected."

"I'll try that line with the NUMA bean counters who keep an eye on the travel budget. You'll be having lunch at Kinkaid's while I'm dining on rubber chicken at thirty-five thousand feet. Tell me, what other conditions did Becker impose?"

"No press conferences allowed on Danish soil. There can be no attempts to salvage the *Sea Sentinel*. And the only way we will ever step foot in Denmark is if we smuggle ourselves in as guest workers. Again, I can't thank you enough for all you've done."

"Everything comes with a price. Tell me all you know about Oceanus."

"Of course, I'll be glad to. As I said last time, Oceanus is a

multinational corporation dealing in fish products and transport. It operates fleets of fishing boats and transport vessels
around the world."

"That could describe a dozen corporations." Austin smiled.
"Why do I have the feeling you're hiding something?"

Therri looked shocked. "Is it *that* obvious?"

"Only to someone who's used to dealing with people who
think that telling some of the truth gets them off the hook for
all of it."

She frowned and said, "I deserved that. It's an old lawyer
habit. We attorneys like to keep something in reserve. SOS is
very much in your debt. What would you like to know?"

"Who *owns* the company, for starters?"

"SOS asked itself the same question. We ran into a thicket
of intertwining shadow corporations, paper companies and
murky trusts. One name kept coming up: Toonook."

"Huh. That name reminds me of a film I saw when I was a
kid, an old documentary called *Nanook of the North*. Is he an
Eskimo?"

"That's my guess. We can't confirm it, but we dug up some
circumstantial evidence pointing in that direction. It took an
incredible amount of research. We learned that he's a Canadian citizen, and that he's very good at keeping his face hidden. That's all I can tell you about him, and that's the *whole*
truth."

Austin nodded, thinking about the swarthy dark-skinned
guards who'd shot at him. "Let's go back to Oceanus. What
first brought them to the attention of SOS?"

"They were one of the few companies that ignored our
Faroes boycott. We'd been aware of fish-farming as an environmental issue, but it was the company's attempts to hide its
operations that got Marcus interested. When he learned about
the fish farm in the Faroes, he thought that he might stir things
up if he focused the spotlight on the operation."

"There are two ships on the bottom of the ocean that prove
he was right."

"Let me ask *you* something," Therri said, leveling her gaze.
"What do *you* know about Oceanus that you haven't told *me*?"

"Fair enough. While you were negotiating with Mr.
Becker, I poked into an Oceanus fish farm in the Faroes."

"Did you learn anything?"

Austin felt a twinge of pain in his chest wound. "I learned that they don't like people poking into their business. I'd advise you and your friends to give them a wide berth."

"*Now* who's the evasive one?"

Austin only smiled. As much as he wanted to trust Therri, he did not know the extent of her loyalty to SOS and its leader. "I've told you enough to keep you out of trouble."

"You must know that throwing me a tidbit of information is only going to stir up my curiosity."

"Just remember that curiosity killed the cat. I wouldn't want to see you suffer a similar fate."

"Thanks for the warning." She smiled her beguiling smile.

"You're welcome. Maybe we can continue this conversation when we get back to Washington."

"I can think of any number of hotel lobbies that would be conducive to an accidental rendezvous. We can pledge not to talk business."

"Let's begin now." Austin signaled the waiter and ordered two Peter Heering cherry liqueurs.

"What would you like to talk about, then?" Therri said.

"Tell me about SOS."

"That could be construed as business."

"Okay, I'll ask you a personal question. How did you come to be involved with the Sentinels?"

"Fate," she said with a smile. "Before I became a whale-hugger, I was a tree-hugger. My future was ordained from the moment of birth. My folks named me Thoreau after Henry David."

"I wondered where the Therri came from."

"I suppose I was lucky they didn't name me *Henry*. My father was an environmental activist before there was such a thing. My mother was from an old Yankee family that got rich on slaves and rum. When I graduated from Harvard Law School, it was expected that I go into the family guilt business. My turn now. How did you get into NUMA?"

Austin gave Therri the Cliff's Notes version of his career.

"There's an unaccountable gap in time in your life history," she said.

"You're much too alert. I worked for the CIA during that

period. My division was disbanded after the Cold War ended. Can't tell you more than that."

"That's all right," she said. "An air of mystery adds to your attractiveness."

Austin felt like an outfielder about to catch an easy pop fly. Therri had moved the conversation to a slightly more intimate level, and he was about to respond in kind when he noticed her looking over his shoulder. He turned and saw Marcus Ryan making his way toward their table.

"Therri!" Ryan said, with his matinee-idol smile. "What a nice surprise."

"Hello, Marcus. You remember Kurt Austin from the hearing in Tórshavn."

"Of course! Mr. Austin gave the only unbiased testimony during that whole fiasco."

"Why don't you join us?" Therri said. "You don't mind, do you, Kurt?"

Austin minded very much. The encounter smelled strongly of a staged meeting, but he was curious about the reason for the setup. He motioned to a chair and shook hands with Ryan. The grip was surprisingly firm.

"Only for a minute," Ryan said. "I don't want to intrude on your dinner, but I'm glad for the opportunity to thank Mr. Austin for helping SOS."

"Your appreciation is misdirected. I didn't do it to help SOS. It was a personal favor for Miss Weld. She's the one who persuaded me to take a close look at your boat."

"I don't know of many people who can resist her persuasiveness, and she deserves a lot of credit. Nevertheless, you did a great service for the creatures of the sea."

"Spare me the hearts and flowers, Mr. Ryan. I gave Therri the evidence of sabotage because it was the right thing to do, not because I believe in your cause."

"Then you know I had no responsibility for that collision."

"I know that you purposely ratcheted up the tension, hoping something would happen so you could get it on the TV cameras."

"Desperate times call for desperate measures. From what I know about NUMA, your organization isn't above using unorthodox methods to achieve its goals."

"There's a big difference. Every one of us, right up to Admiral Sandecker, is ready to bear responsibility for our actions. We don't take refuge behind posters of puppy-faced little harp seals."

Ryan's face turned the color of a cooked beet. "I've always been willing to take the consequences for my actions."

"Sure, as long as you knew there was a way out."

Ryan smiled over his anger. "You're a difficult man, Mr. Austin."

"I try to be."

The waiter arrived just then with their dinners.

"Well, I won't spoil your evening," Ryan said. "It was fun talking to you, Mr. Austin. I'll give you a call later, Therri."

With a jaunty wave, he joined the throngs moving past the restaurant.

Austin watched Ryan depart and said, "Your friend takes an exalted view of himself. I thought the oceans already had a god. Neptune or Poseidon, depending on your language of choice."

He expected Therri to defend Ryan, but she laughed instead. "Congratulations, Kurt. It's nice to know that Marcus isn't the only one who has a talent for irritating people."

"It comes naturally to me. You should tell him that the next time you set up an accidental meeting."

She glanced at the Ferris wheel, avoiding his steady gaze, then toyed with her fork before answering. "Was it that transparent?"

"Any more transparent and it would be invisible."

She sighed heavily. "Sorry for the clumsy attempt to deceive you. You didn't deserve it. Marcus wanted to meet you so he could thank you. He was sincere about that. I didn't expect you to get into a spitting match. Please accept my apology."

"Only if you'll have a nightcap in the Palace lounge after we take a long walk around the neighborhood."

"You drive a hard bargain."

Austin gave her a devilish grin. "As your friend Mr. Ryan said, I'm a difficult man."

18

COPENHAGEN SEEMED TO be in the midst of a major celebration, but the bash was only a normal night in one of Europe's liveliest cities. Music issued from dozens of cafés. The parks and squares along an expansive pedestrian mall named Stroget teemed with strollers and street performers. The party atmosphere was fun, but it was hard to carry on a conversation. Austin suggested that they turn down a quiet street lined with closed boutiques and make their way back to the hotel.

The deserted street was dark except for a few shop windows and softly glowing gas lamps. Austin was listening to Therri tell an anecdote about Becker, when he noticed movement ahead and saw two figures step out of the shadows into a puddle of yellow light.

Austin knew the Danes to be low-key and extra polite, and Copenhagen was relatively crime-free. It didn't bother him when the two men took up a stance blocking the sidewalk. Maybe they'd had too much aquavit. He took Therri's arm and prepared to walk around the pair. He reassessed the situation when the men produced long clubs from behind their backs.

Hearing a scraping footfall, Austin glanced over his shoulder. Two more men, also wielding clubs, were approaching from behind. Therri had become aware of the threat without comprehending it and had stopped talking. In what looked like a rehearsed strategy, the men began to encircle them.

Austin looked around for a weapon. Figuring that anything was better than nothing, he grabbed the lid from a row of trash cans. The heavy-duty cover was made of thick, solid aluminum, he was glad to see. He stepped protectively in front of Therri and used the lid like a medieval infantryman's shield to fend off a clanging blow from the nearest attacker. The man brought the club up to strike again, but Austin went from defense to offense and straight-armed the heavy lid into the attacker's face. The man yelped with pain, and his knees buckled. Austin lifted the lid in both hands and brought it down on the man's head, where it made a sound like a gong. His hands hurt at the shock of the impact, but the attacker was even worse off, crumpling onto the sidewalk in a dark heap.

Another attacker swiftly closed in. Austin jammed the lid in his face, but the attacker anticipated the move, stepping back out of range and clubbing the lid harmlessly aside. Austin was trying to keep the tender left side of his rib from being hit. The assailant sensed a weakness and landed a glancing blow to Austin's head. Austin saw whirling galaxies. At the same time, he heard Therri's scream. One attacker held her while the other pulled her back by the hair to expose her throat. A hard blow to her windpipe could be fatal.

Austin blinked the stars from his eyes and tried to go to her aid. His assailant stepped in front of him and brought his club down as if he were wielding a two-handed broadsword. Austin deflected the blow, but it knocked the lid from his hand, and he lost his balance. Down on one knee, Austin raised his arm to protect his head. He saw wide faces and glittering eyes, clubs raised in the air, and braced himself for a shower of blows to rain down on his skull. Instead, he heard thuds and grunts and men yelling in two different languages, one incomprehensible, the other Spanish. The attackers who had encircled him melted away like snowflakes.

He struggled to his feet and saw figures running *away* from him. Clubs rattled to the pavement. Shadows were moving in every direction, and he was reminded of the scene in the movie *Ghost* where the shades of the dead take the damned to the underworld. Then the shadows disappeared. He and Therri were alone, except for the slumped form of the man he had clouted. The attacker's friends had apparently abandoned him.

"Are you all right?" Austin said, taking Therri's arm.

"Yes, I'm fine, but as you can tell, I'm *very* shaky. What about you?"

He lightly touched the side of his head. "My head feels like raw hamburger and my skull is full of twittering sparrows, but other than that I'm fine. It could have been worse."

"I *know*," she said with a shudder. "Thank goodness those men saved us."

"*What* men? I was a little busy with my imitation of Ivanhoe."

"They came out of nowhere. I think there were two of them. They went after the others and chased them away."

Austin kicked the battered trash-can lid. "Hell, I thought I scared them off with my head-masher." He brushed the dirt off his ripped and dirty pants. "Damn, this is the first new suit I've bought in years."

Therri couldn't help laughing. "*Incredible.* You narrowly missed being beaten to death, and you're worried about your suit." She embraced him in a warm hug.

Therri was holding him tightly. He didn't even complain about the pressure of her body against his knife wound. He was thinking that she smelled very good, when suddenly she stiffened, backed away from him and looked over his shoulder with horror in her eyes.

"Kurt, watch out!"

Austin turned and saw that the attacker who'd been lying on the sidewalk was slowly getting to his feet. The man stared at them for a few seconds, apparently still dazed. Austin clenched his fists and started toward the man, ready to send him back to la-la land. He stopped in midstep when a small circle of intense red appeared on the man's forehead.

"Get down!" Austin yelled at Therri. When she hesitated, he pulled her to the sidewalk, shielding her body with his.

The man started toward them, then he stopped as if he had walked into an invisible wall, went down on his knees and fell facedown onto the sidewalk. Austin heard footsteps and saw a

figure running down the street. Austin pulled Therri to her feet
and apologized for knocking her down.

"What happened?" She seemed to be in a daze.

"Someone shot our friend. I saw the spot from a laser
sight."

"Why would they do that?"

"Maybe his company has a strict severance policy."

"Or maybe they didn't want him talking," she said, staring
at the dead body.

"Either way, this isn't a healthy place to be."

Austin took Therri by the arm and guided her away from
the scene. He kept a sharp eye out for a return of their attackers, not relaxing until the lights of the Palace Hotel were in
sight. The hotel cocktail lounge seemed like another world.
Austin and Therri sat in a corner booth surrounded by the
cheerful Babel of voices and the tinkling of a jazz piano playing Cole Porter. Austin had ordered two double scotches.

Therri took a deep swallow of her drink and looked around
at the other patrons. "Did that *really* happen out there in the
street?"

"It wasn't a production of *West Side Story,* if that's what
you mean. Can you tell me what you remember?"

"It all happened so fast. Two of those men with the clubs
grabbed me." She frowned. "*Look* what those SOBs did to my
hair." Anger was replacing her fear. "Who *were* those jerks?"

"The attack was well-coordinated. They knew we were in
Copenhagen and must have been watching us tonight in order
to set up the ambush. What's your guess?"

She replied without hesitation. "Oceanus?"

Austin nodded grimly. "As I learned in the Faroes,
Oceanus has the thug power, the violent inclination and the
organization. What happened next?"

"They let me go. Just like that. Then they were running
away, with the other men chasing after them." She shook her
head. "I wish our Good Samaritans had stayed so I could
thank them. Should we tell the police what happened?"

"Normally, I'd say yes. But I don't know if it would do any
good. They might pass it off as an attempted mugging. Given
your relationship with the Danish authorities, you might be
detained here longer than you'd like."

"You're right," Therri said. She drained the last of her glass. "I'd better get back to my room. My flight leaves early in the morning."

Austin walked Therri to her door, where they paused. "You're sure you'll be okay?"

"Yes, I'm fine. Thanks for the interesting evening. You certainly know how to show a girl a good time."

"That was nothing. Just wait until our next date."

She smiled and kissed him lightly on the lips. "I can hardly wait."

He was impressed at how quickly Therri had recovered. She was proving to be an iron butterfly. "Call me if you need anything."

She nodded. Austin wished her a good night's sleep and headed for the elevator. She watched until the elevator doors had closed. Then she pulled her key out of the lock, walked down the hall and knocked on another door, which was opened by Marcus Ryan. His smile disappeared when he saw the strain in her face. "Are you all right?" he said with concern in his voice. "You look a little pale."

"Nothing a little makeup won't cure." She brushed by him and stretched out on the sofa. "Whip me up a strong cup of tea, then have a seat and I'll tell you all about it."

They sat down, and she told them about their attack and rescue.

After hearing her story, Ryan tented his fingers and stared off into space. "Austin is right. It's *Oceanus*. I'm *sure* of it."

"Me, too. I'm less sure who our rescuers were."

"Austin didn't know who they were?"

She shook her head. "He said no."

"Was he telling the truth?"

"He may suspect who they were, but I didn't press him on that. Kurt doesn't strike me as someone who lies."

"Well, well, my tough-minded legal counsel has a soft side after all. You like him, don't you?" Ryan said with a foxy grin.

"I won't deny it. He's—different."

"I'm different, too, you must admit."

"That you are," she said with a smile. "That's why we're professional colleagues and not lovers."

Ryan sighed theatrically. "Guess I'm fated to be a bridesmaid, never a bride."

"You'd make a hideous bride. Besides, you had your chance to be a bride. As you recall, I didn't like playing second fiddle to SOS."

"Didn't blame you. I am something of a warrior monk when it comes to the Sentinels."

"Crap! Don't give me that monk stuff. I happen to know you've got a girlfriend in every port."

"Hell, Therri, even a monk has to get out of the monastery and kick up his heels from time to time. But let's talk about your intriguing relationship with Austin. Do you think he's smitten by your charms, enough to have him wrapped around your finger?"

"From what I've seen, Kurt doesn't wrap around *any*one's finger." Her eyes narrowed. "What's going on in that tangle of plots and schemes that you call a mind?"

"Just a thought. I'd like to get NUMA on our side. We need muscle if we're going to tackle Oceanus."

"And if we can't get NUMA to help us?"

He shrugged. "Then we'll have to go it alone."

Therri shook her head. "We're not big enough to do that. This is not a street gang we're dealing with. They're too big and powerful. You saw how easily they sabotaged our ship. If someone like Kurt Austin is nervous, then we should pay attention. We can't risk any more lives."

"Don't underestimate SOS, Therri. Muscle isn't everything. Strength can come from knowledge."

"Don't talk in riddles, Marcus."

He smiled. "We may have a winning card. Josh Green called yesterday. He has stumbled onto something big, and it concerns an Oceanus operation in Canada."

"What sort of operation?"

"Josh wasn't sure. It came out of Ben Nighthawk."

"The college intern in our office?"

Ryan nodded. "As you know, Nighthawk is a Canadian Indian. He's been getting these weird letters from his family in the North Woods. A corporation took over a big tract of land near their village. As a favor to Ben, Josh looked into the ownership. The land was purchased by a straw corporation set up by Oceanus."

In her excitement, Therri put aside her fears. "This may be the lead we're looking for."

"Uh-huh. I thought the same thing. Which is why I told Josh to check it out."

"You sent him up there alone?"

"He was on his way to Canada to meet Ben when he called. Nighthawk knows the lay of the land. Don't worry. They'll be careful."

Therri bit her lower lip as she thought back to the savage attack on a quiet Copenhagen street. She respected Ryan for a hundred different reasons, but sometimes his zeal to attain a goal got in the way of his judgment.

Fear clouded her eyes. "I hope so," she murmured.

19

THE GIANT TREE trunks soared like columns in an ancient temple. Their intertwining branches blocked the sun's rays and created an artificial twilight on the forest floor. Far below the treetops, the dented old pickup lurched and dipped like a boat in a storm as it climbed over ropy tree roots and unyielding rocks.

Joshua Green sat on the passenger side, jouncing on the hard seat. He kept one hand above his head to cushion the impact of his skull against the interior of the truck's roof. Green was an environmental law expert with the Sentinels of the Sea. He was a sandy-haired, thin-faced man whose large, round glasses and birdlike nose made him look like an emaciated owl. He had gamely toughed out the ride without a complaint until the truck hit a bump that practically bounced him through the overhead.

"I'm feeling like a kernel in a popcorn machine," he said to the driver. "How much longer do I have to endure this torture?"

"About five minutes; then we'll start walking," Ben Nighthawk replied. "Don't blame you for getting sick of the bumpy ride. Sorry about the transportation, too. It's the best my cousin could come up with."

Green nodded in resignation and turned his attention back to the deep woods that encroached on every side. Before being assigned to SOS headquarters, he'd been part of the field operations SWAT team. He had been rammed and shot at, and he'd spent short but unforgettable times in jails no better than medieval dungeons. He had acquired a reputation for amazing aplomb under fire, and his professorial appearance disguised a tough interior. But the unnatural darkness of his surroundings unnerved Green more than anything or anybody he had ever encountered at sea.

"The *road* doesn't bother me. It's these damned *woods*," he said, staring out at the forest. "Damned creepy! It's the middle of the day, the sun is shining, and it's dark as Hades out there. Like something out of a Tolkien novel. Wouldn't surprise me if an Orc or an ogre jumped out at us. Whoops, I think I just saw Shrek."

Nighthawk laughed. "I suppose the woods are a little spooky if you're not used to them." He gazed through the windshield, but instead of apprehension, a look of reverence bathed his round, apple-brown features. "It's different when you grow up around here. The forest and the darkness are your friends because they provide protection." He paused and said wistfully, "Most of the time."

A few minutes later, Nighthawk brought the truck to a halt, and they got out and stood in the cathedral gloom. Clouds of tiny flies whirled around their heads. The powerful scent of pine was almost suffocating, but to Nighthawk it was like the finest perfume. He absorbed the sights and smells with a beatific expression on his face, then he and Green donned the backpacks that carried cameras and film, survival tools, water and snacks.

Without consulting a compass, Nighthawk started walking. "This way," he said, as confident as if he were following a dotted line on the ground.

They moved in silence across the thick carpet made up of decades of fallen pine needles, weaving their way through the tree trunks. The air was hot and oppressive, and sweat soaked their shirts within minutes. Except for clusters of ferns and moss hills, no underbrush grew beneath the trees. They made good time without bushes and briars to slow them down. As he loped after Nighthawk, Green reflected on the path that had led him from the comfort of his air-conditioned office to this murky weald.

In addition to his duties with SOS, Green taught part-time at Georgetown University in Washington, which was where he'd met Ben Nighthawk, who was attending his class. The young Indian was in college on scholarship. He wanted to use his education to save the North Woods environment, which was threatened by development. Struck by Ben's intelligence and enthusiasm, Green had asked him to be a research assistant in the SOS office.

The lanky environmentalist and the stocky young Indian were only a few years apart in age, and they had soon become good friends as well as colleagues. Nighthawk was glad for the friendship because he infrequently made it home. His family lived on the shores of a big lake in a remote and almost inaccessible part of eastern Canada. A seaplane owned jointly by the villagers made weekly trips to the nearest town for supplies and emergencies and also carried mail back and forth.

His mother had been keeping Nighthawk up to date about a major construction project on the lake. Someone was probably building a trophy lodge, Nighthawk had assumed with resignation. It was the sort of project he was determined to wage war against when he got out of college. Then, the week before, his mother had written an upsetting letter hinting at dark goings-on, and asking her son to come home as soon as he could.

Green told Nighthawk to take as much time off as he needed. A few days after Nighthawk had left for Canada, he called the SOS office. He sounded desperate. "I need your help," he implored.

"Of course," Green replied, thinking his young friend had run out of money. "How much do you need?"

"I don't need any money. I'm worried about my *family*!"

Nighthawk explained that he had gone to the town nearest to the village and learned that the seaplane hadn't come in for two weeks. The townspeople assumed that the plane had mechanical problems and that someone would eventually come out of the woods by land looking for replacement parts.

He borrowed a truck from a relative who lived in town and followed the crude road that led to the village. He found the road fenced off and guarded by hard-looking men who said that the property was now private. When he said he wanted to get to his village, they waved him off with their weapons and warned him not to come back.

"I don't understand," Green had said on the phone. "Didn't your family live on reservation land?"

"There were only a handful of our people left. A big paper conglomerate owned the land. We were squatters, technically, but the company tolerated us. They even used the tribe in ads to show what nice people they were. They sold the land, and the new owners have been working on a big project on the other side of the lake."

"It's their land; they can do what they want to."

"I know, but that doesn't explain what happened to my people."

"Good point. Have you gone to the authorities?"

"It was the first thing I did. I talked to the provincial police. They said they were contacted by a city lawyer who told them that the villagers had been evicted."

"But where did they go?"

"The police asked the same question. The lawyer said they moved on. Probably squatting on someone else's property, he said. You have to understand, my people are considered eccentric anachronisms. The police here say there is nothing they can do. I need help."

As they talked, Green checked his calendar. "I'll have the company plane run me up there tomorrow morning," he said. SOS leased an executive jet that was on standby.

"Are you sure?"

"Why not? With Marcus tied up in Denmark, I'm nominally in command, and to be honest, having to deal with all the egos and turf wars in this office is driving me bonkers. Tell me where you are."

True to his word, Green had flown into Quebec the following day. He caught a connector flight on a small plane that took him to the town Nighthawk had called from. Ben was waiting at the tiny airport, the truck packed with camping supplies and ready to go. They drove several hours along back roads and camped overnight.

Looking at the map by the light of the camp lantern, Green saw that the forest covered a huge area, pockmarked with large bodies of fresh water. Ben's family lived off the land, fished and hunted for a living and brought in hard cash revenue from the sport fishermen and hunters.

Green had suggested hiring a floatplane to take them in, but Nighthawk said that the heavily armed guards he encountered had made it clear that trespassers would be shot. The access road they guarded wasn't the only way to get to the village, Nighthawk said. The next morning, they'd driven a few more hours, never encountering another vehicle, until they'd come to the track that led into the deep woods.

After leaving the truck, they walked now for about an hour, moving like shadows in the silence of the tall trees, until Nighthawk stopped and raised his hand. He froze in place, eyes half-closed, moving his head slightly back and forth like a radar antenna focusing on an incoming target. He seemed to have forsaken the ordinary senses of sight and hearing and was using some inner direction-finder.

As Green watched, fascinated, he thought, You can take the Indian out of the forest, but you can't take the forest out of the Indian. At last, Nighthawk relaxed, reached into his pack and unscrewed a canteen. He handed it to Green.

"I hate to be a pest," Green said, taking a swig of warm water, "but how much farther do we have to walk?"

Nighthawk pointed toward the line of trees. "About a hundred yards that way is a hunter's trail that will take us to the lake."

"How do you know?"

Ben tapped his nose. "No big deal. I've been following the water smell. Try it."

After a sniff or two, Green found to his surprise that he could pick up the faint scent of rotting vegetation and fish mixed with the fragrance of pine. Nighthawk took some water and tucked the canteen back into his pack. Lowering his voice, he said, "We'll have to be very careful from here on in. I'll communicate with hand signals."

Green gave him the okay sign, and they set off again. Almost immediately, the scenery began to change. The trees grew shorter and slimmer as the soil under their feet became sandier. The undergrowth thickened, and they had to push their way through thorns that ripped at their clothes.

Shafts of light streamed in from breaks in the trees overhead. Then, quite suddenly, they could see the sparkle of water. At a signal from Nighthawk, they got down on their hands and knees and made their way to the edge of the lake.

After a moment, Nighthawk stood and walked to the water's edge, with Green following. An elderly Cessna floatplane was tied up at a rickety dock. Nighthawk inspected the plane, finding nothing out of place. He removed the cowling and gasped when he saw the engine.

"Josh, look at this!"

Green peered at the engine. "Looks like someone took an ax to it."

The hoses and connections hung loose where they had been cut. The engine was scarred in a dozen places where it had been hit with something hard.

"This is why no one could fly out of here," Nighthawk said. He pointed to a foot-worn trail that led away from the floatplane dock. "That path leads to the village."

Within minutes, they were making their way to the edge of a clearing. Nighthawk held out his hand for them to stop. Then he squatted on his haunches and peered with sharp eyes through the bushes. "There's no one here," he said finally.

"Are you sure?"

"Unfortunately, yes," Nighthawk said. He walked unafraid into the open, with Green hesitantly taking up the rear.

The village consisted of a dozen or so sturdy-looking log houses, most with porches. They were built on both sides of a swath of packed-down dirt in a rough approximation of a small town's Main Street, complete with one structure that had a general-store sign on it. Green expected someone to burst out the front door at any moment, but the store and every other house in the village were as still as tombs.

"This is my house, where my parents and my sister lived," Nighthawk said, stopping in front of one of the larger structures. He went up on the porch and went inside. After a few minutes, he came out, shaking his head. "No one. Everything is in place. Like they just stepped out for a minute."

"I poked my head in a couple of the other places," Green said. "Same thing. How many people lived here?"

"Forty or so."

"Where could they have gone?"

Nighthawk walked to the edge of the lake a few yards away. He stood, listening to the quiet lap of the waves. After a moment, he pointed to the opposite shore and said, "Maybe over there?"

Green squinted across the lake. "How can you be sure?"

"My mother wrote that there was funny stuff going on across the lake. We've got to check it out."

"What kind of funny stuff?"

"She said big helicopters were coming in and unloading material night and day. When the village men went over to investigate, they were run off by guards. Then one day, some guys with guns came over to the village and looked around. They didn't hurt anyone, but my mother figured they'd be back."

"Wouldn't it be better to go tell the authorities? They could send someone in by plane."

"I don't think there's time," Nighthawk said. "Her letter is more than two weeks old. Besides, I can feel danger and death in the air."

Green shuddered. He was stuck in the middle of nowhere, and the only person who could get him out was raving like a medicine man in a B movie.

Sensing his friend's nervousness, Nighthawk smiled and said, "Don't worry, I'm not going native. That's a good suggestion about the cops. I'd feel better if we checked things out first. C'mon," he said, and they headed back to the knoll they had climbed a few minutes before. They came to a natural overhang of rock. Nighthawk pulled away some branches that covered the opening. Lying upside-down on a crude rack was a birch-bark canoe. Nighthawk ran his hand lovingly over the shiny surface.

"I made this myself. Used only traditional materials and techniques."

"It's beautiful," Green said. "Straight out of *Last of the Mohicans.*"

"*Better.* I've gone all over the lake in it."

They dragged the canoe to the beach, dined on beef jerky and rested as they waited for the sun to go down.

With the approach of dusk, they threw their packs into the canoe, pushed it into the water and started paddling. Night had fallen by the time they drew close to the shore. They had to stop when the canoe hit something solid in the water.

Nighthawk reached down, thinking they had hit a rock. "It's some kind of metal cage. Like a bait box." He scanned the water with his sharp eyes. "The water is filled with them. I smell fish, lots of them. It must be some sort of hatchery operation."

They found a breach in the floating barricade and pointed the canoe toward land. Something stirred and splashed in the metal cages, confirming Nighthawk's theory of a fish hatchery. Eventually they came to the outer end of a floating dock lit by dim ankle-high lights they had seen from the water. Tied up to a series of finger piers were several Jet Skis and powerboats. Next to the smaller watercraft was a large catamaran. It had a conveyor belt running down the middle, and Nighthawk guessed that it was used in the hatchery operation.

"I've got an idea," Green said. Working systematically, he pulled the ignition keys from the Jet Skis and the boats and threw them into the water. Then they tucked the canoe in between the other craft, covered it with a borrowed tarp and climbed onto the pier.

Where the dock joined the shore, it continued as a blacktop walkway that led inland. Nighthawk and Green decided to keep to the woods. After walking a few minutes, they encountered a wide dirt track, as if a big bulldozer had plowed its way through the forest. They followed the swath and came up on a row of trucks and earth-moving machinery arranged in neat rows behind a huge storage building. Using the shed as a shield, they peered around the corner and saw that they were at the edge of an open area carved out of the woods. It was brightly illuminated by a ring of portable halogen lights. Mechanized shovels were flattening down the dirt, and great road-building machines were laying down swaths of blacktop. Work crews armed with shovels were smoothing out the hot asphalt in preparation for it to be flattened down by the steam-rollers.

Nighthawk said, "What do we do next, Professor?"

"How long do we have until daybreak?"

"About five hours to first light. It would be smart to be back on the lake before then."

Green sat with his back against a tree. "Let's keep an eye on what's going on until then. I'll take the first watch." Shortly after midnight, Ben took over. Green stretched out on the ground and closed his eyes. The cleared area was now almost deserted except for a few armed men lounging around. Nighthawk blinked his eyes and reached over to tap Green's shoulder.

"Uh, Josh—"

Green sat up and looked toward the plaza. "What the hell—?"

Beyond the clearing, where there were only woods before, was a huge dome-shaped structure whose mottled surface glowed bluish white. It seemed to have appeared by magic.

"What *is* that thing?" Ben whispered. "And where did it come from?"

"You got me," Green said.

"Maybe it's a hotel."

"Naw," Green said. "Too functional-looking. Would you stay in a place like that?"

"I grew up in a log cabin. Any place bigger than that is a hotel."

"I don't mean to disparage your home territory, but can you see fishermen and hunters flocking here? That thing belongs in Las Vegas."

"We're talking North Pole, man. Looks like an overgrown igloo."

Green had to admit the dome had the same contours as the Eskimo shelters he had seen in *National Geographic*. But instead of hard snow, the surface appeared to be a translucent plastic material. Huge hangar doors were set into the base of the dome, overlooking the open area, which was being built as a plaza.

As they watched, there were signs of new activity. The

plaza was becoming busy again. The construction crew had returned, along with more armed men, who could be seen glancing up at the night sky. Before long, the sound of engines could be heard from above. Then a gigantic object moved across the night sky and blotted out the stars.

"Look at the dome," Nighthawk said.

A vertical seam had appeared in the top of the structure. The seam widened into a wedge, then the top half of the dome peeled back like the sections of an orange until it was completely open. Light streamed out of the dome's interior and bathed the silvery skin of a gigantic torpedo-shaped object that moved slowly to a position exactly above the vast opening.

"We were *both* wrong," Nighthawk said. "Our Las Vegas hotel is a blimp hangar."

Green had been studying the contours of the enormous aircraft. "You ever see that old news footage about the *Hindenburg,* that big German airship that caught fire and burned back in the 1930s?"

"But what's something like that doing *here*?"

"I think we may find out very soon," Green said.

The descending airship sank into the structure, and the sections of the dome moved back into place and restored the round shape. Before long, the doors overlooking the plaza slid open, and a group of men emerged from inside the structure. They were dressed in black uniforms, and all had dark, swarthy complexions. They swarmed around a man whose bullish head was set on powerful shoulders.

The man walked over to the edge of the plaza and inspected the progress of the work. Nighthawk had paid little attention to the workers before. But now he could see that, unlike the uniformed men, these people were dressed in jeans and work shirts, and armed guards were watching them.

"Oh hell!" he whispered.

"What's wrong?" Green said.

"Those are men from my village. That's my brother and father. But I don't see my mother or any of the other women."

The leader continued on his inspection tour, walking around the edge of the plaza. The men who had been guarding the workers watched their leader's progress. Taking advantage of their inattention, one of the laborers had edged closer to the woods. Then he dropped his shovel and made a break for freedom. Something about the way he ran, with a slight limp, looked familiar to Nighthawk.

"That's my cousin," he said. "I can tell by the way he runs. He hurt his foot bad when we were kids."

One of the guards glanced back and saw the fleeing man. He raised his gun to fire, but lowered it at an apparent command from the bullheaded man. He stepped over to a stack of tools and snatched up a sharp-tipped metal pike from the pile. He held it lightly in two hands, drew back like a javelin thrower, then snapped the pike forward with all the strength of his squat, powerful body.

The missile flew through the air in a metallic blur. It had been thrown expertly ahead of the runner in a high looping trajectory and timed so that it caught him between the shoulder blades. He went down, pinned like a butterfly in a collection book. By then, the leader had turned his back and didn't even see him fall.

The whole scene—the aborted escape and the killing of his cousin—had taken only a few seconds. Nighthawk had watched, frozen in place, but now he lunged forward and, despite Green's attempts to hold him back, broke from cover and ran toward his cousin's body.

Green scrambled after the young Indian and brought him down in a flying tackle. He was on his feet a second later, pulling Nighthawk to his feet by the scruff of his neck. They were clearly visible in the bright glare of lights. Nighthawk saw the guns pointed in their direction, and his instincts took over.

He and Green dashed for the woods. Shots rang out and Green fell. Nighthawk stopped and went to help his companion, but the bullet had caught Green in the back of the head and destroyed his skull. Nighthawk turned and ran, geysers of earth erupting around his feet. He dove into the forest, while a fusillade from the plaza shredded the branches over his head. Under a shower of twigs and leaves, he dashed through the trees until he came to the edge of the lake and his feet pounded onto the dock.

He saw the Jet Skis and wished Green had kept one ignition key. Nighthawk unsheathed a hunting knife from his belt and sliced the mooring lines. Then he shoved the watercraft as far away from the dock as he could. He whipped the tarp from the canoe, pushed off and began to paddle furiously. He was in open water when he saw muzzle flashes from the dock area and heard the rattle of automatic-arms fire. The shooters were firing blind, and their bullets were hitting the water off to one side.

The canoe flew across the lake until it was out of range. Nighthawk continued to paddle with all his strength. Once he had gained the other shore, he could lose himself in the deep woods. It is never entirely dark on water, which catches and magnifies even the tiniest speck of light. But now, the lake around him began to glow as if it were infused with a luminescent chemical. He turned and saw that the light was not coming from the lake, but was a reflection.

Behind him, a wide shaft of light was shining toward the heavens. The dome was opening. The airship was rising slowly into the air. When it was a few hundred feet over the trees, the airship headed toward the lake. Bathed in the eerie light from below, the airship looked like an avenging monster out of some time-shrouded myth. Instead of approaching on a straight line, the airship turned sharply and moved along the shore. Beams of light shot out from its underbelly and probed the surface of the lake.

After making its first pass, the airship turned onto a parallel track. Rather than make a random thrust into the space over the lake, the airship was conducting a thorough search, using a lawn-mowing pattern. Nighthawk was paddling for all he was worth, but it would be only a matter of minutes before the searchlights dancing over the lake's surface caught the canoe.

The airship made another turn and started back on a course that would take it directly over the canoe. Once spotted, the canoe would be an easy target. Nighthawk knew there was only one option available to him. He drew his hunting knife and slashed a hole in the bottom of the canoe. Cold water poured in and surged around his waist. The water was up to his neck, as the airship blotted out the sky almost directly overhead. The guttural noise of its engines blocked out all other sound.

Nighthawk ducked his head and held on to the sinking canoe to keep it below the surface. Above him, the water glowed white from the moving bull's-eyes, then went black again. He stayed under as long as he could, then, gasping for breath, he popped his head out of the water.

The airship had turned for another pass. Nighthawk could hear another sound mingling with the throb of engines. The whine and snarl of Jet Skis. Someone must have had spare ignition keys. Nighthawk swam off at an angle, away from the village.

Minutes later, he saw lights scudding across the lake at great speed as the Jet Skis made directly for the deserted village. Nighthawk kept swimming until he felt soft muck under his feet. He crawled up onto the shore, exhausted from the swim, but he rested only long enough to wring water out of his shirt.

Lights were coming his way along the beach.

Nighthawk took one last, sorrowful look across the lake, before he melted into the woods like a sodden wraith.

20

ABROAD SMILE crossed Austin's bronzed face as the taxi crunched onto the long gravel driveway in Fairfax, Virginia. Austin paid his fare from Dulles Airport and sprinted up the steps of the Victorian boathouse, part of an old estate fronting on the Potomac River. He dropped his bags inside the door, swept his eye around the combination study-den and the familiar line from Robert Louis Stevenson came to mind.

Home is the sailor, home from sea.

Like Austin himself, his house was a study in contrasts. He was a man of action whose physical strength, courage and quickness made him a force to be reckoned with. Yet he possessed a cool intellect, and he often drew inspiration from the great minds of centuries past. His work often involved the latest in high-tech gadgets, but his respect for the past was crystallized in the brace of dueling pistols that hung over his fireplace. It was part of a collection of more than two hundred sets, to which he was always adding, despite the limitations of a government salary.

The dichotomy in his personality was reflected in the comfortable dark-wood Colonial furniture that contrasted with the plain white walls, like those in a New York art gallery, that were hung with contemporary originals. His extensive book-shelves groaned under the weight of hundreds of books that included first editions of Joseph Conrad and Herman Melville, and well-worn volumes containing the writings of the great philosophers. While he could spend hours studying the works and wisdom of Plato and Kant, his extensive music library was heavy on progressive jazz. Curiously, there was little to indicate that he spent most of his working days on or under the sea, except for a primitive painting of a clipper ship and a few other sailing vessels, a photo of his catboat under full sail and a glass-encased model of his racing hydroplane.

Austin had lovingly converted the boathouse into a residence, doing much of the work himself. His assignments for NUMA, and before that for the CIA, took him all over the globe. But when his work was done, he could always return to his safe harbor, drop sail and throw the anchor over the side. All that was needed to make the nautical analogy complete, he reflected, was a ration of grog.

He went into the kitchen and poured himself a glass of dark rum and Jamaican ginger beer. The ice tinkled pleasantly in his glass as he threw the doors open to release the musty smell. He went out onto the deck, where he filled his lungs with the fresh river air and surveyed the slow-moving Potomac in the vanishing light. Nothing had changed. The river was as beautiful and serene as ever.

He stretched out in a wood-slatted Adirondack chair, lay back and stared at the sky as if the stars could tell him what was behind the events of the last few days. His misadventures in the Faroe Islands and in Copenhagen would have been the stuff of dreams if not for the itch on his chest where the knife wound was healing and the tender swelling under his hair where a club had connected with his noggin. He could draw a straight line from the sabotage of the SOS ship to the attack on a quiet Copenhagen street. The dark impulses that had inspired the sabotage of the SOS ship were obviously a means to an end. Simply put, someone wanted SOS out of the picture. When Austin had gotten nosey, he'd become a target, first in Skaalshavn and later in Copenhagen.

The situation could be summed up in a simple equation: Whenever someone got too close to a company called Oceanus, the results could be disastrous. His thoughts drifted back to the Faroe Islands fish farm and the thing in the fish tank that had scared the hell out of him. A miasma of pure evil seemed to hang over the Oceanus operation. What had Jorgensen said? *Unholy.* Then there was the Basque tycoon, Balthazar Aguirrez, and his Quixotic quest. What was *that* all about?

Austin went over the events of the past several days in his mind until he felt his eyelids drooping. He downed the last of his drink, climbed the stairs to his bedroom in the turret surmounting the mansard roof, and turned in. He slept soundly and was up and dressed early the next morning, refreshed by a night's sleep and stimulated by a pot of strong Kona coffee. He telephoned an old friend at the CIA to make sure he would be in, then called his NUMA office to say he'd be late.

Unlike his colleague Dirk Pitt, who collected antique autos and relished driving them, Austin was indifferent when it came to ground transportation. Driving a sedan from the NUMA car pool, nondescript except for its turquoise color, he headed to Langley, along a route he knew well from his days with the CIA, and parked his car next to dozens of other government vehicles. Security at the sprawling complex was tighter since 9/11.

Herman Perez, whom he had called earlier, was waiting in the visitors' area. Perez was a slightly built man with an olive complexion and dark-brown eyes that matched his thinning hair. Perez helped speed the check-in process through security and led Austin through the labyrinth of corridors to an office uncluttered by a scrap of paper. The only objects on the desktop were a computer monitor, a telephone and a photo of an attractive woman and two cute children.

"Kurt, it's great to see you!" Perez said, motioning for Austin to sit down. "Thinking of jumping Sandecker's ship to come back into the Company? We'd love to have you. The cloak-and-dagger stuff you're so good at has become respectable at Langley once again."

"Admiral Sandecker might have something to say about that. But I'll have to admit that I still get misty-eyed when I think about the fun we had on our last job."

"The secret missile retrieval job we did off Gibraltar," Perez said with a boyish grin. "Oh boy, that was something."

"I was thinking about that on the drive over this morning. How long has it been?"

"*Too* damned long. You know something, Kurt, I still hear little flamenco dancers in my head whenever I drink Spanish wine." A dreamy look came into Perez's face. "By God, we had some good times, didn't we?"

Austin nodded in agreement. "The world has changed a lot since then."

Perez laughed in reply. "Not for *you*, old pal! Hell, I read about that amazing rescue you pulled off in the Faroe Islands. You haven't changed a bit, you old sea dog. Still the same swashbuckling Austin."

Austin groaned. "These days, for every minute swashing buckles, I spend an hour at my desk dealing with reports."

"I hear you! I could do without the paperwork, although I've gotten to like my nine-to-five schedule since I became a father. Two kids, would you believe it? Being a desk jockey isn't all bad. You might want to try it."

"No, thanks. I'd rather have my eyeballs tattooed."

Perez laughed. "Well, you didn't come here to talk about the good ol' days. You said on the phone that you were looking for background info on Balthazar Aguirrez. What's your interest in him, if you don't mind my asking?"

"Not at all. I ran into Aguirrez in the Faroe Islands. He seemed like a fascinating character. I know he's a shipbuilding magnate, but I suspected there was more to him than meets the eye."

"You *met* him?"

"He was fishing. So was I."

"I should have known," Perez said. "Trouble attracts trouble."

"Why is he trouble?"

"What do you know about the Basque separatist movement?"

"It's been around a long time. Every so often, Basque terrorists blow up a public building or assassinate an innocent government official."

"That pretty much sums it up," Perez said. "There's been talk for decades of a separate Basque state that would straddle Spain and France. The most radical separatist group, ETA,

started fighting for an autonomous Basque state in 1968.
When Franco died in 1975, the new Spanish government gave
the Basques more political power, but the ETA wants the
whole enchilada. They've killed more than eight hundred people since taking up the cause. Anyone who is not on their side
is an enemy."

"A familiar story around the world, unfortunately."

"The political wing of the separatist movement is the Batasuna party. Some people have compared it to Sinn Fein, the
public face of the IRA. The Spanish government threw up its
hands after more assassinations and the discovery of a big
ETA weapons cache. Autonomy wasn't working, so they
banned Batasuna and started to crack down on the whole separatist movement."

"Where does Aguirrez fit in to this bloody little picture?"

"Your instincts were right about there being more to him
than meets the eye. He has been a major backer of Batasuna.
The government has accused him of financing terrorism."

"I liked him. He didn't look like a terrorist," Austin said,
recalling his benefactor's bluff and down-to-earth manners.

"Sure, and Joe Stalin looked like somebody's grandfather."

Austin remembered the yacht's tough-looking crew and
the heavy-duty armament that the vessel carried. "So, are the
charges true?"

"He freely admits to supporting Batasuna, but points out
that it was a legitimate party when he gave them money. The
government suspects he's still channeling money into the
movement. They have no proof, and Aguirrez is too well-
connected to bring into court with flimsy evidence."

"What's your take on the guy?"

"In all my years in Spain, I never met him, which was why
I was surprised when you said you had. I think he's a moderate who'd like to see a peaceful separatist solution, but the
ETA murders have undermined his cause. He's afraid the
crackdown will rekindle the conflict and endanger innocent
citizens. He may be right."

"Sounds like he's walking a very thin tightrope."

"Some people say that the pressure's made him unhinged.
He's been talking about a way to rally European public opinion in favor of a Basque nation. Did he give you any hint of

what's on his mind?" Perez narrowed his dark eyes. "Surely you didn't talk just about fishing."

"He struck me as very proud of his Basque heritage—his yacht is named the *Navarra*. He didn't say a word about politics. We talked mostly about archaeology. He's an amateur archaeologist with strong interest in his own ancestors."

"You make him sound like a contender for the nutty professor. Let me give you a warning, old friend. The Spanish police would love to nail him to the wall. They have no direct proof linking him to terrorist acts, but when they do, you don't want to be in their way."

"I'll remember that. Thanks for the heads-up."

"Hell, Kurt, it's the least I could do for a former comrade-in-arms."

Before Perez had the chance to start reminiscing again, Austin glanced at his watch. "Got to get moving. Thanks for your time."

"Not at all. Let's get together for lunch sometime. We miss you here. The brass is still ticked off about Sandecker grabbing you for NUMA."

Austin rose from his chair. "Maybe we'll work on a joint operation someday."

Perez smiled. "I'd like that," he said.

The Washington traffic had let up, and before long, Austin saw the sun gleaming on the green glass façade of the thirty-story NUMA building overlooking the Potomac. He groaned when he walked into his office. His efficient secretary had neatly piled the pink call-back slips in the center of his desk. In addition, he would have to dig himself out of an avalanche of e-mail messages before he got down to preparing a report on Oceanus.

Ah, the exciting life of a swashbuckler! He scrolled through his e-mail, deleted half of it as nonessential and shuffled through his pink slips. There was a message from Paul and Gamay. They had gone to Canada to check into an Oceanus operation. Zavala had left a call on his answering machine saying he would be home that night in time for a hot date. Some things never change, Austin thought with a shake of his head. His handsome and charming partner was much in demand among Washington's female set. Austin sighed and began to tap away at his computer. He was wrapping up the first draft when the phone rang.

"Good afternoon, Mr. Austin. I was hoping I'd find you in your office."

Austin smiled at the sound of Therri's voice. "I'm already pining for the high seas. Your flight home on the Concorde went well, I trust."

"Yes, but I don't know why I hurried back. My in-box is filled with depositions and briefs. But I didn't call to complain. I'd like to get together with you."

"I'm halfway out the door. A walk maybe. Cocktails and dinner. Then, who knows?"

"We'll have to put the 'who knows?' on hold for now. This is business. Marcus wants to talk to you."

"I'm really starting to dislike your friend. He keeps getting in the way of what may be the love affair of the century."

"This is important, Kurt."

"Okay, I'll meet with him, with one condition. We make a date for tonight."

"It's a deal."

She gave Austin a time and place for the meeting. Therri's charm notwithstanding, he had agreed to talk to Ryan because he had come to a dead end and thought he might learn something new. He hung up, leaned back in his swivel chair and laced his fingers behind his head. It was easy to bring his thoughts around to Oceanus. His chest ached when he raised his arm, and the pain made an effective memory aid.

He wondered if the Trouts had turned up anything. They hadn't called since leaving their message. He tried to reach them on their cell phone and got no answer. He didn't worry. Paul and Gamay were fully capable of taking care of themselves. Next, he called Rudi Gunn, NUMA's assistant director, and set up a luncheon meeting. Rudi's famed analytical skills might help guide him through the dense thicket surrounding the mysterious corporation.

Gunn was bound to hone in on Aguirrez when he read the report, questioning whether there was any link between Basque terrorism and Oceanus violence. Aguirrez had mentioned his ancestor, Diego. Austin pondered the Basque's obsession with his forebear and thought that Aguirrez might be on to something. From his own experience, Austin knew that the past is always the key to the present. He needed someone who could guide him back five centuries. One person came to mind immediately. Austin picked up the phone and punched out a number.

21

THE WORLD-FAMOUS MARINE historian and gourmand, St. Julien Perlmutter, was in an agony of ecstasy. He sat outside a three-hundred-year-old Tuscan villa whose shaded terrace had a breathtaking view of rolling vineyards. Visible in the distance, dominating the Renaissance city of Florence, was the Duomo. The wide oak table before him groaned with Italian cuisine, from pungent sausage made locally, to a thick, rare beefsteak Florentine. There was so much wonderful food, and so many wonderful colors and fragrances, in fact, that he was having a hard time trying to decide where to start.

"Get a grip on yourself, old man," he muttered, stroking his gray beard as he stared at the spread. "Wouldn't do to starve to death amid all this plenty."

At four hundred pounds, Perlmutter was in little danger of wasting away. Since arriving in Italy ten days before, he had eaten his way up the Italian boot on a promotional tour for an Italian-American food magazine. He had trudged through wineries, trattorias and smokehouses, posed for photo opportunities in refrigerator rooms full of hanging prosciutto, and delivered lectures on the history of food going back to the

Etruscans. He had dined on sumptuous feasts everywhere he stopped. The sensory overload had brought him to his present impasse.

The cell phone in his suit pocket trilled. Grateful for the distraction from his quandary, he flipped the phone open. "State your business in a concise and businesslike manner."

"You're a hard man to find, St. Julien."

The sky-blue eyes in the ruddy face danced with pleasure at the sound of the familiar voice of Kurt Austin.

"To the contrary, Kurt m'lad. I'm like Hansel and Gretel. Follow the food crumbs, and you'll find me nibbling at the gingerbread house."

"It was easier to follow the suggestion of your house-keeper. She told me you were in Italy. How's the tour going?"

Perlmutter patted his substantial stomach. "It's very fulfilling, to say the least. All goes well in the District of Columbia, I trust?"

"As far as I know. I just flew back from Copenhagen last night."

"Ah, the city of Hans Christian Andersen and the Little Mermaid. I remember when I was there some years ago, there was this restaurant I dined at—"

Austin cut Perlmutter off before he launched into a course-by-course account of his meal. "I'd love to hear about it. But right now, I need your historical expertise."

"Always willing to talk about food or history. Fire away." Perlmutter was often asked to lend his expertise to NUMA queries.

"Have you ever come across a Basque mariner by the name of Diego Aguirrez? Fifteenth or sixteenth century."

Perlmutter dug into his encyclopedic mind. "Ah yes, something to do with the *Song of Roland,* the epic French poem."

"*Chanson de Roland?* I struggled through that as part of a high school French course."

"Then you know the legend. Roland was the nephew of the emperor Charlemagne. He held off the Saracens at Roncesvalles with the help of his magic sword, *Durendal.* As he was dying, Roland beat his sword against a rock to keep it out of the hands of his enemies, but it wouldn't break. He blew his horn to summon help. Charlemagne, hearing it, came with his armies, but it was too late. Roland was dead. Through the centuries, Roland became a Basque hero, a symbol of their stubborn character."

"How do we get from Roland to Aguirrez?"

"I recall a reference to the Aguirrez family in an eighteenth century treatise on pre-Columbian voyages to the Americas. Aguirrez was said to have made many fishing trips to North American waters decades before Columbus's voyage. Unfortunately, he ran afoul of the Spanish Inquisition. There were unverified reports he had been entrusted with the Roland relics."

"From what you say, the Roland story was not just a legend. The sword and the horn actually existed."

"The Inquisition apparently thought so. They feared the relics could be used to rally the Basques."

"What happened to Aguirrez and the relics?"

"They both disappeared. There is no record of a shipwreck that I can recall. May I ask what prompts your interest in the subject?"

"I met a descendant of Diego Aguirrez. He's retracing the voyage of his long-lost ancestor, but he never said anything about sacred relics."

"I'm not surprised. Basque separatists are still setting off bombs in Spain. Lord knows what would happen if they got their hands on potent symbols like this."

"Do you remember anything else about Aguirrez?"

"Not off the top of my head. I'll dig around in my books when I get home." Perlmutter owned one of the world's finest marine libraries. "I'll be back in Georgetown in a few days, after a stop-off in Milan."

"You've been a great help as usual. We'll talk again. *Buon appetito.*"

"*Grazie,*" Perlmutter said, clicking off his phone. He turned his attention back to the table. He was about to dig in to a plate of marinated artichoke hearts when his host, who owned the villa and the surrounding vineyards, came in with the bottle of wine he had gone for.

Shock registered on the man's face. "You're not touching your food. Are you ill?"

"Oh no, Signor Nocci. I was distracted by a telephone call regarding a question of a historical nature."

The silver-haired Italian nodded. "Perhaps a taste of the *chingali,* the wild boar, will help your memory. The sauce was made from truffles found in my woods."

"A splendid suggestion, my friend." With the dam breached, Perlmutter dug into the food with his usual gusto. Nocci politely held his curiosity at bay while his guest devoured the repast. But when Perlmutter dabbed his small mouth and set his napkin aside, Nocci said, "I am an amateur historian. It is impossible not to be when one lives in a country surrounded by the remnants of countless civilizations. Perhaps I can help you with your question."

Perlmutter poured himself another glass of 1997 Chianti and recounted his conversation with Austin. The Italian cocked his head. "I know nothing about this Basque, but your story brings to mind something I came across while doing some research in the *Biblioteca Laurenziana.*"

"I visited the Laurentian Library many years ago. I was fascinated by the manuscripts."

"More than ten thousand masterpieces," Nocci said, nodding his head. "As you know, the library was founded by the Medici family to house their priceless collection of papers. I have been writing a paper on Lorenzo the Magnificent which I hope to publish some day, although I doubt if anyone will read it."

"Be assured, *I* shall read it," Perlmutter said grandly.

"Then it will have been worth my labor," Nocci said. "Anyway, one of the hazards of research is the temptation to wander away from the highway, and while I was at the library, I traveled a side road that led to the Medici Pope Leo X. With the death of King Ferdinand in 1516, his seventeen-year-old successor, Charles V, encountered pressure to restrict the power of the Inquisition. In the great humanist tradition of the Medici family, Leo favored curtailing the Inquisitors. But Charles's advisors persuaded the young king that the Inquisition was essential to maintain his rule, and the persecution continued another three hundred years."

"A sad chapter in human history. It's comforting to know that Aguirrez had the courage to speak out, but the dark forces are strong."

"And none was darker than a Spaniard named Martinez.

He sent a letter to the king urging him to support the Inquisition and expand its powers. As far as I can determine, the letter was forwarded to Leo for his comment and came to the library with the Pope's other papers." He shook his head. "It is the fanatical raving of a monster. Martinez hated the Basques, wanted them wiped from the face of the earth. I remember there was a mention of Roland, which I recall thinking was unusual in this context."

"What was the nature of this reference?"

Nocci heaved a great sigh and tapped his head with his forefinger. "I can't remember. One of the consequences of growing old."

"Perhaps you'll remember after more wine."

"I trust the *wine* more than my memory," Nocci said, with a smile. "The assistant curator at the library is a friend of mine. Please relax, and I will make a telephone call." He was back in a few minutes. "She says she would be happy to produce the letter I mentioned for us any time we want to look at it."

Perlmutter pushed his great bulk back from the table and rose to his feet. "I think perhaps a little exercise would do me some good."

The trip to Florence took less than fifteen minutes. Nocci usually drove a Fiat, but in expectation of Perlmutter's visit, he had leased a Mercedes, which more comfortably accommodated his guest's wide girth. They parked near the leather and souvenir stalls that abounded in the Piazza San Lorenzo and went through an entrance to the left of the Medici family's old parish chapel.

Passing into the quiet cloisters, they left the bustle of commerce behind them and climbed the Michelangelo stairs into the reading room. The sturdy frame that supported Perlmutter's large figure allowed more agility than would have seemed possible under the laws of gravity. Still, he was puffing from the exertion of climbing the staircase and gladly agreed when Nocci said that he would fetch his friend. Perlmutter strolled past the rows of carved straight-backed benches, basking in the light that was filtering through the high windows as he breathed in the musty odor of antiquity.

Nocci returned after a minute with a handsome middle-aged woman, whom he introduced as Mara Maggi, the assistant curator. She had the reddish-blond hair and fair Florentine complexion that showed up so often in Botticelli paintings.

Perlmutter shook her hand. "Thank you for seeing us on such short notice, Signora Maggi."

She greeted Perlmutter with a radiant smile. "Not at all. It is a pleasure to open our collection to someone of such repute. Please come with me. The letter you wish to see is in my office."

She led the way to a space whose window overlooked the cloister garden and settled Perlmutter in a small anteroom that had a spare desk and a couple of chairs. Several pages of wrinkled parchment lay in an open vellum-bound wooden box. She left the two men alone and said to call if they needed any help.

Nocci gingerly lifted the first parchment page from the folder and held it by the edges. "My Spanish is not too bad. If you'll allow me . . ."

Perlmutter nodded and Nocci began to read. As he listened, Perlmutter decided that he had seldom heard writing that dripped with so much venom and bloodthirsty hatred. The diatribe was a litany of charges directed at the Basques—witchcraft and Satanism among them. Even the uniqueness of their language was used in evidence. Martinez was obviously a madman. But behind his ravings was a clever political message to the young Medici king: To restrict the Inquisition would diminish the power of the throne.

"Ah," Nocci said, adjusting his reading glasses, "here is the passage I was telling you about. Martinez writes:

But it is their tendency to rebellion I fear the most. They are attached to relics. They have the Sword, and the Horn, to which they attribute great powers. It gives them the power to rebel. Which will threaten the authority of the church and of your kingdom, my lord. There is one among them, a man called Aguirrez, who is at the heart of this sedition. I have vowed to pursue him to the ends of the earth, to reclaim these relics. Sire, if our Sacred Mission is not allowed to continue its work until heresy is uprooted from the land, I fear the call of Roland's Horn will summon our enemies to battle and that his Blade will lay waste to all we hold dear."

"Interesting," Perlmutter said, knitting his brow. "First of all, he seems to be saying that the relics are real. And second, that this fellow Aguirrez has them in his possession. This certainly backs up the legendary accounts of Roland's fall."

Signora Maggi poked her head in the door and asked if they needed anything. Nocci thanked her and said, "This is a fascinating document. Do you have any more papers authored by this man Martinez?"

"I'm very sorry, but there is nothing I can think of."

Perlmutter tented his fingers and said, "Martinez comes across in his writings as a man of great ego. I would be surprised if he did not keep a journal of his day-to-day activities. It would be wonderful if such a book existed and we could get our hands on it. Perhaps at the state archives in Seville."

Signora Maggi was only half-listening. She was reading a sheet of paper that had been tucked into the box with the other records. "This is a list of all the manuscripts in this box. Apparently, one of the documents was taken from this file by a previous curator and sent on to the Venice State Archives."

"What sort of document?" Perlmutter asked.

"It is described here as an 'Exoneration of a Man of the Sea,' written by an Englishman, Captain Richard Blackthorne. It was supposed to be returned, but there are more than ninety kilometers of archives covering a thousand years of history, so sometimes things fall through the cracks, as you Americans say."

"I'd love to read Blackthorne's account," Perlmutter said. "I'm due in Milan tomorrow, but perhaps I can divert to Venice."

"Perhaps it won't be necessary." She took the file into her office, and they could hear the soft clicking of a computer keyboard. She reappeared after a moment. "I have contacted the Venice State Archives and asked for a virtual search of the records. Once the document is found, it can be copied and transmitted through the Internet."

"Well done!" Perlmutter said. "And my heartfelt thanks."

Signora Maggi kissed Perlmutter on both fleshy cheeks, and before long he and Nocci were driving through the suburbs of Florence. Exhausted by the activities of the day, Perlmutter took a nap and awoke just in time for dinner. He and Nocci dined on the terrace. He had regained his gustatory equilibrium and had no trouble downing his veal and pasta dishes. After finishing up with a spinach salad and a simple *dolci* of fresh fruit, they watched the sun go down, silently sipping on glasses of *limoncello*.

The phone rang and Nocci went to answer it, while Perlmutter sat in the dark, savoring the smell of earth and grapevines, carried to his tulip nose by a light evening breeze. Nocci appeared a few minutes later and summoned Perlmutter into a small state-of-the-art computer room.

Noting his guest's upraised eyebrow, Nocci said, "Even a business as small as mine must use the latest in communications in order to survive in the global market. That was Signora Maggi," he said, sitting down in front of the monitor. "She apologizes for the delay, but the document you requested had to be retrieved from the Museo Storico Navale, the naval museum, where it had been languishing. Here," he said, and rose to give up his seat.

The sturdy wooden chair creaked in protest when Perlmutter settled in. He scanned the title page, on which the author declared the journal to be "an account of an unwilling mercenary in the service of the Spanish Inquisition."

Perlmutter leaned forward, stared into the screen and began to read the words that had been written five centuries before.

22

THE BEER TRUCK rounded a sharp curve, and the driver slammed on his brakes to avoid hitting the battered wreck in the road. The car that lay on its side a few yards from the edge looked as if it had been dropped from a great height. Two more wrecks smoldered at the bottom of the drop-off hundreds of feet below. The driver hurried from his truck and peered into the car window. He was surprised to discover that the people inside were still alive.

The trucker called for help on his CB radio. The rescue crew had to use mechanical jaws to extricate the Trouts, and then the couple was taken to a small but well-equipped hospital. Paul suffered from a broken wrist, Gamay had a concussion, and they were both covered with bumps and bruises. They spent the night under observation, went through another exam the next morning and were pronounced fit to go. They were signing out at the front desk, when two men wearing rumpled suits arrived, identified themselves as provincial police and asked to talk with them.

They settled into an unoccupied visitors' lounge, and the Trouts were asked to tell what happened. The senior man was named MacFarlane. In a classic good-cop, bad-cop pairing, he was the friendly one who tut-tutted, while his partner, a man named Duffy, was the belligerent officer who tried to pick holes in their story.

After replying to a particularly pointed question, Gamay, who could never be mistaken for a shrinking violet, stared at Duffy and gave him a smile. "I may be wrong, Officer, but it sounds as if we're being accused of something."

MacFarlane fidgeted with his hands. "It's not that, ma'am, but look at it from our point of view. You and your husband arrive in town from out of nowhere. Within twenty-four hours, a fisherman you were seen with goes missing, along with his boat. Then four men are killed in a very unusual accident."

"Damned bloody death plague if you ask me," Duffy growled.

"We've told you everything," Paul said. "We were on vacation, and went out with a fisherman named Mike Neal, whom we met at a waterfront restaurant. You can check with the bartender. Mr. Neal was looking for work and offered to take us out for a cruise."

"Pretty expensive cruise," Duffy sneered. "The boatyard says you paid off Neal's bill of nearly a thousand dollars."

"We're both ocean scientists. When we learned about the problems the fishermen had been having with low catches, we asked Mr. Neal to do some survey work."

"What happened next?"

"We stayed overnight at a bed and breakfast. The next morning, we learned that Mr. Neal and his boat had been lost. We were continuing our trip, when we were caught between two very bad drivers driving two very big cars."

"From what you said," Duffy said, making no attempt to hide his skepticism, "it sounds like these folks were trying to run you off the road."

"It seems that way."

"That's what we can't figure," Duffy said, scratching the stubble on his chin. "Why would they try to kill a couple of innocent tourists?"

"You'll have to ask them," Paul said.

Duffy's ruddy face went an even deeper red. He opened his mouth to respond.

MacFarlane raised his hand to shush his partner. "Those

folks are in no condition to answer questions," he said with a wan smile. "But you see, this presents another problem. The young lady here stopped at a general store and asked about a fish plant in town. The four gentlemen who were killed were all employees of the same plant."

"I'm a marine biologist," Gamay said. "My interest in fish is nothing odd. I don't mean to tell you how to do your job," she said, in a tone that indicated that was exactly what she was doing, "but maybe you should talk to someone at the plant."

"That's another funny thing," Duffy said. "The plant's closed."

Gamay hid her surprise with a shrug and girded herself for more questions, but just then, MacFarlane's cell phone rang, saving them from another round of the third degree. He excused himself, got up and moved into the hall, out of earshot. A few minutes later, he came back in and said, "Thanks for your time, folks. You can go."

"I won't argue with you, Officer, but could you tell us what's going on?" Paul said. "A minute ago, we were public enemies one and two."

The worried expression that had been on MacFarlane's face earlier was replaced by a friendly smile. "That was the station. We made some inquiries when we saw the ID cards in your wallets. Just got a call from Washington. Seems like you two are pretty important people at NUMA. We'll prepare a couple of statements and get them to you for additions and signatures. Anywhere we can take you?" He seemed relieved at the resolution of a difficult situation.

"A rental-car agency might be a good start," Gamay said.

"And a pub would be a good finish," Paul said.

On the drive to the car rental office, Duffy dropped his bad-cop act and told them how to get to a pub where the beer and food were good and cheap. The policemen, who were going off-duty, invited themselves along, too. By the time they got into their second pint, the detectives were very talkative. They had retraced the Trouts' footsteps, talking to the B-and-B owners and a few regulars around the waterfront. Mike Neal was still missing, and the man named Grogan had also disappeared. There was no telephone number for the Oceanus plant. They were still trying to contact the corporation's international office, but were having little luck.

Gamay ordered another beer after the police officers left. She blew off the foamy head and, in an accusatory tone, said, "That's the last time I take a drive in the country with you."

"At least *you* didn't break any bones. I have to drink my beer with my left hand. And how am I going to tie my bow ties?"

"Heaven forbid you use snap-ons, you poor boy. Have you seen the dark circle under my eye? I believe it's what we called a mouse when I was a kid."

Paul leaned over and lightly kissed his wife on the cheek. "On you, it looks exotic."

"I suppose that's better than nothing," Gamay said, with an indulgent smile. "What do we do now? We can't go back to Washington with nothing to show but a few lumps and repair bills for a nonexistent boat."

He sipped his beer. "What was the name of that scientist Mike Neal tried to contact?"

"Throckmorton. Neal said he was at McGill University."

"Montreal! Why not drop by and see him, as long as we're in the neighborhood?"

"Brilliant idea!" Gamay said. "Enjoy your beer, Lefty. I'll update Kurt on our plans."

Gamay took her cell phone to a relatively quiet corner of the pub and called NUMA. Austin was out, so she left a message saying they were following the Oceanus trail to Quebec and would be in contact. She asked Austin's secretary to track down a telephone number for Throckmorton and to see if she could put together a flight to Montreal. Several minutes later, the secretary called back with the phone number and two reservations on a flight leaving later that day.

Gamay called Throckmorton. She said she was a NUMA marine biologist and wondered if he had any time to talk about his work. He was delighted and flattered, he said, and would be free after his last class. Their Air Canada flight landed at Dorval Airport around midafternoon. They dropped their baggage off at the Queen Elizabeth Hotel and caught a cab to the McGill University campus, a cluster of gray granite older buildings along with more modern structures on the side of Mont Royal.

Professor Throckmorton was wrapping up his lecture as the Trouts arrived, and emerged from his classroom surrounded by a flock of chattering students. Throckmorton's eye caught Gamay's stunning red hair and took in Paul's tall figure. He shooed away the students and came over to greet the newcomers.

"The Doctors Trout, I presume," he said, pumping their hands.

"Thank you for seeing us on such short notice," Gamay said.

"Not at all," he said warmly. "It's an honor to meet scientists from NUMA. I'm flattered that you're interested in my work."

Paul said, "We were traveling in Canada, and when Gamay learned about your research, she insisted that we make a detour."

"Hope I'm not the source of marital discord," he said, bushy eyebrows jumping like startled caterpillars.

"Not at all," Gamay said. "Montreal is one of our favorite cities."

"Well, then, now that we've got that settled, why don't you come up to the lab and see what's on the slab, as they say."

"Didn't they say that in *The Rocky Horror Picture Show*?" Gamay said.

"Correct! Some of my colleagues have taken to calling me the mad scientist Frank N. Furter."

Throckmorton was of shorter-than-average height, chubby rather than plump, and the roundness of his body was repeated in his moon-shaped face and his circular eyeglasses. Yet he moved with the quickness of an athlete, as he led the way to the lab.

He ushered the Trouts through a door and into a large, brightly lit space and motioned for them to sit down at a lab table. Computers were scattered at stations around the room. Aerators bubbled in a series of tanks on the far side of the lab, and a briny smell of fish filled the room. Throckmorton poured three lab beakers of iced tea and sat down at the table.

"How did you hear about my work?" he said, after a sip from his beaker. "Something in a scientific journal?"

The Trouts exchanged glances. "To be honest," Gamay said, "we don't know what you're working on."

Seeing Throckmorton's puzzled expression, Paul jumped in and said, "We got your name from a fisherman by the name of Mike Neal. He said he had contacted you on behalf of the men in his fleet. Their catches were off, and they thought it might have something to do with an odd type of fish he and the other fishermen in his town were landing."

"Oh, yes, Mr. Neal! His call was directed to my office, but I never talked to him. I was out of the country when he called, and I've been too busy to get back to him. Sounded quite intriguing. Something about a 'devilfish.' Maybe I can give him a call later today."

"I hope you get good long-distance rates," Paul said. "Neal is dead."

"I don't understand."

"He was killed in a boat explosion," Gamay said. "The police don't know what caused it."

A stunned expression crossed Throckmorton's face. "Poor man." He paused, then said, "I hope this doesn't seem callous, but I suppose now I'll never know about this strange devilfish."

"We'll be glad to tell you what we know," Gamay said.

Throckmorton listened intently as Gamay and Paul took turns describing their trip with Neal. As each detail unfolded, the cheerfulness drained from Throckmorton's rosy-cheeked face. He gazed solemnly from Gamay to Paul. "Are you absolutely certain of everything you told me? You're quite sure of the size of the fish and the strange white color. And its aggressiveness?"

"See for yourself," Paul said, producing the videotape shot on Neal's boat.

After viewing the tape, Throckmorton rose, solemn-faced, from his chair and paced back and forth, hands clasped behind his back. Over and over, he muttered, "This is not good, not good at all."

Gamay had a disarming way of cutting to the chase. "Please tell us what's going on, Professor."

He stopped his pacing and sat down again. "As a marine biologist, you must know about transgenic fish," he said. "The first one was developed practically in your backyard, at the University of Maryland Biotechnology Institute."

"I've read a number of papers, but I can't say I'm an expert on the subject. From what I understand, genes are spliced into fish eggs to make them grow faster."

"That's right. The genes come from other species, even from insects and humans."

"Humans?"

"I don't use human genes in my experiments. I agree with the Chinese, who are heavily into biofish research, that using human genes in this manner is unethical."

"How are the genes used?"

"They produce unusually high levels of growth hormones and stimulate the fish's appetite. I've been developing transgenic fish with the Federal Department of Fisheries and Oceans lab in Vancouver. The salmon grown there are fed twenty times a day. The constant feeding is essential. These super-salmon are programmed to grow eight times faster, forty times larger than normal in the first year. You can see what a boon this is for a fish farmer. He brings a fatter fish to market in a fraction of the time."

"Thus ensuring a larger profit."

"To be sure. Those pushing to bring biofish to market call it the 'Blue Revolution.' They admit they'd like to increase profits, but they say they have an altruistic motive as well. DNA-altered fish will provide a cheap and plentiful source of food for the poorer nations of the world."

"I think I heard the same arguments in favor of DNA-modified crops," Gamay said.

"With good reason. Genetically modified fish were a logical outgrowth of the biotech food trend. If you can engineer corn, why not do the same for higher living organisms? This is likely to be far more controversial, though. The protests have already started. The opponents say transgenic fish could mess up the environment, wipe out the wild fishery and put the small fisherman out of business. They're calling these biotech creations 'Frankenfish.' "

"Catchy name," said Paul, who had been listening with interest to the conversation. "Can't see it selling too many fish."

"Where do you stand on this issue?" Gamay said.

"Since I created some of these fish, I have a special responsibility. I want to see more study before we start raising these creatures on fish farms. The push to commercialize what we've been doing worries me. We need extensive risk assessment before we trigger what could be a disaster."

"You sound very worried," Gamay said.

"It's what I *don't* know that concerns me. Things are spinning out of control. Dozens of commercial operations are pushing to bring their own fish to market. More than two dozen fish species are being researched in addition to salmon. The potential is enormous, although some fish farmers are turning away from transgenics because of the controversy. But big corporations have been moving in. There are dozens of patents for gene changes in Canada and the U.S."

"An economic and scientific juggernaut like that will be hard to stop once it gets going."

"I feel like King Canute trying to shout down the ocean." The frustration was apparent in his voice. "Billions of dollars are at stake, so the pressure is enormous. That's why the Canadian government funds transgenic research. The feeling is that if we don't lead the way, others will. We want to be ready when the dam bursts."

"If there is so much pressure and money involved, what's holding back the biofish tide?"

"A potential public relations nightmare. Let me give you an example. A New Zealand company called King Salmon was developing biofish, but word about two-headed and lump-covered fish leaked out, and the press whipped the public into a frenzy. King had to stop its experiments and destroy everything, because people were worried that these Frankenfish might escape into the wild and start mating with normal ones."

"Is something like that a possibility?" Gamay said.

"Not with contained fish-farming, but I have no doubt that transgenic fish would escape if they were placed in open-water cages. They are aggressive and hungry. Like a convict who yearns for freedom, they'd find a way. The government fisheries lab in Vancouver is as tight as Fort Knox. We've got electronic alarms, security guards, double-screened tanks to keep fish from getting away. But a private company might be less cautious."

Gamay nodded. "We've had invasions of foreign species in

U.S. waters, with potentially damaging results. The Asian swamp eel has been found in some states—it's a voracious creature that can slither across dry land. Asian carp are in the Mississippi River, and there are worries they can get into Lake Michigan. They grow up to four feet long, and there have been stories of them jumping out of the water and knocking people out of boats, but the real worry is the way they suck up plankton like a vacuum cleaner. Then there's the lionfish, a real cutie. They carry spines that can poison humans, and they compete for food with native species."

"You make an excellent point, but the situation with transgenic fish is even more complicated than a competition for food. Some of my colleagues are more worried about the 'Trojan gene' effect. You recall the story of the Trojan horse, naturally."

"The wooden horse filled with Greek soldiers," said Paul. "The Trojans thought it was a gift, brought it inside their city walls—and that was the end of Troy."

"An appropriate analogy in this case," Throckmorton said.

He tapped his finger against the cover of a thick staple-bound report that was lying on the table. "This was published by English Nature, the group that advises the British government on conservation matters. It contains the results of two studies. As a result of the findings, English Nature is opposing release of transgenic fish unless they are made infertile, and a House of Lords committee wants an outright ban on GM fish. The first study was done at Purdue University, where researchers found that transgenic male fish have a fourfold advantage in breeding. Larger fish are preferred as mates by females."

"Who says size isn't important?" Paul said, with his usual dry humor.

"It happens to be *very* important in fish. The researchers looked at the Japanese medaka, whose transgenic offspring were twenty-two percent larger than their siblings. These big males made up eighty percent of the breeding against twenty percent for the smaller males."

Gamay leaned forward with her brow furrowed. "It would eventually be a disaster for the wild population."

"Worse than a disaster. More like a *catastrophe*. If you had one transgenic fish in a population of 100,000, GM fish would become fifty percent of the population within sixteen generations."

"Which isn't long in fish terms," Gamay commented.

Throckmorton nodded. "You can cut that time even further. Computer models show that if you introduced sixty DNA-altered fish into a population of sixty thousand, it would take only forty generations to pollute the gene pool to extinction."

"You said there was a second study."

Throckmorton rubbed his hands together.

"Oh yes, it gets even better. The researchers at universities in Alabama and California gave salmon growth-promoter genes to some Channel catfish. They found that these transgenic fish were better at avoiding predators than were their natural counterparts."

"To put it succinctly, you think one of these superfish might get into the wild, where it would outbreed and outlive the natural species, quickly driving them to extinction."

"That's it."

Paul shook his head in disbelief. "Given what you've just told us," he said, "why would *any* government or company be fooling around with genetic dynamite like this?"

"I understand what you're saying, but in the hands of a professional, dynamite can be extremely useful." Throckmorton rose from his chair. "Come see, Dr. Frankenstein's work-bench is right this way."

He led them to the other side of the lab. The fish swimming in the tanks ranged in size from finger-length to a couple of feet long. He stopped in front of one of the larger tanks. A silver-scaled fish with a dark ridge along its spine was swimming slowly from one end of the tank to the other.

"Well, what do you think of our latest genetically modified monster?"

Gamay leaned close so that her nose was inches from the glass. "Looks like any other well-fed salmon you might see swimming in the Atlantic Ocean. Maybe a little more girth around the middle than normal."

"Appearances can be deceiving. How old would you say this handsome fellow is?"

"I'd guess it's about a year old."

"Actually, only a few weeks ago, it was a mere egg."

"Impossible."

"I would agree with you if I hadn't played midwife at its birth. What you're looking at is an eating machine. We've managed to soup up its metabolism. If that creature were placed in the wild, it would quickly out-eat the native stocks. Its little brain shouts one message over and over. 'Feed me, I'm hungry!' Watch."

Throckmorton opened a cooler, extracted a bucket of small bait fish and threw a handful into the tank. The salmon pounced on the fish, and within moments it had devoured its meal. Then it devoured the floating shreds.

"I practically grew up on a fishing boat," Paul said with wide eyes. "I've seen shark go for a hooked cod and schools of blues drive bait fish onto the beach, but I've never come across anything like this. Are you sure you didn't insert some piranha genes into your little baby?"

"Nothing that complicated, although we did some physical engineering as well. Salmon have weak, brittle teeth, so we gave this model sharper, more durable dentures that allow it to eat more quickly."

"Amazing," Gamay said, equally impressed by the display.

"This fish was only slightly modified. We've built some real monsters, true Frankenfish. We destroyed them immediately so that there was no chance they might escape into the wild. We found that we could control size, but I started to worry when I saw how aggressive our creations were, even though they looked fairly normal."

Gamay said, "The fish we caught was aggressive *and* abnormal in size."

The worried look came back onto Throckmorton's face. "There's only one conclusion I can draw. Your devilfish was a mutant created in a lab. Someone is doing research that has gotten out of control. Instead of destroying their mutants, they've allowed them into the wild. It's a shame the fish you caught was destroyed. I can only hope that it was sterile."

"What would happen if genetically engineered fish like the one we may have seen start to propagate?"

"A biotech fish is basically an alien species. It's no different than an exotic life-form brought in from Mars and introduced into our environment. I see environmental and economic damage on an unprecedented scale. They could destroy whole fishing fleets, causing huge economic hardship, like that experienced by Mr. Neal and his fellow fishermen. It would totally upset the balance of nature in the waters along our coasts, where the most productive areas are. I have no idea what the long-term consequences would be."

"Let me play devil's advocate," Gamay said after some thought. "Suppose these so-called superfish *did* supplant the natural population. The commercial fishermen would in effect become the predators who keep the population within reasonable limits. You would still have fish that could be harvested and sold at market. They would just be bigger and meatier."

"And meaner," Paul noted.

"There are too many unknowns to take the risk," Throckmorton said. "In Norway, hybrid salmon escaped into the sea and bred successfully with the native fish, but were less able to survive in the wild. So you could have a case where the superfish that replaces the wild stock dies out as a species, eliminating itself as well as the natural population."

A sardonic voice said, "My dear Throckmorton, are you trying to frighten these poor people with your dire warnings?"

A man wearing a lab coat had quietly slipped into the lab and was observing them, a wide smile on his face. "Frederick!" Professor Throckmorton said, beaming. Turning to the Trouts, he said, "This is my esteemed colleague, Dr. Barker. Frederick, these are the Doctors Trout from NUMA." In an audible aside, Throckmorton said, "They may call me Frankenstein, but this is Dr. Strangelove."

Both men laughed over the shared joke. Barker came over and shook hands. He was in his early fifties, with an imposing physique, a shaved head and sunglasses that hid his eyes. His skin had a bleached-out look to it.

"It's a great pleasure to meet someone from NUMA. Please don't let Throckmorton frighten you. You'll never eat a salmon amandine again after listening to him. What brings you to McGill?"

"We were on vacation and heard about Dr. Throckmorton's work," Gamay said. "As a marine biologist, I thought there might be something in it NUMA would be interested in."

"A busman's holiday! Well, let me defend myself against this slander. I am a strong proponent of transgenic fish, which makes me suspect in the eyes of my friend here."

"The doctor is more than a proponent. He is affiliated with some of the biotech companies that are pushing to bring these creatures to market."

"You make it sound like a dark conspiracy, Throckmorton. My friend forgets to tell you that I am working with the full complicity and financial support of the Canadian government."

"Dr. Barker would like to create a designer salmon, so that people could have a different flavor every day of the week."

"That's not a bad idea, Throckmorton. Do you mind if I borrow it?"

"Only if you claim full responsibility for creating such a monster."

"The professor worries too much." He gestured toward the fish tank. "That fine fellow is proof there is no need to create a transgenic fish of monstrous size. And as he said, biotech fish are less able to survive in the wild. It's easy enough to sterilize the fish so they won't replicate themselves."

"Yes, but sterilization techniques are less than one hundred percent reliable. You might not be so casual after you hear the news that the Trouts have brought me."

Throckmorton asked the Trouts to tell their story and run the video again. When they were finished, he said, "What do you make of it, Frederick?"

Barker shook his head. "I'm afraid I share some blame. I got the message from Neal when he called. But I never called him back."

"And what do you think?"

Barker's smile had disappeared. "I would say that it was impossible, if it had not been witnessed by two qualified observers and videotaped. This has all the earmarks of a transgenic experiment gone wrong."

"Who would be so irresponsible as to let a fish like this escape into the wild? Apparently, there are others, if we are to believe the fishermen. We must get someone in the field immediately."

"I agree wholeheartedly. It's evident that this white devilfish is already competing with the wild species for food. Whether it can pass along its genes is another question."

"That's what has bothered me all along about this whole issue, its unpredictability," Throckmorton said.

Barker glanced at his watch. "What is not unpredictable is my next class, which meets in a few minutes." He bowed slightly and shook hands with Paul and Gamay. "I'm sorry that I have to run. A pleasure meeting you."

"Your colleague is fascinating," Gamay said. "He looks more like a professional wrestler than a geneticist."

"Oh yes, Frederick is one of a kind. The female students love him. He rides a motorcycle around the city, which they think is very cool."

"Is there something wrong with his eyes?"

"You noticed the sunglasses, of course. Frederick tends toward albinism. As you can see from his lack of complexion, he avoids the sun, and his eyes are very sensitive to light. His handicap hasn't hindered his accomplishments, though. Everything I said about his brilliance is true, though, unlike me, he is putting his expertise to work in the private sector. He'll probably become a millionaire. Anyway, we must both thank you for alerting us. I'll start immediately to put a field team together."

"We've taken enough of your time," Gamay said.

"Not at all. It's been a treat to talk to you. I hope we'll meet again."

Throckmorton asked if he could copy the video. Minutes later, Paul and Gamay were in a cab headed down the hill to the hotel.

"Interesting afternoon," Paul said.

"More so than you think. While Throckmorton and I were copying the tape, I asked him who Barker's employers were. I thought it wouldn't hurt to have another lead to chase down. He said the company was named Aurora."

"Pretty name," Paul said with a yawn. "What did he say about it?"

Gamay smiled mysteriously. "He said Aurora is a subsidiary of a larger company."

Paul blinked. "Don't tell me—"

She nodded. "Oceanus."

He thought about it for a moment, then said, "I tried to look at this as if I were creating a computer graphic, but the problem is more like a kid's picture puzzle. Barker is one dot, the guys who tried to drive us off the road are another dot. If we connect the two, we can start to sketch out a picture. So our course of action is very clear."

"And what might that be?" Gamay said with skepticism.

Paul gave her a lopsided grin. "We have to come up with more dots."

23

THE LOCATION RYAN had suggested for a rendezvous was only a few minutes from NUMA headquarters. Austin drove along the George Washington Parkway to a sign that said THEODORE ROOSEVELT ISLAND. He parked his car, walked over the footbridge that spanned a narrow waterway called Little River and followed a path to the Roosevelt Memorial, a wide plaza edged by low benches. Ryan was standing with his back to the bronze statue of the president, apparently keeping an eye out for Austin.

Ryan waved him over. "Thanks for coming, Kurt."

Ryan turned and gazed up at the statue. TR stood with legs wide apart, fist raised high in the air. "Ol' Teddy up there got me into this crazy business. He put millions of acres under federal protection, saved endangered birds from the plume hunters and made the Grand Canyon a national park. He wasn't afraid to push the law to its limits when he thought he was acting in the public good. Whenever I have doubts about what I'm doing, I think of this guy staring down the fat cats."

Austin couldn't help feeling that Ryan was posing for a

photo op. "It's hard to believe you have doubts about anything, Marcus."

"Oh I *do*, believe me. Especially when I think of the task I've carved out for myself: protecting the world's oceans and the critters that live in them."

"If I recall my mythology, the sea-god position has been filled for the last few thousand years."

Ryan smirked like a guilty child. "Yeah, I guess I do sound godlike at times. But mythology also tells us that gods commonly appoint themselves to their positions."

"I'll remember that if I ever lose my job at NUMA. Therri said you wanted to talk to me about something important."

"Yes," Ryan said, looking past Austin's shoulder. "There she is now, as a matter of fact."

Therri was walking across the plaza with a young man Austin guessed to be in his early twenties. He had reddish-brown skin, a broad face and high cheekbones.

"Good to see you again, Kurt," Therri said, extending her hand. Her manner was businesslike in front of the other men, but her eyes told Austin she hadn't forgotten the goodnight kiss in Copenhagen; or at least that's what he hoped they said. "This is Ben Nighthawk. Ben is a research assistant in our office."

Ryan suggested that they move off to the side of the memorial. When he was sure they could talk out of the earshot of any wandering tourists, he wasted no time. "Ben has uncovered some important information on Oceanus," he said.

With a nod from Ryan, the young Indian began to tell his story.

"I come from a tiny village in northern Canada. It's pretty remote, on a big lake, and usually it's pretty quiet up there. A few months ago, my mother wrote me a letter saying someone had bought a huge tract of land across the lake from the village. Big corporation, she thought. I hope to work against overdevelopment of the Canadian wilds when I get out of college, so I got really interested when she said they were building night and day on the lake. Helicopters and floatplanes were coming in at all hours. I asked my mother to keep me up to date, and the last time I heard from her was more than two weeks ago. She was really worried."

"About what?" Austin said.

"She didn't say, only that it had something to do with the stuff going on across the lake. So I got worried and went home to take a look—and my family was gone."

"You're saying they disappeared?" Austin said.

Nighthawk nodded. "Everyone in the village had vanished."

"Canada's a big place, Ben. Where was your village located?"

Nighthawk glanced at Ryan. "In good time, Kurt," Ryan said. "Tell Mr. Austin what happened next, Ben."

"I went looking for my family," Nighthawk continued. "I found them being kept prisoner on the other side of the lake. Guys with guns were forcing the men from my village to work, clearing land around a big building."

"Do you know who they were?"

"I never saw them before. They were dressed in black uniforms." He looked at Ryan for encouragement, then went on. "It's crazy, but when we got there—"

"We?"

Ryan said, "Josh Green, my next in command, went along with Ben. Don't be afraid to tell Mr. Austin everything you saw, no matter how wild it seems."

Nighthawk shrugged. "Okay, then. When we first got there, we didn't see anything but forest, except for where they were clearing. Then this huge building suddenly appeared out of nowhere." He paused, waiting for Austin to reply with disbelieving laughter.

Austin kept his blue-green eyes leveled. "Go on," he said, his face impassive.

"That's *it*. Instead of trees, we were looking at a giant dome. Josh and I thought it looked like an Eskimo igloo, only hundreds of times bigger. While we were watching, the top of the thing opened like this." He cupped his hands to form an open clamshell. "Turned out it was a hangar for a blimp."

Austin said, "Something like the Goodyear blimp?"

Nighthawk screwed up his mouth in thought. "Naw. Bigger and longer. More like a rocket ship. It even had a name on the fin. *Nietzsche*."

"Like the German philosopher?"

"I guess so," Ben said. "We saw the thing land in the

hangar, and the roof closed again, and then a bunch of guys came out the front door. My cousin was in a work gang, and he tried to run for it, and one of those bastards killed him." Nighthawk's voice became choked with emotion.

Ryan put his hand on Nighthawk's shoulder. "That's enough for now, Ben."

Austin said, "I'd like to help. But I'm going to need more details."

Ryan said, "We'll be glad to fill you in, but the information comes with a price."

Austin raised an eyebrow. "I'm a little short of change today, Marcus."

"We're not interested in money. We want SOS and NUMA to work together to bring Oceanus down. We share the information. You include us in any mission."

Austin showed his teeth in a wide grin. "You'd be better off calling in the marines, Ryan. NUMA is a scientific organization dedicated to gathering knowledge. It's not a military organization."

"C'mon, Kurt, you're being disingenuous," Ryan said, with a knowing smile. "We researched your job at NUMA. This Special Assignments Team you run has come up against some pretty hard cases. You didn't stop the bad guys by whacking them over the head with a scientific treatise."

"You flatter me, Marcus. I don't have the power to authorize a joint mission. I'd have to run it by higher-ups."

Ryan took the answer as a qualified yes. "I *knew* you'd come around," he said triumphantly. "Thank you so much."

"Save your thanks. I have no intention of going to the head honchos."

"Why not?"

"NUMA would be putting its reputation on the line if it worked with a fringe organization like SOS. On the other hand, you'd gain public support for the Sentinels by putting them under NUMA's umbrella of legitimacy. Sorry. It's a one-sided deal."

Ryan brushed back his hair. "We haven't told you everything, Kurt. I have a personal stake in this, as well. It wasn't just Ben's cousin—Josh Green was killed."

"It was my fault," Ben said. "I ran into the open, and he tried to stop me. They shot him."

"You did what anyone would have done in your place," Ryan said. "Josh was a brave man."

"You're talking about *two* murders now," Austin said. "Have you reported them to the police?"

"No. We want to deal with this ourselves. And there's something else that may persuade you to change your mind. We tracked down the new owner of the land around Ben's lake. It was a real-estate straw corporation . . . set up by Oceanus."

"You're sure of that?"

"Positive. Are you with us now?"

Austin shook his head. "Before you buckle on your six-shooters and ride off, let me remind you what you're up against. Oceanus has money, and worldwide connections, and as you've seen, they don't hesitate to commit cold-blooded murder. They'd swat you and anyone you brought in from SOS like a fly. I'm sorry about Ben's cousin and your friend getting killed, but it only proves what I've been saying. You'll be putting your people in similar danger." He glanced pointedly at Therri.

"They're willing to take any risk for the environment," Ryan said. "Apparently, NUMA doesn't give a damn about it."

"Hold on, Marcus," Therri said. She had seen Austin's jaw harden. "Kurt has a point. Maybe we could offer a compromise. SOS could work *behind* the scenes with NUMA."

"Spoken like a true lawyer," Austin said.

Therri hadn't expected Austin's quick rebuff. "What's that supposed to mean?" she said, a hint of coldness creeping into her voice.

"I think this is less about the whales and the walruses and dead friends, and more about your friend's ego." He turned back to Ryan. "You're still ticked off about the loss of the *Sea Sentinel*. She was your pride and joy. You were going to play the martyr in front of the cable news cameras, but the Danes beat you to the punch when they dropped the charges and quietly kicked you out of their country."

"That's not true," Therri said. "Marcus is—"

Ryan silenced her with a wave of his hand. "Don't waste your breath. It's apparent that Kurt is a fair-weather friend."

"Better than no friend at all," Austin said. He pointed toward the statue of Roosevelt. "Maybe you should go back and read that guy's resumé again. He didn't ask others to stick their necks out. Sorry to hear about your cousin, Ben, and about Josh Green. Nice to see you again, Therri."

Austin had had his fill of Ryan's self-aggrandizement. He'd been hopeful when he heard Nighthawk's story, but angry at Ryan for slamming the door on a possible lead. He was striding down the path when he heard footsteps from behind. Therri had followed him from the memorial. She caught up with him and grabbed him lightly by the arm. "Kurt, please reconsider. Marcus really needs your help."

"I can see that. But I can't agree to his conditions."

"We can work something out," she pleaded.

"If you and Ben want help from NUMA, you'll have to cut loose from Ryan."

"I can't do that," she said, bringing the power of her lovely eyes to bear.

"I think you can," Austin said, boring back with his own, equally intense gaze.

"Damnit, Austin," she said with exasperation, "you're one stubborn bastard."

Austin chuckled. "Does that mean you won't go out to dinner with me?"

Therri's face darkened with anger, and she spun on her heel and strode off along the path. Austin watched her until she disappeared around a curve. He shook his head. The sacrifices I make for NUMA, he thought. He started off toward the parking lot, only to stop short a minute later when a figure popped out of the woods. It was Ben Nighthawk.

"I made an excuse to get away," Nighthawk said breathlessly. "I told Marcus I had to use the rest room. I had to talk to you. I don't blame you for not wanting to hook up with SOS. Marcus has let all the publicity go to his head. He thinks he's Wyatt Earp. But I saw those guys kill my cousin and Josh. I tried to tell him what he's up against, but he won't listen. If SOS goes in, my family is dead meat."

"Tell me where they are and I'll do what I can."

"It's tough to explain. I'll have to draw you a map. Oh, hell—"

Ryan was striding up the path toward them, an angry expression on his handsome face. "Call me," Austin said.

Ben nodded and walked back to meet Ryan. They became engaged in what looked like a heated discussion. Then Ryan put his arm around Ben and guided him back to the memorial. He turned back once, to glare at Austin, who shrugged off the evil eye and headed back to his car.

Twenty minutes later, Austin strolled into the Air and Space Museum on Independence Avenue. He took the elevator to the third floor, and was headed toward the library, when he encountered a middle-aged man in a wrinkled tan suit who had stepped out of a side room.

"Kurt Austin, as I live and breathe!" the man said.

"I wondered if I'd bump into you, Mac."

"Always a good chance of that around here. I practically live within these walls. How's the pride of NUMA these days?"

"Fine. How's the Smithsonian's answer to St. Julien Perlmutter?"

MacDougal chortled at the question. Tall and lean, with fine sandy hair and a hawk-nose that dominated his narrow face, he was the physical antithesis of the portly Perlmutter. But what he lacked in girth he made up for with an encyclopedic knowledge of air history that was every bit the equivalent of Perlmutter's grasp of the sea.

"St. Julien carries much more, um, weight in the historical world than I do," he said, with a twinkle in his gray eyes. "What brings you into the rarified atmosphere of the Archives Division?"

"I'm doing some research on an old airship. I was hoping I'd find something in the library."

"No need to go to the archives. I'm on my way to a meeting, but we can talk on the way."

Austin said. "Have you ever come across a mention of an airship called the *Nietzsche*?"

"Oh, sure. Only one airship had that name—the one that was lost on the secret polar expedition of 1935."

"You know it, then?"

He nodded. "There were rumors that the Germans had sent an airship to the North Pole on a secret mission. If it had succeeded, it was meant to cow the Allies and tout the glories of German *Kultur* in the propaganda war. The Germans denied it, but they couldn't explain the disappearance of two of their greatest airship pioneers, Heinrich Braun and Herman Lutz. The war came along, and the stories faded."

"So that was it?"

"Oh no. After the war, papers were discovered that suggested strongly that the flight had indeed taken place, with an airship similar to the *Graf Zeppelin*. The airship supposedly sent a radio message as it neared the pole. They had discovered something of interest on the ice."

"They didn't say what?"

"No. And some people believe it was a fabrication, anyhow. Maybe something Josef Goebbels made up."

"But *you* believe the accounts."

"It's entirely possible. Certainly the technology was there."

"What could have happened to the airship?"

"There are all sorts of possibilities. Engine failure. Sudden storm. Ice. Human error. The *Graf Zeppelin* was a highly successful aircraft, but we're talking about operating in extreme conditions. Other airships have come to similar fates. It could have crashed into the pack ice, been carried hundreds of miles away and gone into the sea when the ice melted." His face lit up. "Don't tell me! You've found traces of it at the bottom of the sea?"

"Unfortunately, no. Someone mentioned it to me . . . and, well, my scientific curiosity got the better of me."

"I know exactly what you mean." He stopped in front of a door. "Here's my meeting. Come by again and we'll talk some more."

"I will. Thanks for your help."

Austin was glad that Mac wasn't pressing him further. He didn't like being evasive with old friends.

MacDougal paused with his hand on the doorknob. "The

fact that we're talking about the Arctic is a funny coincidence. There's a big reception tonight to open a new exhibition on Eskimo culture and art. 'People of the Frozen North,' or something like that. Dogsled races, the whole thing."

"Dogsled races in Washington?"

"I said the same thing, but apparently it's so. Why don't you come by and see for yourself?"

"I may just do that."

As he was leaving the museum, Austin stopped at the information booth and picked up a brochure for the exhibition, which was in fact called *Denizens of the Frozen North*. The opening night reception was by invitation only. He ran his eye down the brochure and stopped at the name of the sponsor: Oceanus.

He tucked the brochure in his pocket and drove back to his office. A few calls later, he had wrangled an invitation, and, after working awhile longer on his report to Gunn, he went home to change. As he walked past the bookshelves in his combined living room–library, he ran his fingers along the spines of the neatly shelved volumes. The voices of Aristotle, Dante and Locke seemed to speak to him.

Austin's fascination with the great philosophers went back to his college days and the influence of a thought-provoking professor. Later, philosophy provided a distraction from his work and helped shed light on the darker elements of the human soul. In the course of his assignments, Austin had killed men and injured others. His sense of duty, justice and self-preservation had shielded him from crippling, and perhaps dangerous, self-doubt. But Austin was not a callous man, and philosophy gave him a moral compass to follow when he examined the rightness of his actions.

He extracted a thick volume, flicked on the stereo so that the liquid notes flowed from John Coltrane's saxophone, then went out on the deck and settled into a chair. Riffling through the pages, he quickly found the quote he'd been thinking about since MacDougal had mentioned a blimp named *Nietzsche*.

Whoever fights monsters should see to it that in the process he does not become a monster. And when you look into an abyss, the abyss also looks into you.

He stared off into space for a few moments, wondering if he had seen the abyss, or more important, whether it was looking back at him. Then he closed the book, put it back on the shelf and went to get ready for the reception.

24

A HUGE BANNER emblazoned with the words *Denizens of the Frozen North* was draped over the Mall entrance to the National Museum of Natural History. Painted on the banner, so there would be no mistaking the subject of the show, were figures in hooded fur parkas riding dogsleds across a forbidding Arctic landscape. Mountainous hulking icebergs loomed in the background.

Austin walked between the portico columns and stepped into the museum's expansive octagonal rotunda. At the center of the eighty-foot-wide space was a masterpiece of taxidermy, an African elephant charging across an imaginary savanna. The twelve-ton animal dwarfed the petite docent standing under its upraised trunk.

"Good evening," the young woman said with a smile, handing Austin a program. She was wearing a lightweight facsimile of traditional Eskimo dress. "Welcome to the *Denizens of the Frozen North* exhibition. Go through that door and you'll see the displays in the special exhibition hall. A movie on Eskimo culture will be showing every twenty minutes in the Imax Theater. The sled dog and harpoon competitions will be held on the Mall in about fifteen minutes. Should be quite exciting!"

Austin thanked the guide and trailed the guests into the special exhibit area. The well-lit display cases were filled with Eskimo artwork and ivory carvings, tools for hunting and fishing, cleverly fashioned skin suits and boots that would keep their owners warm and dry in the coldest of Arctic temperatures, driftwood sleds, canoes and whaleboats. A doleful chant backed by the beat of a tom-tom came from speakers scattered around the hall.

The chattering crowd was the usual combination of Washington politicians, bureaucrats and press. For all its importance in the world, Washington was still a small town, and Austin recognized a number of familiar faces. He was talking to a historian from the Navy Museum who was a kayak enthusiast, when he heard his name called. Angus MacDougal from the Air and Space Museum was making his way through the milling guests. He took Austin's arm.

"Come over here, Kurt, there's someone I want you to meet."

He led Austin to a dignified-looking gray-haired man and introduced him as Charles Gleason, the curator of the exhibition.

"I told Chuck that you were interested in Eskimos," MacDougal said.

"Actually, they prefer to be called 'Inuit,' which means, 'the People,'" Gleason said. "'Eskimo' was a name the Indians gave them. It means 'eaters of raw flesh.' Their name for themselves is 'Nakooruk,' which means 'good.'" He smiled. "Sorry for the lecture. I taught college for many years, and the pedagogue in me keeps reasserting itself."

"No apology necessary," Austin said. "I never resist the opportunity to learn something new."

"That's very kind of you. Do you have any questions on the exhibition?"

"I was wondering about the sponsor," Austin said. He read the placard stating that items in the case were on loan from Oceanus, and he decided to take a long shot. "I've heard the head of Oceanus is a man named Toonook."

"*Toonook?*"

"That's right."

Gleason gave him a wary look. "You're serious?"

"*Very.* I'd like to meet the gentleman."

Gleason replied with a strange half smile and made a sound between a chortle and a snicker. Unable to contain himself, he burst forth with a loud guffaw. "Sorry," he said, "but I'd hardly call Toonook a *gentleman.* Toonook is the Inuit name of an evil spirit. He's considered to be the creator and destroyer."

"You're saying Toonook is a *mythological* name?"

"That's right. The Inuit say he's in the sea, the earth and the air. Every time there's an unexpected noise, like the ice cracking underfoot, it's Toonook, looking for a victim. When the wind howls like a pack of hungry wolves, it's Toonook."

Austin was confused. Toonook was the name Therri had given him as the head of Oceanus. "I can see why my question made you laugh," Austin said, with an embarrassed smile. "I must have misunderstood."

"There's no misunderstanding as far as the Inuit are concerned," Gleason said. "When they travel alone, they keep an eye out for Toonook. They carry a bone knife and wave it around to keep Toonook at bay."

Austin's eye drifted past Gleason's shoulder. "Something like the little pig sticker in that display case?"

Gleason tapped the glass in front of the ornately carved white blade. "That's a very rare and unusual item."

"In what way?"

"Most Inuit knives were tools mainly used for skinning. That knife was made with one purpose: to kill other human beings."

"Odd," Austin said, "I had always heard that the Eskimos were a peaceful and good-natured people."

"Very true. They live in close quarters in a harsh and demanding environment where tempers could easily flare into violence. They know cooperation is vital to survival, and so they've evolved a whole set of rituals and customs to diffuse aggression."

"That knife looks about as aggressive as it gets."

Gleason nodded in agreement. "The Inuit are subject to the same dark passions as the rest of humankind. The people who made that weapon were from a tribe that broke the peaceful mold. We think they came from Siberia in prehistoric times and settled in northern Quebec. They tended toward rape, pillage, human sacrifice . . . very nasty. The other communities banded together many years ago and drove them off. They named them 'Kiolya.' "

"Doesn't ring a bell."

"It's the Inuit name for the aurora borealis, which the Arctic people regard as the manifestation of evil. The real name of the tribe, no one knows."

"What happened to the Kiolya?"

"They scattered around Canada. Many of them ended up in the cities, where their descendants formed criminal enterprises. Murder for hire and extortion, mainly. Some of them retained their old tribal customs, such as the vertical tattoos over the cheekbones, until they found that it identified them easily to the police."

"I'm curious. How is an exhibition like this pulled together?"

"In many different ways. With this one, a public relations firm from Oceanus approached the museum and asked if we would be interested in placing the show. They said the sponsors had a strong interest in educating the public on Inuit culture, and they would organize the exhibition and pay all costs. Well, we couldn't resist. It's a fascinating show, don't you think?"

Austin stared at the Kiolya knife, which was identical to the weapon that had slashed his chest open at the Faroe Islands fish farm. He was thinking about the vertical tattoos on the face of the man who'd wielded the knife. "Yes, fascinating," he said.

"Since I can't introduce you to Toonook, perhaps you'd like to meet the representative from Oceanus."

"He's here?"

"I just spoke to him a few minutes ago in the diorama room. Follow me."

The lights in the diorama room had been dimmed to simulate the Arctic night. Lasers projected a moving display of the northern lights on the ceiling. Standing alone in front of a life-sized diorama showing a seal hunt was a tall, well-built man with a shaved head. Dark sunglasses covered his eyes.

Gleason approached the man and said, "Dr. Barker, I'd like you to meet Kurt Austin. Mr. Austin is with the National Underwater and Marine Agency. You must know of it."

"I would have to come from another planet not to know NUMA."

They shook hands. Austin felt like his fingers were clutching a frozen side of beef.

"I hope you don't mind if I share our little joke," Gleason said to Kurt. "Mr. Austin thought that the head of Oceanus was named Toonook."

"Mr. Gleason explained that Toonook was not a man, but an evil spirit," Austin said.

Barker stared at Austin through the dark lenses. "It's more complicated than that," he said. "Toonook *is* considered to be evil in the Inuit culture. He is the embodiment of that clever light display on the ceiling. But like others through history, the people of the North worshipped the thing they feared the most."

"Toonook is a god, then?"

"Sometimes. But I assure you that the head of Oceanus is very human."

"I stand corrected. If it's not Toonook, what is his real name?"

"He prefers to keep his identity a secret. If you'd like to call him Toonook, feel free to do so. He has been called worse names by his competitors. He stays out of the limelight, and it falls upon his employees to represent him. In my case, I work for a company named Aurora, which is a subsidiary of Oceanus."

"What sort of work do you do for Aurora?"

"I'm a geneticist."

Austin glanced around the room. "This is a wide departure from genetics."

"I like to get out of the lab. I suggested that Oceanus sponsor this exhibition. I have a direct interest in the Kiolya. My great-great-grandfather was a New England whaling captain. He stayed with the tribe and tried to stop the walrus hunting that led to its dissolution."

"Mr. Gleason tells me that the other Eskimos ran the Kiolya off because they were thieves and murderers."

"They did what they had to do to survive," Barker said.

"I'd love to continue this discussion," Gleason said, "but you'll have to excuse me. I see an assistant who needs my attention. Please give me a call sometime, and we can talk at length, Mr. Austin."

When Gleason was gone, Austin said, "Tell me, Dr. Barker, what sort of business is Oceanus involved in that would require the services of a geneticist?"

The frozen smile disappeared. "Come on, Austin. We're alone, so we don't need to play games, anymore. You know very well what Oceanus does. You broke into our Faroe Islands operation, caused a lot of damage and killed one of my men. I won't forget it."

"Gee," Austin said. "Now you've got me confused. You've obviously mistaken me for someone else."

"I don't think so. The Danish press published your picture everywhere. You're quite the hero in Denmark, you know, for rescuing their sailors after that collision."

"A collision which your company engineered," Austin said, dropping all pretense.

"And which would have worked, except for your meddling." The soft, cultivated voice had become a snarl. "Well, that ends now. You've interfered in my business for the last time."

"*Your* business? I thought you were a humble employee for Oceanus, Dr. Barker . . . or should I call you Toonook?"

Barker removed his glasses and stared at Austin with pale-gray eyes. The moving colors played across his ashen features as if projected on a screen. "Who I am is not important. *What* I am has a direct bearing on your future. I am the instrument of your death. Turn around."

Austin glanced over his shoulder. Two swarthy men stood behind him, blocking the way. They had closed the door to keep the other guests out. Austin wondered which would offer him the better chance, pushing Barker through the display glass or bulling his way between the men at the door. He had already decided he didn't like either option and was groping for a third, when there was a knock at the door and MacDougal stuck his head in.

"Hey, Kurt," he called out. "I'm looking for Charlie Gleason. Sorry to interrupt you."

"Not at all," Austin said. MacDougal wasn't the Seventh Cavalry, but he would do.

The guards looked to Barker for direction. He replaced his sunglasses, gave Austin his glacial smile and said, " 'Til we meet again," and made for the door. The guards stepped aside to let him through, and a second later, all three men were lost in the crowd.

Austin's reunion with MacDougal didn't last long. As they merged with the crowd, Mac spotted a senator who was a friend of the Smithsonian, and he dashed off to collar him for funding. Austin mingled with the other guests until he heard an announcement saying that the dogsled races were about to begin. He was heading back to the rotunda when he caught a glimpse of chestnut hair cascading to bare shoulders. Therri must have felt his attention. She turned and glared in his direction. Then she smiled.

"Kurt, what a nice surprise," she said. As they shook hands, she eyed him from head to toe. "You look quite handsome in your tuxedo."

Austin hadn't expected the friendly greeting after the acrimony of their parting exchange on Roosevelt Island. "Thanks," he said. "Hope it doesn't smell too strongly of mothballs."

She adjusted one of his lapels as if she were his prom date. "You smell quite nice, as a matter of fact."

"And so do you. Does this flowery exchange of compliments mean that we're friends again?"

"I was never angry at you. *Frustrated,* perhaps." She pouted, but her eyes twinkled. The girl-next-door wholesomeness couldn't mask an underlying sensuality.

"Let's call a truce, then, and start over."

"I'd like that." Therri glanced around at the crowd. "I'm curious about what brought you to the reception."

"The same thing that attracted you. I'm sure it didn't escape your attention that these displays are the property of Oceanus."

"That's the main reason we're here." Therri glanced off to the side of the rotunda, where Ben Nighthawk stood. He looked uneasy in his black tuxedo, unsure of what to do with his hands, shifting his weight from one foot to the other. She waved him over.

"You remember Ben," Therri said.

"Good to see you again," Austin said, shaking hands. "Nice tux."

"Thanks," Nighthawk said, without enthusiasm. "It's rented." He glanced around at the other guests. "I'm a little out of my element."

"Don't worry," Austin said. "Most of the people who come to these receptions are here for the food and the gossip."

"Ben agreed to escort me," Therri said. "Marcus thought Ben's memory might be jogged by something he saw."

"Has it been?"

"Not yet," Therri said. "What about you? Have you learned anything?"

"Yes," he said with a tight smile. "I've learned that you don't listen to warnings of possible danger."

"That's ancient history," Therri said, like someone trying to be patient with an annoying child. Austin took in the challenging gaze and decided he was wasting his breath trying to change her mind.

"I'm on my way outside to see the dogsled races," he said. "Would you like to join me?"

"Thank you," she said, hooking her arm in Nighthawk's. "We were headed that way ourselves."

A guide directed them outside. Traffic on Madison Drive had been stopped to allow spectators to cross to the National Mall. It was a beautiful night. Lit by floodlights, the red sandstone turrets of the Smithsonian Castle were clearly visible across the eight-hundred-foot width of greensward. Toward the Potomac, the plain white spike of the Washington Monument soared into the night sky.

A large section of open grass had been marked off with yellow police tape and was brightly illuminated by portable lights. Inside the enclosure, orange pylons were arranged in a rectangle. Hundreds of reception guests in evening attire, and passersby attracted by the lights and crowd, ringed the perimeter. A few National Park Service uniforms could be seen. From the other side of the racecourse, where several trucks were lined up, came a sound like a kennel at feeding time. Then the excited yelps and barks were drowned out by a male voice on the public address system.

"Welcome to the *Denizens of the Frozen North* exhibition, ladies and gentlemen," the announcer said. "You're about to see the most exciting part of the show, the dogsled competition. This is more than a race. The contestants, from two different Inuit communities in Canada, will demonstrate the skills needed to survive in the Arctic. The hunter must speed to the kill and use his harpoon with unerring accuracy. As you know, we don't have much snowfall in Washington this time of year." He paused, to allow for the laughter. "So the racers will have wheels on their sleds instead of runners. Enjoy the show!"

Figures milled around the trucks, then broke into two groups, each pushing a sled toward an opening in the taped enclosure. The sleds, one bright blue, the other fire-engine red, were brought to the starting point and placed side by side. The wolflike sled dogs were taken from the kennel trailers and hooked into their harnesses.

Excited by the prospect of a run, the huskies grew more agitated. The barking reached a crescendo as the impatient dogs pulled against their harnesses. The nine-dog teams, with eight in pairs and one as leader, exerted an amazing amount of muscle power when harnessed together. Even with the brakes set and handlers holding on, the sleds inched forward.

Two men, the drivers obviously, detached themselves from the others and climbed onto their sleds. A second later, the starting gun went off. The drivers shouted commands, the dogs dug their paws in, and the sleds took off like twin rockets. The dogs immediately went into an all-out run. Unsure of the conditions on the grassy course, the drivers slowed slightly as they came into the first turn. There was some skidding, but the sleds came out of the turn side by side and stayed neck and neck into the second curve, successfully navigating it.

The sleds were moving at full tilt again as they raced toward the spot where Austin stood behind the yellow tape, next to Therri and Ben. The drivers urged the dogs on with loud kissing sounds. In deference to the mild evening, the drivers were not dressed in hooded fur parkas, instead wearing skin pants tucked into their boots. Sweat glistened on their bare chests.

The sleds were modified tube steel rigs like those used to train dogs when there is no snow for the runners to glide upon. Steel mesh platforms about six feet long and more than a yard wide nestled between four rubber airplane tires. The sleds were steered by a small wheel at the top of a vertical tube frame. The drivers stood with feet placed on narrow side extensions that flanked the main platform, bodies hunched over the steering posts to cut wind resistance and lower the center of gravity. As the sleds flashed by with whirring wheels, the faces of the drivers were only a blur.

The racers were still abreast as they came into the third turn. The red one was on the inside. Looking for a gain, the driver tried to cut the turn tightly. But the sled caught an edge, and the wheels on the other side lifted off the ground a few inches. The driver skillfully compensated with the weight of his body and a touch of the brake, and the wheels slammed down again. The blue-sled driver took advantage of the lost gamble. He could have gone wide, but he finessed the turn with admirable skill and gained a quarter of a length in the straightaway.

The crowd was cheering madly, and it went wild when the blue sled increased the lead to half a length. Another few feet and the blue sled would be able to pull over in front of the red one, blocking the way and controlling the race. The blue driver kept glancing over his shoulder, looking for an opportunity. He got his chance in the fourth and last curve.

The leading sled, on the outside, came into the turn at a perfect speed and angle to put him completely ahead of the other racer. But the red sled suddenly veered to the right, and its front wheel caught the leader's rear-left tire. The blue sled fishtailed from the impact, and the driver fought to bring it under control. The dogs sensed the whiplash about to take place and tried to compensate by pulling harder, but the centrifugal forces acting on the light vehicle proved too potent.

The blue sled went up on two wheels and flipped. The driver went airborne, like a circus performer shot out of a cannon. He hit the grass hard, rolled several times and lay still. The dogs kept running and dragged the sled on its side until they could pull it no farther. Then they began to fight among themselves. The handlers ducked under the yellow tape and rushed in to get the dogs under control, while others tended to the fallen driver.

The red-sled driver pushed ahead at full speed, although he had the race won, not slowing until he had passed over the finish line. The sled was still moving when he jumped off it and grabbed a harpoon from a barrel. Without pausing to aim, he sent the spear winging toward an archery target set up near the course. The spear hit the bull's-eye at dead center. Then he pulled a hatchet from his belt and hurled it at the target as well. Bull's-eye again.

The victorious driver raised his fists high in the air and let out a chilling cry of victory, then strutted around the perimeter of the racecourse, his wide mouth set in a grin, his face like a malevolent jack-o'-lantern. His arrogant posturing put to rest any doubts that the collision was an accident. A lone boo issued from the stunned crowd, then was joined by others, growing into an angry chorus as the spectators showed their disapproval of the winning tactics. Disgusted with the race, guests began to move back to the museum.

The driver gestured at the departing spectators as if daring someone to step forward. His gaze swept the crowd—looking for anyone brave or foolish enough to take him on—when it fell on Austin. The dark eyes narrowed into slits. Austin tensed. Standing only a few feet away was the man who had slashed him and tossed a hand grenade into his boat at the Mermaid's Gate. He would have recognized the man from the hate burning in his feral eyes even without the vertical tattoo lines on the cheekbones and the mangled knot of flesh where Austin had bashed him in the nose.

The thick lips in the dark, wide face formed a silent word. *Austin.*

Austin was stunned that the man knew his name, but he hid his surprise.

Using his most mocking tone, he said, "Long time no see, Nanook. You owe me for the plastic surgery I did on your pretty face."

The driver stepped closer until they were a foot or so apart, separated only by the yellow tape. Austin could smell the man's fetid breath.

"The name is Umealiq," he said. "I want you to call my name when you beg me for mercy."

"Don't blame you for being dissatisfied with your nose job," Austin said evenly. "You didn't give me a lot to work with. Pay me for the boat you blew up and we'll call it even."

"The only payment you will get is *death*," the man snarled.

His thick fingers dropped down to his belt, and he began to slide the bone knife from its scabbard. Although most of the spectators had left, there were still knots of people hanging around. Austin sensed that there was no safety in numbers and the man would not hesitate to kill him, even in front of dozens of witnesses. He clenched his right fist, ready to send it crashing into the broken nose, where it would inflict the most damage and pain.

Then, out of the corner of his eye, he saw a sudden movement. Ben Nighthawk had hurled himself at the driver. The Indian was too light and his tackling form too imperfect to do any damage. The driver grunted, and his squat body shuddered slightly from the impact, but he kept his footing and swatted Nighthawk aside with a mighty blow.

Again the hand groped for the knife, and he took a step forward, only to freeze at the sound of a commotion. The blue-sled driver was making his way across the Mall, accompanied by several angry handlers. Dirt and blood stained his face. Umealiq whirled to face the newcomers. They exchanged angry words, obviously arguing over the race tactics. With a quick burning glance back at Austin, the red-sled driver pushed his way through the others and made his way back to the trucks.

Therri was down on her knees, tending to Nighthawk. Austin went to her side and saw that the Indian's only injury was a bruise where he'd been struck under the eye. As they helped him to his feet, he spit the words out: "That was the man who killed my cousin."

"You're *sure*?" Therri said.

Nighthawk nodded dumbly. His dazed eyes fixed on the figure walking across the Mall, and he stumbled forward. Austin saw where he was going and stepped in front of him, barring his path. "He and his pals will kill you."

"I don't care."

"Now is not the time," Austin said, in a voice that said he wasn't yielding.

Nighthawk saw that his determination wasn't enough to get him past Austin's wide shoulders. He swore in his native language and stalked across the Mall toward the museum.

Therri said, "Thanks for stopping Ben. We should tell the police."

"Not a bad idea. But it might be a problem."

A group of men was striding onto the Mall from the direction of the museum. In the lead was the tall figure of Dr. Barker. He hailed Austin like a long-lost buddy.

"Nice to see you again, Austin. I'm on my way out and stopped to say good-bye."

"Thanks, but I'm not going anywhere."

"Oh, but you *are*. Umealiq is waiting for you and your friend. You're about to learn why he is named after the stone-headed lance the Inuit use on seal hunts."

Barker pointed to where Scarface stood in the middle of the racecourse. Then, escorted by two bodyguards, he strode off to where a limo awaited, leaving the rest of his men behind.

Others came running over from where the trucks were parked. Austin did a quick count and estimated that there were about twenty men in all. Not exactly great odds. Their prospects didn't get any better when a couple of men ran over to the portable lights that had illuminated the racecourse and snapped them off.

The Mall had become a big and lonely place. The nearest police presence was a traffic cop on Madison Drive stopping cars so the guests could return to the museum. The remaining guests were making their way back to the reception, and the passersby had resumed their strolls. Austin's sharp eye followed the shadows that were moving across the grass in a classic encircling maneuver.

He took Therri's arm and tried to guide her toward the museum, but Barker's men barred their way. It was a repeat of the scene in Copenhagen, but this time Austin had no trash-can lid to use as a shield and a weapon. He could see several strollers, and even a couple of National Park Service people, walking through the Mall unmindful of the unfolding drama, but decided against calling for help. Anyone he talked to would be put in immediate danger.

One light had been left on. Standing in the bull's-eye of illumination, like an actor in the spotlight, was Umealiq. His hand was on his scabbard. His men were closing in from the sides and behind. Austin had no choice. He took Therri's hand, and they slowly began to walk toward what was certain death.

25

DESPITE THE AURA of death in the air, Austin maintained an uncanny serenity. He had developed the ability to shift his brain into what could best be described as a mental overdrive. While his synapses continued to crackle, an inner voice slowed his thought processes, calmly taking in details fed to it by the senses and formulating a plan of action.

He and Therri faced two possible fates. At a signal from their leader, the men pacing on both sides could carve them up with their hatchets. More likely, Austin judged, Scarface would do the job, as he himself had promised. Austin was working on a third option, although it wouldn't have been apparent to their escorts. He glanced fearfully around him, giving the impression of being consumed with panic and confusion, while mentally he mapped out an escape route and calculated the odds.

Therri squeezed his hand until his knuckles hurt. "Kurt, what should we do?" she said, with only the slightest tremor in her voice.

The question gave Austin a sense of relief. It told him that, far from having given up hope, Therri was also looking for a way out of their predicament. Her determination suggested that she could call upon untapped reserves. She would need them, Austin thought.

"Keep walking. Just think of it as a stroll in the park."

Therri glanced sideways at their silent escorts. "Some stroll. Some park. I haven't had so much fun since our Copenhagen date."

The spark of humor was a good sign. They took a few more steps.

Austin murmured, "When I say 'mush,' I want you to follow my lead."

"Did you say 'mush'?"

"That's right. Stay with me. Climb up on my heels if you have to. No matter where I go, stay close."

Therri nodded, and they continued to walk at a snail's pace. Austin and Therri had advanced close enough to Scarface to see the hard eyes glittering like black diamonds under the low-cut bangs. The others seemed in no hurry, probably trying to draw out the terror as long as possible. In their black coveralls, the men looked like mourners at a wake. Austin saw them only as dangerous obstacles to be removed or eluded. The real focus of his attention lay off to the left. The red dogsled had been left unattended. The dogs sat or lay curled up on the grass, eyes half-closed, mouths open in a canine grin.

Austin took a deep breath. Timing would be everything. Another step closer to the end of their lives.

Scarface anticipated their arrival. His hand dropped to the hilt of the bone knife in its scabbard, the cruel mouth widened in a smile, like someone licking his chops over a tender steak. He said something in an unintelligible language. It was only a few words, probably a gloating remark, but it caught the attention of his men, who all looked in their leader's direction.

Austin gripped Therri's hand. "Ready?" he whispered.

She squeezed back.

"Mush!"

Austin sidestepped to his left, yanked Therri practically off her feet, and lunged toward a gap in the line of pickets. The guards saw them break out and tried to head them off, like defensive linebackers converging to stop a runner with the ball. They raced toward the closing gap. At the last moment, Austin changed direction. He shook off Therri's hand, and putting all the weight of his body behind his shoulder, smashed into the midsection of the guard to his left. The man let out a sound like a malfunctioning steam engine and doubled over.

The other guard charged in, hatchet in hand. Using the bounce from his first encounter, Austin came out of his crouch and slammed into the man with his other shoulder. The impact lifted the other man off his feet. The hatchet went flying onto the grass.

Therri was right behind him. A few more steps and they were at the sled. The dogs noticed their approach and perked their ears up. Austin grabbed the sled's upright framework and held it tight. He didn't want the dog team to bolt off. Without being instructed, Therri rolled onto the steel-mesh platform, then sat up, legs extended forward, hands gripping the uprights in front of her. Austin kicked off the brake.

"Hike!" he snapped in a clear, commanding voice.

The sled's regular driver probably used an Inuit command, but the team knew from his tone what Austin wanted. Mushers don't use the word "mush" to get dogs moving. The word is too soft. Austin was a man of the sea, but he wasn't above developing land-based skills. Dogsledding, unfortunately, wasn't among them. He had tried dogsled driving a few times as a diversion on ski trips, and after being thrown into snowdrifts a couple of times, he discovered that it looked easier than it was. The driver had to balance on runners that seemed as thin as knife blades, while trying to control a pack of animals only a few generations removed from their wolf brethren. Sled dogs were deceptively small, but welded together in a team, they produced an incredible explosion of power with their short legs.

He knew, too, that a dogsled driver had to come across as the leader of the pack if the strong-willed dogs were to respond to his commands. The team was on its feet even before he shouted the command. The gang line connecting the dogs to the sled went taut, and the wheel almost jerked out of his hands. Austin ran several steps, helping the sled along, then he jumped on board and let the dogs do all the work. They bayed loudly, happy doing what they did best, which was to run their hearts out.

From the instant he had gotten his hand on the sled, the

whole operation had taken only a few seconds. Scarface's men tried to cut the sled off. The dogs were too fast. They barked gleefully as they outdistanced their pursuers. Once they were in the clear, Austin experimented with the steering. He tried "gee" and "haw" commands to make the dogs go right and left, and he was glad to see that the team was multi-lingual. Steering required a tender touch on the wheel, especially on the curves. Turn too sharply and the sled acted like the business end of a bullwhip, although the weight of two people kept all four wheels on the ground.

The combined load also kept their speed down. Austin hadn't considered this a problem, figuring that they could still outdistance a running man, especially the burly Scarface and his short-legged cohorts. His confidence drained away when he looked back. Umealiq was on the other sled in hot pursuit. Austin steered off the grass onto a paved walkway. The sled picked up speed on the smooth asphalt. But he had to share the walkway, and this was presenting a problem, as he wove around obstacles like a slalom racer. He narrowly missed a young couple, then brushed by a man walking a toy poodle that yapped at Austin. He drove a woman on Rollerblades up on the turf, and she swore creatively at him. Angry shouts and curses followed the sled as he pushed the dogs to even greater speed.

He tried to figure out how long the team would last, running at full tilt, and decided he didn't have much time. Sled dogs are accustomed to running in the cold and snow, and with their thick fur coats they would quickly become overheated in the warm evening temperatures. He glanced around to get his bearings. They were moving across the Mall, away from the museum, toward the Castle and the Smithsonian quad. He looked behind him. Umealiq had gained ground, and it would be only a matter of time before he caught up.

"Easy," he commanded the dogs, and he put pressure on the brake to reinforce his command. They slowed.

"What are you doing?" Therri said.

"Get off!"

"What?"

"Get off and make a run for the lights and people around the Smithsonian. I can't outrun him with you on board. It's me he really wants."

Therri reluctantly overcame her natural inclination to argue. Comprehending the danger, she rolled off the sled, then got to her feet and started running. Austin shouted at the dogs to get moving. The team took off again in a neck-snapping start. He made a right-angle turn onto another path. The sled felt lighter and more responsive, and he was moving faster than before. He was glad to see Scarface still chasing him. Therri was safe, but pausing to let her off had given Umealiq the chance to gain ground.

Austin's eyes were blurred with the sweat running down his forehead. He wiped away the moisture with the sleeve of his tux and glanced over his shoulder. Scarface had cut the distance in half. Austin dodged another pedestrian and looked ahead. He could see the white spike of the Washington Monument in the distance. There might be armed security guards around the monument, but he would never make it that far. The dogs were becoming weary. He could feel them slow their pace slightly, and the sled was acting like a car running out of gas. He urged the team on with the kissing sound he had heard the drivers use during the race.

Cars were moving along the street ahead of him. With luck and timing, he could put the traffic between him and his pursuers. The sled emerged from the Mall onto the sidewalk. Austin saw an opening between two moving vehicles and steered for it, hoping to whisk through to the other side of the street. The dogs hesitated, but he urged them on. The paws of the lead dog had left the curb when one of the ubiquitous limos that prowled the streets of Washington came out of nowhere and cut him off.

Austin cut the steering wheel hard. The lead dog was way ahead of him and had already changed directions, dashing off to the right with the team and the sled behind him. The sled heeled over at an angle like a boat sailing close to the wind. Austin compensated with his body, and the sled slammed back down on all four wheels and straightened out. The dogs were pulling the sled along the sidewalk. Scarface had cut the angle and was pacing Austin along the sidewalk a few yards away.

The two sleds raced along the sidewalk like the chariot racers in *Ben-Hur.* The dogs swerved around pedestrians. Austin had just about relinquished control, conceding that the dogs could steer the sled far better than he could, and simply concentrated on hanging on. Even at top form, his skills would have been no match for the other driver. The sleds were running side by side, almost close enough to touch. Then Scarface upped the ante and aimed a pistol at Austin from a few feet away.

Austin had the feeling that someone had just painted a bull's-eye on his forehead. But getting a clean shot wouldn't be easy. Scarface held the wheel with his left hand and the pistol in his right. Without the stability of two hands holding on to the wheel, the sled wavered from side to side, and Scarface was finding it impossible to keep the pistol barrel leveled. He tried a shot anyhow.

The bullet missed Austin and went high. Austin took little comfort from the wild shot. Scarface would keep trying until he emptied his gun. Even if the flying lead missed Austin, someone else could be hurt or killed. Acting more on instinct than intellect, Austin quickly touched his brakes. The Eskimo's sled pulled slightly ahead of him. Borrowing a page from Umealiq's book of dirty race tactics, Austin angled his sled to the right. His front wheel slammed into the rear wheel of the other sled, and Scarface fought to maintain control.

The maneuver was risky, but it had the desired effect. With only one sweat-soaked hand gripping the steering wheel, Scarface was unable to stop the rim from spinning. The sled's front wheels jackknifed. The sled itself fishtailed, then flipped, and Scarface tumbled off, the pistol flying out of his hand and clattering onto the sidewalk. He rolled several times before coming to a stop. His dog team kept on running, dragging the sled on its side, before they figured out it was a waste of time.

Austin was in no position to celebrate. His team was pulling the sled toward Constitution Avenue. He yelled a command to stop and jammed his foot down on the brakes, but it was no use. The dogs had been spooked by the gunshot and unnerved by Austin's erratic driving, and he realized he was simply along for the ride. They plunged into the busy boulevard without looking.

The sled flew off the curb, became airborne and slammed

down on all four wheels. Austin's teeth rattled in his skull. There was a banshee screech as an SUV as big as a house slammed on its brakes, its massive chrome grille only inches away. Austin caught a glimpse of the horrified face behind the wheel, the driver's eyes popping out of his head as he watched a man in a tux drive a sled team across Washington's busiest boulevard.

The best Austin could do was to hang on and try to keep the sled upright. His ears were filled with the squeal of brakes, and then he heard a thud as someone rear-ended another car. There were several more thuds as the chain reaction continued. The air reeked of the smell of burnt rubber. Then he was safely across the avenue, and the dogs were scrambling onto the opposite sidewalk. The sled was moving slow enough for him to jump off before it hit the curb. The dogs were exhausted from running in the unaccustomed heat and had no desire to keep moving. They simply plopped down where they were, their sides heaving and their tongues dripping like faucets.

Austin looked back across the trail of chaos he had left on Constitution Avenue. Traffic on his side had come to a stop, and angry people were getting out of their cars to trade registration and license numbers. Scarface stood on the opposite curb, blood streaming down his face. He pulled his knife from his belt. Holding it close to his chest, he stepped off the curb, only to pause at the sound of sirens. Then one of the kennel trucks Austin had seen near the racecourse screeched to a stop, hiding the Eskimo from view for a few seconds. When it took off a second later, the man had vanished.

Austin went over to the panting dogs and patted each one on the head.

"We'll have to do this again, but not too soon," he said.

He brushed the knees and elbows of his tuxedo, but he knew he must look as if he were coming off a weekend binge. Shrugging in resignation, he walked back to the museum. Therri was standing on the Constitution Avenue side of the four-story granite edifice. The expression of anxiety on her face disappeared when she saw Austin trudging toward her, and she ran over to throw her arms around him.

"Thank goodness you're all right," she said, hugging him in a tight embrace. "What happened to that awful man?"

"He got thrown for a loop by the Washington traffic and called it a night. Sorry I had to kick you off back there."

"That's all right. I've been dumped by guys before, although this is the first time it's been off a moving dogsled."

Therri said that after she had been unceremoniously kicked off the sled, she had found a police cruiser parked near the Castle. She'd told the police that her friend was in danger of being murdered on the Mall, and though the police had looked at her as if she were crazy, they did go to investigate. She had come back to the museum to look for Ben, but there'd been no sign of him. She was trying to decide what to do next when she heard the sirens, walked onto the boulevard and saw Austin plodding down the avenue. They shared a cab back to their cars and parted with a lingering kiss and the promise to get in touch the next day.

A turquoise NUMA vehicle was in Austin's driveway when he got home, and the front door was unlocked. He walked into the house and heard the Dave Brubeck Quartet playing "Take Five" on the stereo. Sitting in Austin's favorite black leather chair with a drink in his hand was Rudi Gunn, second in command at NUMA. Gunn was a wiry little man, slim with narrow shoulders and matching hips. He was a master of logistics, a graduate of Annapolis and a former commander in the navy.

"Hope you don't mind my breaking into your house," Gunn said.

"Not at all. That's why I gave you the lock code."

Gunn pointed to the glass. "You're getting a little low on your Highland malt scotch whiskey," he said, his lips turning up in his typical mischievous grin.

"I'll talk to the butler about it." Austin recognized the book that Gunn was holding. "Didn't know you liked Nietzsche."

"I found it on the coffee table. Pretty heavy stuff."

"It might be heavier than you think," Austin said, going over to the bar to mix himself a Dark and Stormy.

Gunn put the book aside and picked up a bound folder from a side table. "Thanks for getting your report to me. I found it far more interesting than Mr. Nietzsche's writings."

"Thought you might," Austin said, settling into a sofa with his drink.

Gunn pushed his thick horn-rimmed glasses up onto his thinning hair and leafed through the folder. "At times like this, I realize what a boring life I lead," he said. "You've really missed your calling. You should be writing scripts for video games."

Austin took a big gulp of his drink, savoring the deep flavor of the dark rum and the tingle of the Jamaican ginger beer. "Naw. This stuff is too far-fetched."

"I beg to differ, old pal. What's far-fetched about a mysterious corporation that sinks ships by remote control? A long-lost cave with fantastic wall art in the Faroe Islands. A creature out of *Jaws* that knocks you on your ass." He started to chuckle uncontrollably. "Now *that's* something I would have liked to witness."

"There's no such thing as respect anymore," Austin lamented.

Gunn got his composure back, and he turned a few more pages. "The list goes on and on. Murderous Eskimo thugs who hunt humans instead of seals. Oh yes, a female attorney with a radical environmental group." He looked up from his reading. "She has long slim legs, I suppose."

Austin thought about Therri's figure. "About average in length, I'd say, but quite shapely."

"Can't have everything, I suppose." Gunn put the folder on his lap and gave Austin the once-over, taking in his scuffed shoes, crooked bow tie and the hole in the knee of the tuxedo. "Did the bouncer throw you out of the museum reception? You look a little, ah, rumpled."

"The reception was fine. But I learned that Washington is going to the dogs."

"Nothing new there. Hope that tux wasn't rented," Gunn said.

"Worse," Austin replied. "I own it. Maybe NUMA will buy me a new one."

"I'll take it up with Admiral Sandecker," Gunn said.

Austin refreshed their drinks, then laid out the story of the meeting with Marcus Ryan and the evening's events.

After absorbing the account without comment, Gunn tapped the report on his lap. "Any thoughts on how your dogsled adventure fits in with this wild tale?"

"Lots of thoughts, but nothing coherent. I'll sum up what I know in a single sentence. The people who run Oceanus deal ruthlessly with anyone who gets in their way."

"That would be my conclusion, too, based on what you've said." Gunn paused for a moment, brow furrowed. He had the capacity to think as coldly and clearly as a computer. He processed the mountain of information, separating the wheat from the chaff. After a few moments, he said, "What about this Basque character, Aguirrez?"

"Interesting fellow. He's the wild card in this poker game. I talked to a friend at the CIA. Aguirrez may or may not be allied with Basque separatists. Perlmutter is looking into the family background for me. All I know for now is that he's either a Basque terrorist or an amateur archaeologist. Take your pick."

"Maybe he could bird-dog this thing for us. Too bad you can't get in touch with him."

Austin set his drink down, pulled his wallet from his pocket and extracted the card Aguirrez had given him as he was leaving the Basque's yacht. He handed the card to Gunn, who noted the phone number on the back. "Why not?" he said, and handed the card back.

Austin picked up a phone and punched out the number. He was tired from the night's exertions, and his expectations were low. So he was startled when he heard the familiar *basso* voice on the line.

"What a pleasant surprise, Mr. Austin. I had the feeling we'd be talking again."

"Hope I'm not interrupting anything important."

"Not at all."

"Are you still in the Faroes?"

"I am in Washington on business."

"Washington?"

"Yes, the fishing in the Faroes didn't live up to its reputation. What can I do for you, Mr. Austin?"

"I called to thank you for pulling me out of some difficulties in Copenhagen."

Aguirrez made no attempt to deny that his men had chased away the club-yielding thugs who'd attacked Austin and

Therri Weld. He simply laughed and said, "You have a way of getting yourself in difficult situations, my friend."

"Most of my troubles have to do with a company called Oceanus. I was hoping we might chat about that subject again. Maybe you could bring me up to date on your archaeological investigation as well."

"I'd like that very much," Aguirrez said. "I have meetings in the morning, but tomorrow afternoon would be convenient."

They agreed on a time, and Austin jotted down the directions Aguirrez gave him for an address in Washington. He hung up and started to fill Gunn in on the short conversation, when the phone rang. It was Zavala, who had returned from Europe. Joe had fixed the problems with the *Sea Lamprey*, then had jumped ship when the *Beebe* had been invited by the Danish vessel *Thor* to join in a Faroe Islands research project.

"Just wanted to let you know I'm home. I've hugged my Corvette, and I'm about to head out for a nightcap with a beautiful young lady," Zavala said. "Anything new since I last saw you?"

"The usual stuff. Tonight, a crazy Eskimo on a dogsled chased me through the Mall with murder in his heart. Other than that, things are quiet."

There was silence at the other end of the line. Then Zavala said, "You're not kidding, are you?"

"Nope. Rudi's here. Drop by my place and you'll get the whole sordid story."

Zavala lived in a small building in Arlington, Virginia, that had once housed a district library. "Guess I'm cancelling that date. Be by in a few minutes," he said.

"One more thing. Still got that bottle of tequila we were going to break into back in the Faroes?"

"Sure, it's in my duffel bag."

"I think you better bring it with you."

26

THE NEXT MORNING, Austin stopped at the Museum of Natural History on the way to NUMA headquarters. Gleason was in the exhibition hall when Austin arrived, and he didn't look happy. The guests, music and food of the reception had disappeared, but that wasn't the main cause of his concern. The display cases were empty. Not even a placard remained.

Gleason was beside himself. "This is terrible, absolutely terrible," he was saying.

"Looks like you had a fire sale," Austin said.

"*Worse.* This is a total disaster. The sponsors have pulled the exhibition."

"Can they do that?" Austin realized it was a dumb question, even as the words left his mouth.

Gleason waved his arms. "Yes, according to the small print in the contract they insisted we sign. They are allowed to break up the exhibition any time they want to and give us a small monetary compensation instead."

"Why did they close the show?"

"Damned if I know. The PR firm that set the whole thing up said they're just following orders."

"What about Dr. Barker?"

"I tried to get in touch with him, but he's vanished into thin air."

"You've been closer to Oceanus than most people," Austin said, getting to his real reason for stopping by the museum. "What do you know about Dr. Barker?"

"Not much, I'm afraid. I know more about his ancestor."

"The whaling captain he mentioned?"

"Yes, Frederick Barker, Sr. One of the Kiolya knives you saw on display originally belonged to him. It was more than a hundred years old. Dreadful thing, and razor-sharp. Gave me a stomachache just looking at it."

"Where would I look for information on Captain Barker?"

"You can start in my office." Gleason cast a woeful glance at the empty display cases. "C'mon. Not much for me to do here."

The office was in the administrative wing. Gleason gestured for Austin to take a seat, then plucked an old volume from the shelf. The title was *Whaling Captains of New Bedford.* He opened the book to a page and plopped it in front of Austin.

"I dug this out of our library when the exhibition first came through. That's Captain Barker. The New England whaling skippers were a tough·lot. Many became captains in their twenties. Mutinies, destructive storms, hostile natives—all in a day's work to them. The adversity made some men ogres, others humanitarians."

Austin examined the grainy black-and-white photograph in the book. Barker was dressed in native garb, and it was hard to make out his features. A fur parka framed his face, and bone goggles with horizontal slits in them covered his eyes. White stubble adorned his chin.

"Interesting eyewear," Austin said.

"Those are sunglasses. The Inuit were very aware of the dangers from snow blindness. They would have been particularly important to Barker, whose eyes were probably sensitive to light. There was albinism in Barker's family. They say that's why he spent so many winters in the frozen north, to avoid the direct sunlight."

Gleason explained that in 1871, Barker's ship, the *Orient,* was wrecked, and the captain was the only survivor. "The natives saved Barker's life, and he spent the winter in an Eskimo settlement. He recounts how the chief's wife pulled off his boots and thawed his frozen feet out with the warmth of her naked bosom."

"I can think of worse ways to thaw out. Where does the Kiolya tribe come in?"

"They were the ones who saved him."

"That seems out of character with what you told me of their bloodthirsty ways. I would have expected them to kill a stranger."

"That would have been the normal case, but don't forget that Barker stood out from the ordinary whale hunter. With his pure white hair, pale skin and eyes, he must have looked like some sort of snow god."

"Toonook, perhaps."

"Anything is possible. Barker didn't go into detail about some things. Quaker society in New Bedford would not have approved of one of their number posing as a god. The experience transformed him, though."

"In what way?"

"He became a staunch conservationist. When he got home, he urged his fellow whale men to stop slaughtering the walrus. The Kiolya muscled in on the walrus hunting grounds like a street gang taking over new drug turf. They even took women and tools from those they conquered. The other Inuit tribes practically starved as a result, until they banded together and drove the Kiolya away. Barker saw this conflict over walrus meat and wanted to end it. He was grateful to the Kiolya and thought if the walrus were saved, they might change their marauding ways."

"Was he right?"

"Barker was naïve, in my view. I don't think anything would have changed their behavior, short of brute force."

Austin pondered over the answer. As a student of philosophy, he was a great believer in the theory that past is present. The Kiolya might be the key to unraveling the tangled skein that surrounded Oceanus.

"Where could I go to learn more about the tribe?"

"Canadian police blotter, for the most part, I'd venture.

There isn't much information between their diaspora and the present, but I did find a crazy story that verifies what I said earlier about the god thing." He rummaged around in a filing cabinet and produced a 1935 clip from the *New York Times,* encased in a plastic envelope. It was datelined Hudson Bay. Austin took a minute to read the story:

The Arctic north added another mystery to its history of exploration when a half-crazed German crawled out of the frozen tundra claiming that he was the sole survivor of an airship disaster.

Canadian authorities said the German, who identified himself as Gerhardt Heinz, was brought in by a group of unknown Eskimos who had apparently rescued him. The *Times* found Mr. Heinz in a hospital ward, where he died a short time later. In the interview, Mr. Heinz said,

"I was on a secret trip to the North Pole for the greater glory of the Fatherland. We landed at the pole, but on the way back, we sighted the wreck of a boat frozen in the ice. The captain insisted on landing on the ice to investigate. It was a boat of great antiquity, probably hundreds of years old. We removed a frozen body, which we placed in the airship cooler, along with some unusual items.

"After rising from the ice and traveling a distance, we experienced mechanical problems, and had to land. The survivors decided to try to cross the ice, but I stayed to guard the zeppelin. I was near death when the local natives found me, and I was nursed back to health."

Mr. Heinz said that the natives spoke no English, but he learned that their name was 'Kiolya.' He said that they thought he was a god, having come from the skies, and when he requested through sign language that they bring him to the nearest settlement, they complied.

German authorities contacted by the *Times* said that they had no knowledge of Mr. Heinz nor of any dirigible voyage to the North Pole.

Austin asked Gleason to run off a copy of the article and thanked him for his time and information. "Sorry about your exhibition," he said on the way out.

"Thank you." Gleason shook his head. "It simply astounds me why they pulled up stakes so abruptly. By the way, have you heard about Senator Graham? That's another disaster. One of our strongest supporters."

Austin said, "I think I saw Graham last night at the reception."

"You did. While he was driving home to Virginia, his car was forced off the road by a truck. He's in critical condition. Hit-and-run."

"Sorry to hear about that, too."

"Damn," Gleason said. "Hope it's not true about bad things running in threes."

"There may be a simpler explanation for your run of bad luck," Austin said.

"Oh, what's that?"

Austin pointed to the sky, and in all seriousness, said: "Toonook."

27

Sᴛ. Jᴜʟɪᴇɴ Pᴇʀʟᴍᴜᴛᴛᴇʀ stepped into his spacious Georgetown carriage house and cast an appreciative glance around at the hundreds of volumes, old and new, that spilled off the sagging wall shelves and flowed like a vast river of words, breaking off into tributaries that ran into every room.

An ordinary human being confronted with this seeming confusion would have fled the premises. A beatific smile came to his lips, as his eye lingered on one stack, then moved on to another. He could rattle off titles, even quote whole pages, from what was generally acknowledged to be the world's most complete collection of literature regarding historic ships.

He was starving after dealing with the rigors of a trans-Atlantic flight. Finding space aboard a plane to accommodate his substantial bulk was not a problem; he simply reserved two seats. But even the culinary offerings of first class were, to Perlmutter's way of thinking, the equivalent of a church ham-and-bean supper. He headed for the kitchen like a heat-seeking missile and was glad to see that the housekeeper had followed his shopping instructions.

Even though it was early in the day, before long he was dining on a Provençale-style stuffed lamb with potatoes perfumed with thyme and washed down with a simple but well-balanced Bordeaux. Thus fortified, he was dabbing at his mouth and magnificent gray beard with a napkin when the phone rang.

"Kurt!" he said, recognizing the voice on the line. "How in blazes did you know I was back?"

"There was a report on CNN that Italy had run out of pasta. I assumed you would be coming home for a square meal."

"No," Perlmutter boomed. "Actually, I returned because I missed being taunted on the phone by impertinent young whippersnappers who should know better."

"You sound in fine fettle, St. Julien. It must have been a good trip."

"It was, and I *do* feel as if I've eaten all the pasta in Italy. But it's good to be back on my own turf."

"I wondered what you had turned up on my historical query."

"I was going to call you later today. Fascinating material. Can you drop by? I'll brew up some coffee, and we can talk about my findings."

"Five minutes. I just happen to be driving through Georgetown."

When Austin arrived, Perlmutter served two giant cups of café latte. He pushed aside a pile of books to reveal a chair for Austin, and another stack to make room for his own wide haunches on an oversized sofa.

Perlmutter sipped his coffee. "Well, now, getting down to business . . . After you called me in Florence, I discussed your query about the Roland relics with my host, a Signor Nocci. He remembered a historical reference he had seen in a letter to the Medici Pope penned by a man named Martinez, who was a fanatical supporter of the Spanish Inquisition, particularly where it applied to the Basques. Mr. Nocci put me in touch with an assistant curator at the Laurentian Library. She dug out a manuscript written by Martinez in which he directs particular venom at Diego Aguirrez."

"The ancestor of Balthazar, the man I met. Good work."

Perlmutter smiled. "That's only the start. Martinez says flatly that Aguirrez had the sword and the horn of Roland and that he would pursue him, and I quote, 'to the ends of the earth,' to retrieve these objects."

Austin let out a low whistle. "That establishes that the Roland relics were real and puts them directly in the hands of the Aguirrez family."

"It would seem to verify the rumors that Diego was in possession of the sword and horn."

Perlmutter passed over a folder. "This is a copy of a manuscript from the Venice State Archives. It was found at the naval museum in a file having to do with war galleys."

Austin read the title on the first page. "An Exoneration of a Man of the Sea." The publication date on the frontispiece was 1520. The preamble described the work as, *An account by Richard Blackthorne, an unwilling mercenary in the service of the Spanish Inquisition, a humble sailor who has always stood in defence of His Majesty's name, in which he proves infamies that have been brought against him to be untrue and warns any and all never to trust the murdering Spaniards.*

He glanced up at Perlmutter. "Blackthorne is surely a master of the never-ending sentence, but what does he have to do with Roland and the long-dead Aguirrez?"

"Everything, m'lad. *Everything.*" He looked into the bottom of his coffee cup. "While you're up, old boy, would you fetch me a refill? I'm feeling peaked after the rigors of travel. Get one for yourself."

Austin had no intention of getting up, but he rose from his chair and went for the refills. He knew that Perlmutter functioned best when he was eating or drinking.

Perlmutter sipped his coffee and ran his hand over the manuscript as if he were reading it with his fingers. "You can study this at your leisure, but I'll give you a quick summary now. Apparently, Blackthorne fell afoul of rumors that he had willingly served the hated Spaniard, and he wanted to set the record straight."

"That came across loud and clear in the preamble."

"Blackthorne was worried about the stain on his name. He was born of a respectable merchant family in Sussex. He went to sea as a youth and worked his way up from cabin boy to master of a merchant vessel plying the Mediterranean. He was captured by Barbary pirates and forced to become a rower on an Algerian galley. The galley was shipwrecked, and he was rescued by the Genoese, who turned him over to the Spanish."

"Remind me never to be rescued by the Genoese."

"Blackthorne was a hot potato. According to the Inquisition system, any Englishman was a heretic, and subject to torture, arrest and execution. English and Dutch sailors shunned Spanish ports for fear they would be arrested. If you were caught with a copy of an English Bible or possessed some ancient classic deemed heretical, you were, to put it literally, toast."

Austin glanced down at the folder. "Either Blackthorne survived or his memoirs were ghostwritten."

"He had nine lives, our Captain Blackthorne. He actually escaped once from the Spanish but was recaptured. He was eventually dragged from his dark cell in irons to stand trial. The prosecutor called him an enemy of the faith and 'other opprobrious names,' as he put it. He was condemned to death and was headed for the stake, when fate intervened in the unlikely form of *El Brasero*."

"Isn't that the name of a Mexican restaurant in Falls Church?"

"You're asking the wrong man. I've always considered 'Mexican' and 'restaurant' uttered in the same sentence as no less an oxymoron than 'military intelligence.' *El Brasero* means 'brazier' in Spanish. It was the nickname given the aforementioned Martinez for his zeal in putting the torch to heretics."

"Not the type you would invite to a barbecue."

"No, but he proved to be Blackthorne's savior. The Englishman impressed Martinez with his resourcefulness, and his ability to speak Spanish, but more important, Blackthorne was familiar with war galleys and sailing ships."

"That shows the lengths to which Martinez would go to catch Aguirrez, even sparing a victim."

"Oh, yes. We know from his writings that he thought Aguirrez was especially dangerous because he had been charged with the stewardship of the Roland relics and might use them to rally his countrymen against the Spaniards. When Aguirrez escaped arrest in his ship, Martinez went after him.

Blackthorne was commanding Brasero's lead galley when they caught up with Aguirrez on his caravel off the coast of France in 1515. Although he was becalmed, outnumbered and outgunned, Aguirrez managed to sink two galleys and put Martinez to flight."

"The more I learn about Diego, the more I like him."

Perlmutter nodded. "His strategy was brilliant. I intend to include this fight in a collection I'm preparing of classic sea battles. Unfortunately, Brasero had the services of an informer who knew that Aguirrez always stopped in the Faroe Islands to rest before crossing the ocean to North America."

Austin leaned forward in his chair and murmured, "Skaalshavn."

"You know it?"

"I was in Skaalshavn a few days ago."

"Can't say I'm familiar with the place."

"Can't blame you, it's quite remote. A picturesque little fishing village with a natural harbor of refuge. There are some interesting caves nearby."

"Caves?" The blue eyes danced with excitement.

"Quite an extensive network. I've seen them. From the drawings on the walls, I'd say they've been occupied off and on going back to ancient times. The Basques, or others, may have been using them for hundreds, maybe thousands, of years."

"Blackthorne mentions the caves in his narrative. In fact, they were instrumental in his story."

"In what way?"

"Aguirrez could easily have outdistanced his pursuers and fled to North America, where Brasero would never find him. The Basques were the only mariners intrepid enough to sail the Atlantic in those days. But Diego knew that Brasero would go after his family. And he knew that even if he stashed the relics in North America, when he returned to Europe, Brasero would be waiting."

"Maybe he decided to take a stand for the most primal of reasons," Austin said. "He wanted his revenge on the man who had ruined his life and stolen his fortune."

"No disagreement there. Brasero was just as determined to finish the job he'd started. He had switched from his galley to a warship twice the size of Diego's caravel. He had put Blackthorne in command. The ship bristled with guns that would have made short work of the Basques. But Diego knew from their previous encounter of the informant on board Brasero's ship and prudently moved the caravel away from the caves. Diego stationed a handful of his men on shore, where they could be seen by Brasero, and when Martinez launched his boats, the men ran into the caves, drawing their pursuers after them."

"I smell a trap."

"You've got a better nose than Martinez, although in fairness, he was probably distracted by thoughts of all the fun he was going to have burning Diego and his crew."

"Shades of Custer's Last Stand. That cave system is a labyrinth. Perfect to stage an ambush."

"Then I'm sure you won't be surprised to hear that's what happened. It was a two-pronged strategy. The caravel swept down on the warship and cowed its skeleton crew with a few cannon shots. Then they boarded the ship and took it over. Meanwhile, Diego launched his ambush. He had dragged one of his ship's cannon into the caves and used it to take the wind out of the attack." Perlmutter raised a pudgy fist as if he were reliving the battle. "Brasero was a skilled swordsman, but Aguirrez was better. Instead of killing him, he toyed with Martinez before he doused Brasero's flame forever."

"Where was Mr. Blackthorne in all this?"

"One of Brasero's men went to take a shot at Diego. Blackthorne killed the man. Diego had his men bring Blackthorne to him. The Englishman laid out his story. Diego needed a skilled captain to command the warship, so he made a deal. Blackthorne would take charge of the ship and get Diego's men home safely. Several weeks later, by Blackthorne's account, he sailed up the Thames with his prize."

"What happened to the Roland relics?"

"Blackthorne never mentions them. But by his account, Diego called for a small volunteer crew to stay with him and sent the others home with Blackthorne. Diego no longer needed gunners and cannon crew, only skilled sailors. Even with Brasero dead, he knew the relics would not be safe as long as the Inquisition was alive. So he continued west, never to be heard from again. Another unsolved mystery of the sea."

"Maybe not," Austin said. He handed Perlmutter the news clip about the zeppelin crash.

Perlmutter read the story and looked up. "These unusual 'items' Heinz mentions could be the long-lost relics."

"My thoughts exactly. Which means they're in the hands of Oceanus."

"Would Oceanus give them up?"

Austin thought of his run-ins with the Oceanus thugs. "Not likely," he said, with a rueful chuckle.

Perlmutter gazed at Austin over tented fingers. "It seems there is more to this whole saga than meets the eye."

"A *hell* of a lot more, and I'll be glad to tell you all the gory details over another cup of coffee." Austin lifted his cup. "As long as you're up, old boy, could you fetch me a refill? Get one for yourself."

28

AUSTIN ARRIVED THREE minutes before his appointed meeting time with Aguirrez. After leaving Perlmutter's house, Austin drove down Embassy Row. The gods that look over Washington drivers were smiling, and he found a parking space with no trouble. He walked along Pennsylvania Avenue until he stood in front of a square building that consisted of several dark-glass stories grafted onto some old Washington houses. Austin read the sign next to the front door and wondered if he had the wrong address. Given the troubles the Aguirrez family had had with the Spanish authorities through the centuries, the last place he would have expected to find Balthazar was at the embassy of Spain.

Austin gave his name to a security guard at the door and was passed on to the receptionist, who punched out a number on her intercom phone and spoke in Spanish to someone on the line. Then she smiled and, in a lovely accent that evoked visions of Castile, said, "Mr. Aguirrez is with the ambassador. He'll be with you in a moment."

A few minutes later, Aguirrez came strolling out of a hallway. Aguirrez had shed his blue sweat suit and black beret and was impeccably dressed in a dark-gray suit that would have cost Austin a week's pay. But even the best of tailors couldn't hide the peasant hands and sturdy physique. He was talking to a snowy-haired man who walked beside him, hands behind his back, head lowered in thought as he listened intently to what the Basque was saying. Aguirrez saw Austin and waved at him. The two men broke off their conversation, parting with warm handshakes and smiles. Aguirrez strode over to where Austin stood and wrapped an arm around his shoulder.

"Mr. Austin," he said cheerfully. "How nice to see you again. I'm sorry I didn't introduce you to the ambassador, but he was late for a meeting. Come this way."

Aguirrez led Austin down a hallway to a door into what had been a drawing room in one of the old houses that were part of the embassy complex. The centerpiece was an over-sized marble fireplace, and the room itself was comfortably appointed with plush rugs and heavy, dark wood furniture. Oil paintings of Spanish rural scenes decorated the walls.

As they took their seats, Aguirrez evidently noted the wondering look on Austin's face, because he said, "You look puzzled, Mr. Austin."

Austin saw no reason to beat around the bush. "I'm surprised to find you here—a man accused of being a Basque terrorist within the walls of the Spanish Embassy."

Aguirrez didn't seem offended. "You have obviously looked into my background, which I expected, so you know that the accusations have not been substantiated."

"Still, I noticed that you're not wearing your black beret."

Aguirrez gave out a booming laugh. "In deference to my hosts, I have shed my chapeau, although I miss wearing it. I think that some in this building might think I had a bomb under the beret, and their nervousness would interfere with our work."

"Which is?"

"To settle the Basque problem peacefully once and for all."

"That's a tall order after hundreds of years of conflict."

"I'm confident it can be accomplished."

"What happened to your ancestral quest?"

"The past and the present are inseparable in this cause. The Basque separatists want a homeland. The Spanish government has experimented with autonomy, with unfortunate results. If I find the relics I am looking for, their discovery could set off an emotional wave of Basque nationalism. I know my people. It would tear Spain apart."

"So you have suddenly become very important to the Spanish government."

He nodded. "I have met with high-level officials in Madrid who asked me to inform your State Department people of the situation and assure them I am not a terrorist. I have agreed, once I find the relics, to put them in safekeeping."

"What's to prevent you from going back on your word?"

The Basque frowned, and a dangerous expression came to his dark eyes. "It is a logical question, and one the Spanish government also asked. I told them that I will honor the memory of my ancestor, who was chosen to be the guardian of the relics. In return, the Spanish government will take graduated, meaningful steps toward Basque autonomy."

"You're using the relics as leverage?"

He shrugged. "I prefer to call it a solution that takes into account our mutual interests."

"Not a bad deal, considering the fact that you don't have the relics."

"A technicality," he said, the broad smile returning. "I have unearthed information on the sea routes my ancestor took to the New World. The Basques were in the Faroes as early as 875. After stopping at the Faroes, Diego would head for Newfoundland or Labrador. There is ample precedent for this theory. My people fished for cod and whales off North America as far back as the Middle Ages."

"I've read that Cabot found Indians using words that could have had a Basque origin."

"No doubt about it!" he said, his face flushing with excitement. "My research indicates that there are some unexplored caves near Channel-Port aux Basques in Newfoundland. I will rejoin my yacht there as soon as I clear up my business here, and I am convinced that before long I will hold the sword and horn of Roland in my hands."

Austin paused, wondering how he could gently break the news, then decided that it could not be done. "There may be a problem," he said.

Aguirrez eyed Austin warily. "What do you mean?"

Austin handed over an envelope containing a copy of the Blackthorne manuscript. "This material suggests that the relics may not be where you think they are." Austin proceeded to lay out the story Perlmutter had told him. As Aguirrez listened, storm clouds seemed to move in and perch on his brow.

"I know of St. Julien Perlmutter through my own research. He is highly respected as a sea historian."

"There is none more knowledgeable."

Aguirrez slammed a fist into his palm. "I *knew* Diego wasn't killed by Brasero. He escaped with the relics."

"There's more," Austin said. He handed Aguirrez the news clip detailing the interview with the zeppelin's survivor.

"I still don't understand," the Basque said after reading the article.

"Oceanus is the owner of the zeppelin that found your ancestor's boat locked in the ice."

Aguirrez saw the connection immediately. "You believe that Oceanus has the sacred relics in its possession?"

"It's a good bet if you follow the chain of evidence."

"And in your view, Oceanus can't be approached on this matter?"

"I don't think Oceanus can be approached on *any*thing," Austin said, with a rueful chuckle. "You recall my boating accident? I have a confession to make. An Oceanus security guard blew up my boat with a hand grenade."

"And I must confess that I never believed your story about engine fumes."

"While we're in a confessing mood," Austin said, "maybe you can tell me why your men followed me to Copenhagen."

"A precaution. To be frank, I didn't know what to make of you. I knew from your identity card that you were with NUMA, but I didn't know why you were poking into the Oceanus operation, and assumed it must be an official mission. My curiosity was stirred, so I decided to keep an eye on you. You made no effort to hide your movements. My men happened to be nearby when you were attacked. How is the young lady you were with, by the way?"

"She's fine, thanks to the alertness of your men."

"Then you're not angry at being followed?"

"Not at all, but I wouldn't like to see you make it a habit."

"I understand." Aguirrez paused in thought. "Am I correct to assume the men who attacked you were from Oceanus?"

"That seems a safe conclusion. The attackers resembled the guards I encountered at the Oceanus operation in the Faroes."

"Oceanus tried to kill you twice. Be careful, my friend, they may try again."

"They already have."

Aguirrez didn't ask for details, and it was obvious he had other things on his mind. He rose from his chair and paced the room, Blackthorne's manuscript clutched in his hand. "The people here must not know of this material. Without the relics, the Spanish government will lose its incentive to move on Basque autonomy. But this goes beyond political matters," he said in a hollow voice. "I have failed my ancestor Diego by not finding the relics."

"There may still be a way."

Aguirrez stopped his pacing and fixed Austin with a penetrating stare. "What are you saying?"

"We're both interested in nailing Oceanus to the wall. Let's talk about it, taking account, as you said before, of mutual interests."

Aguirrez hiked his bushy eyebrows, but his face remained impassive. Then he went over to a liquor cabinet and brought back two small glasses and a bottle of greenish-yellow liquor. He poured the glasses full and handed one to Austin, who recognized the distinctive scent of Izzara.

An hour later, Austin slid behind the wheel of his car. He wondered if he had made a deal that might come back to haunt him, but he trusted his instincts, which were all he had to go on at this point. He sensed that Aguirrez was devious but principled, and since they shared the same goals, it would be foolish not to form a loose alliance.

He checked his cell phone and saw that there were two calls. The first was from the Trouts. He was relieved to hear from them. He knew from working with them on the Special Assignments Team that Paul and Gamay were able to take care of themselves, but at the same time, they had gone looking for Oceanus without knowing how dangerous their mission might be.

Gamay answered his call. She and Paul had returned from Canada a few hours before, and dropped their luggage off at their town house. Then they had gone to NUMA headquarters to meet with Zavala, who was going to update them.

"Did you get inside the Oceanus operation?" Austin asked.

"No," Gamay said, "but we bumped into a few of their people."

Gamay was being a little too casual. "I know from personal experience that when you bump into Oceanus, it bumps back. Are you and Paul all right?"

"We're fine. A slight concussion for me and a broken wrist for Paul. The cuts and bruises are healing nicely."

Austin swore under his breath, angry at himself for putting his partners in danger.

"I didn't realize what I was getting you into. I'm sorry."

"*Don't* be. You only asked us to see what we could learn about Oceanus. It was our decision to go flying off to Canada and poke our noses in where they weren't welcome. It was worth the trip, too. We wouldn't have learned about the devilfish otherwise."

The only devilfish Austin had ever heard of was the manta ray. "Are you sure that concussion is on the mend?"

"I've never been more clearheaded, Kurt. In all my years as a marine biologist, I've never encountered anything like this before. Paul calls it 'white death.' "

Austin experienced a quick frisson as he recalled his brush with the large, toothy creature in the Oceanus fish tank. "You can fill me in when I get there."

He hung up and punched out Gunn's number. "Hello, Rudi," he said, without the usual exchange of pleasantries. "I think it's time we had a meeting with Sandecker."

29

THE GIANT VIDEO screen in the conference room glowed blue for a second, then an image appeared. There was a flash of silvery-white scales in a net, and Mike Neal was heard shouting, "Stand way back, folks, we've got a live one!" There was a blurred glimpse of a fish slamming against the deck and a close-up of a toothy mouth snapping a gaff handle in two. The handheld camera showed the same fish being clouted with a baseball bat. The astonished voices of the Trouts were audible in the background.

Paul Trout clicked the remote control and froze the picture. The lights blinked back on, and a crisp, commanding voice was heard to say, "It seems *Jaws* has formidable competition."

Admiral James Sandecker, the driving force behind NUMA, sat at a long conference table, his head enveloped in a purple cloud that belched from the fat cigar in his hand.

"That thing up on the screen is in a class of its own, Admiral," said Gamay, who sat at the table along with Austin, Zavala and Rudi Gunn. "The great white shark attacks when it's hungry or hunted. The creature we're looking at is more like Mack the Knife: just plain mean."

Sandecker blew out a plume of smoke and glanced around

the table. "Now that you've engaged my attention with what must be the shortest monster movie on record, please tell me what in blazes is going on and what that creature has to do with the cast on Paul's wrist."

Gamay and Paul took turns telling the story of their Canadian adventure, from their visit to the Oceanus fish-processing plant to their talk with the geneticists at McGill.

Austin cut in. "Did you say Frederick Barker?"

"Yes," Gamay said. "Do you know him?"

"We've had a passing acquaintance. His men tried to kill me last night."

Austin gave the gathering a quick rundown of his encounter with Barker and the wild dogsled race through the Mall.

"Congratulations, Kurt. The traffic tie-up you caused was page one in *The Washington Post*." Sandecker paused in thought. "Let me see if I understand this story to date. You believe that Oceanus orchestrated the sinking of two ships in Faroe waters to divert attention from a secret project, directed by this man Barker, having to do with the breeding of mutant fish." He gestured at the screen. "Fish similar to the one Paul and Gamay encountered in Canada. And that people from a rogue Eskimo tribe made attempts on your life in the Faroes, in Copenhagen and in Washington."

"Sounds unbelievable when somebody else tells it," Austin said, with a shake of his head.

"Baron Munchausen couldn't have done better. Luckily, Paul and Gamay have verified the existence of these homicidal Eskimos." He turned to Gunn. "What do you make of this fantastic tale, Rudi?"

"Before I answer, I'd like to ask Gamay what could happen if these artificially mutated superfish got into the sea and started breeding."

"According to Dr. Throckmorton, Barker's colleague, in sufficient numbers, they could create a biological time bomb," Gamay said. "They could replace the natural strains of fish within a few generations."

"What's wrong with that?" Sandecker said, playing devil's advocate. "Fishermen would have to catch a few large fish instead of many smaller ones."

"True, but we don't know enough about the long-range effects. What would happen if these Frankenfish had some property that made them unfit for human consumption? What if an unforeseen mutant strain resulted? What if the superfish offspring couldn't survive in the wild? You'd have neither the natural species nor the mutants. The ocean system would be thrown out of whack. Fishermen, processing people and distributors would be idled around the world. This would disrupt whole societies that depend upon fish protein for nourishment. Industrial nations would be damaged, as well."

"That's quite a dismal forecast," Sandecker said.

"I'm being conservative in my assessment. There are so many unknowns. We know that more than twenty-five species are being targeted for genetic modification. It could mean a tragedy of unimaginable proportions if they escape into the sea."

"We're assuming that monster up there *escaped* from a research lab," Rudi said. "Suppose he and others like him were released into the sea *deliberately*?"

Gamay stared at Gunn as if he had grown a set of horns. "Why would anyone risk extinction of a whole species? That would be a terrible thing."

Gunn shook his head. "Not for everyone."

"What are you saying?" Sandecker asked.

"That the fish will vanish from the *sea,* but not from the Oceanus holding tanks. Oceanus has been acquiring international patents for its fish genes. The species would be preserved in Oceanus DNA banks."

"Very clever, Rudi," Sandecker said. "Oceanus would have created a monopoly on a major source of the world's protein."

Paul said, "A monopoly like that could be worth billions of dollars."

"It goes beyond money," Sandecker said. "Fish protein is a major source of nourishment for much of the world. Food is power."

"This explains why Oceanus is so trigger-happy," Austin said. "If the news got out that they were about to deplete the world's oceans, the adverse public reaction would be overwhelming."

"Certainly sounds plausible," Gunn said. "You establish

biofish hatcheries around the world. You could seed the major fish-breeding areas in a short time."

"You wouldn't need many fish," Gamay said. "Each male biofish released could breed with dozens of females. But I'd like to point out there is nothing illegal about dumping fish into the open sea."

"They've been responsible for the loss of two ships and several deaths trying to keep their dirty little secret," Austin said. "They're holding an entire Indian village captive. Last I heard, murder and kidnapping were illegal."

Sandecker said, "But since we can't pin the killings and other crimes on Oceanus yet, we'll have to proceed with care. We can't go through the regular channels. Even the Canadian government can't know of our action. Oceanus could bring the forces of the law down on us. The Special Assignments Team was formed for missions away from official oversight, so it's the perfect vehicle to carry out our plan."

"I didn't know we *had* a plan," Zavala said.

"Seems obvious to me," the admiral said. "We blow Oceanus and their bloody scheme out of the water, like the pirates they are. I realize it won't be easy. Nighthawk's family and relatives could be placed in jeopardy. The fact that we've stumbled onto the scene might make Oceanus act in haste."

"There's another factor we should take into account," Austin said. "Marcus Ryan is determined to get SOS involved. They could compromise our plan and put the captives in real danger."

"That settles it," Sandecker said. "We move immediately. We've got to strike at the heart of this thing, that facility in the Canadian woods. Kurt, did this young Indian give you any inkling where his village was located?"

"Ryan had him on a short leash. Ben seems to have disappeared, but I'll keep trying to find him."

"We can't wait that long." Sandecker's gaze moved over to a scruffy-looking man who had quietly slipped into the room during the discussion and taken a seat in a corner. "Hiram, do you have something for us?"

Hiram Yeager was the director of the vast computer network that covered the entire tenth floor of the NUMA building. The center processed and stored the biggest amount of digital data on the oceans ever assembled under one roof. The brains behind this incredible display of information-gathering power was dressed in his standard uniform, Levi's pants and jacket over a pure white T-shirt. His feet were stuffed into a pair of cowboy boots that looked as if they had come from Boot Hill. His long hair was tied in a ponytail, and his gray eyes peered out at the world through wire-rimmed granny glasses.

"Rudi asked me to see if Max would compile a list of places that have experienced sudden fish kills, and to cross-check when possible with nearby fish-processing plants or farms."

"Do you want us to adjourn this meeting to the data center?" Sandecker asked.

Yeager's boyish face beamed with excitement. "Stay right where you are. You're about to see a demonstration of Portable Max."

Sandecker grimaced. He was impatient to get his troops moving and wasn't interested in Yeager's experiments, only their results. But his respect for the computer genius displayed itself in the same uncharacteristic patience that allowed Yeager to ignore the NUMA dress code.

Yeager connected a laptop computer to various outlets and to the video screen. He clicked the ON button. Anyone who expected an ordinary presentation didn't know Hiram Yeager. The image of a woman appeared on the video screen. Her eyes were topaz brown and her hair a shiny auburn, her shoulders bare down to the first hints of her breasts.

It was hard to believe that the lovely woman on the screen was an artificial intelligence system, the end product of the most complex electronic circuitry imaginable. Yeager had recorded his voice, digitally altering it to give it a feminine tone, and programmed the face of his wife, a successful artist, into the system. Max tended to be just as testy and petulant as she was.

When he was working in the data center, Yeager sat at a huge console and Max was projected in 3-D onto a giant monitor. "With the Portable Max, you don't have to come to the data center to ask questions. The laptop connects to the mainframe, so I can bring her with me wherever I go. Isn't that right, Max?"

Normally, Max responded to the opening question with a dazzling smile, but the face on the screen looked as if she had been sucking on lemons. Yeager fiddled with the connections and tried again.

"Max? Are you okay?"

The eyes looked down to the bottom of the screen. "I'm feeling rather . . . flat."

"You look fine from out here," Yeager said.

"Fine?"

"No, you look *wonderful*!"

Sandecker's patience had run out. "Perhaps you should send the young lady a bouquet of roses."

"That always works for me," Zavala said.

Sandecker shot him a withering look. "Thank you for giving us the benefit of your wide experience, Joe. I'm sure you can include it in your memoirs. Hiram, could you cut to the chase, please?"

Max smiled. "Hello, Admiral Sandecker."

"Hello, Max. Hiram is correct when he says you look wonderful. But I think we should end this Portable Max experiment. In the future, we will visit you in the data center."

"Thanks for your understanding, Admiral. What can I do for you?"

"Please produce the data Hiram requested."

The face instantly disappeared. In its place was a map of the world. Max's voice narrated: "This map shows the locations where there have been fish kills near aquaculture facilities. I can give you specifics for each location."

"Don't bother for now. Please show us those aquaculture sites owned by Oceanus."

Some of the circles vanished, but a substantial number remained.

"Now go to Canada," Sandecker said.

The picture zoomed in on Cape Breton.

"Bingo!" Paul Trout said. "That's where Gamay and I had our run-in with Oceanus."

Austin said, "Max, could you draw a straight line from the Oceanus site to the nearest lake in northern Canada?"

The map displayed a line that connected the coastal facility with the interior, but the lake it showed was too small and too close to civilization. After several tries, Max connected the aquaculture operation to the only lake large and remote enough to fit Nighthawk's description.

"We can run some satellite photos on this site, but my instincts tell me this is the right place," Austin said.

"Thank you, Max. You can shut down now," Sandecker said.

The screen went blank. Sandecker, who was obviously pleased with himself, turned to Zavala and said, "Now *that's* how you handle a woman." His face grew serious. "I think it's time to get moving," he said.

Zavala raised his hand and cleared his throat.

"This is pretty rugged country. Assuming we find these hombres with no trouble, do we just drop in on them?"

Sandecker looked as if the question surprised him. "I'm open to suggestions."

"I've got one. Call in the Royal Canadian Mounties."

"I'm sure you can do it without their help." Sandecker showed his even teeth in a crocodile smile. "You have carte blanche."

"I'd rather have the Mounties," Zavala said. "If they're busy, a contingent of Special Forces might do."

"I don't blame Joe for being doubtful," Austin said, coming to his partner's aid. "As the Trouts and I know, Oceanus shoots first and asks questions later."

"It would take too long to go through the red tape necessary to involve the Canadian military or police. As for Special Forces, we would need presidential authority to trespass on Canadian turf. I don't see that coming."

"In that case, I'd like to make a proposal," Austin said. He related his conversation with Aguirrez.

Sandecker puffed thoughtfully on his cigar. "Let me see. You'd like to use the resources of this Basque, who may or may not be a terrorist, to carry out a NUMA mission in a foreign country?" Sandecker said.

"If we can't use the U.S. Marines or the Mounties, he might be all we have."

"Hmm," Sandecker said. "Can he be trusted?"

"He can be trusted to do whatever he can to find his relics. Beyond that I can't say, other than to remind you that he saved my life on two occasions."

Sandecker tugged at his precisely trimmed beard. The idea of using the Basque appealed to the admiral's unconventional side, but he was reluctant to lose control of the situation. On the other hand, he had complete confidence in Austin and his team.

"Use your best judgment," Sandecker said.

"There's something else," Austin said. He told them about the overnight closing of the museum exhibition and the accident involving Senator Graham.

"But I know Graham well," Sandecker said.

Gunn nodded. "And guess what his commerce committee has been involved in lately? Legislation trying to close loopholes that would allow biofish to be shipped into the U.S."

"Quite a coincidence, isn't it?" Austin said. "Especially since he was returning from a party hosted by Oceanus."

"Are you suggesting," Sandecker said, "that this exhibition was an elaborate cover for an assassination crew?"

"It fits. With Graham out of the way, those loopholes may never be closed."

"I agree. There are certainly enough party hacks around to raise the possibility of bribes," said Sandecker, who had a low opinion of Congress.

Austin said, "Oceanus has cleared away a major obstacle. I think they're about to make their move."

Sandecker rose from his seat and glanced around the table with his cold blue eyes. "Then it's high time we made *ours*," he said.

When Austin returned to his office, a message was waiting for him from the captain of the NUMA research vessel *William Beebe*, working with the Danes in the Faroe Islands. *Call immediately*, the message said, and left a phone number.

"I thought you'd want to know," the captain said, when Austin reached him. "There's been an accident out here. A research vessel working with a Danish scientist named Jorgensen blew up somehow. They lost eight people, including the professor."

Austin had forgotten about Jorgensen's plans to continue his research near the Oceanus plant. Now he recalled warning the professor to be careful.

"Thank you, Captain," he said. "Any idea what caused the explosion?"

"The lone survivor said something about a helicopter in the area before the explosion, but she didn't make sense. She was the one who suggested that we call you, in fact. Seems she was on the boat as a guest of the professor. Name was Pia something."

"She's a friend of mine. How is she?"

"Few broken bones, some burns. But the doctors expect that she'll pull through. Sounds like a tough lady."

"She is. Could you give her a message?"

"Of course."

"Tell her I'll be over to see her as soon as she's feeling better."

"Will do."

Austin thanked the captain and hung up. He stared into space, his jaw muscle working, his blue-green eyes at the topaz level on Moh's scale of hardness. He was thinking of Jorgensen's horsy smile and Pia's kindness. Barker, or Toonook, or whatever his name was, had made the mistake of his life. By killing the professor and injuring Pia, he had made it personal.

30

THE SINGLE-ENGINE FLOATPLANE flew low, looking like a toy against the vastness of the Canadian wilderness. Therri Weld sat next to the pilot in the front passenger seat, where she had a good view of the ranks of sharp, pointed treetops, any one of which could have ripped the belly out of the fuselage.

The first part of the flight had been spent in whiteknuckled terror. Therri had not been reassured when she saw the pair of fuzzy dice hanging in the cockpit. But as the flight proceeded without a hitch, she had concluded that the pilot, an enormous, grizzled man whose name was Bear, actually seemed to know what he was doing.

"Don't get up here very often," Bear shouted over the roar of the engine. "Too remote for most of the 'sportsmen' who come up to go hunting and fishing. Their idea of roughing it is staying at a lodge with inside plumbing." Bear pointed through the windshield at the featureless terrain. "Coming up on Looking Glass Lake. It's really two lakes joined by a short connector. Locals call it the Twins, although one's bigger than the other. We'll drop down on the little guy in a few minutes."

"All I see is trees and more trees," said Marcus Ryan, who sat behind the pilot.

"Yeah, bound to find trees in these parts," Bear said, with a cheerful grin. He glanced over to see if Therri appreciated the joke on Ryan. She smiled gamely, but her heart wasn't in it. She would have felt far more confident if Ben Nighthawk were with them. Her calls to his apartment had gone unanswered. She'd wanted to keep trying, but Marcus had been in a hurry to get rolling.

"You can pull out if you want to," Ryan had said. "Chuck and I can go it alone, but we've got to move fast because the plane's waiting for us." Therri barely had time to pack before Ryan picked her up. Before long, they were piling into the SOS executive jet with Chuck Mercer, the former first mate of the *Sea Sentinel*. With his ship on the bottom, Mercer was eager to see action.

Therri would have been more enthusiastic if she didn't think Ryan was making up his strategy as he went along. Thanks to the information from Ben, Ryan knew where to go. Ben had told him the name and location of the lake. It was Ben, too, who had given him Bear's name.

The bush pilot used to be a drug smuggler and was known to work with no questions asked, if the money was right. He hadn't even blinked when Marcus had spun a cock-and-bull tale about doing a documentary film on native culture and wanting to observe Ben's village without being seen.

Bear was usually discreet, but he had become careless living in a community where everyone was aware of his past. He'd let a few words slip about his job for SOS while he was fueling up the plane. He could not have known that sharp ears were listening, or that unfriendly eyes were watching as his plane took off and headed into the interior.

The lake loomed up suddenly. Therri glimpsed water shimmering in the slanting rays of the late afternoon sun. Seconds later, the plane dropped as if it had hit a downdraft. She felt her heart in her mouth, then the plane bottomed out and slid into a gradually angled trajectory. The floats skimmed the lake's surface a short distance before the plane settled into the water and slowed.

Bear taxied close to shore. When the plane neared a sharply

banked beach a few yards wide, he climbed out of the cockpit onto a float and jumped feetfirst into water up to his waist. He tied an anchor line onto a strut, pulled the other end over his shoulder and towed the plane closer to shore. He tied up to a stump, then helped the others unload a large package and several smaller ones. They untied the largest bundle, and with the help of a CO_2 capsule, quickly pumped up an inflatable boat about eight feet long. Bear watched with interest, hands on hips, as Ryan tested a quiet, battery-operated outboard motor.

"I'll be back tomorrow," he said. "You've got the radio if you need me. Watch your ass."

The plane taxied to one end of the lake, took off and headed back the way it had come. Therri went over to where Ryan and Mercer were checking through the pack. Mercer unwrapped a block of C-4 explosives and examined the detonators.

He smiled and said, "Just like the old days."

"Sure you're up for this, Chuck?"

"You're talking to the guy who sank an Icelandic whaling ship practically single-handed."

"That was a few years ago. We're a lot older now."

Mercer fingered a detonator. "Doesn't take much energy to push a button," he said. "I owe these bastards for our ship." Mercer had been steaming since he'd learned that Oceanus's ships were serviced at the same Shetlands boatyard where the *Sea Sentinel* could have been sabotaged.

"We can't forget Josh, either," Ryan said.

"I haven't forgotten Josh. But are you sure there's no other way?" Therri said.

"I wish there were," Ryan said. "We've got to play hardball."

"I'm not arguing with the *need* to do something, but the *means*. What about Ben's people? You're risking their lives."

"We can't be diverted from our prime goal. We know from our contacts on Senator Graham's staff that Oceanus continued the transgendered fish experiments that were halted in New Zealand. We've got to stop this abomination before it is unleashed."

"*Abomination?* You're scaring me, Marcus. You're talking like a Biblical prophet."

Ryan's face flushed, but he held his temper. "I have no intention of making Ben's people collateral damage. Oceanus will be too busy dealing with our little gifts to do anything. In any case, we'll call the authorities as soon as we're finished here."

"It would only take a few bursts from an automatic weapon to kill Ben's people. Why not call in outside help now?"

"Because it would take time we don't have. We're talking search warrants and legal process. The villagers could be dead by the time the Mounties decide to investigate." He paused. "Remember, I tried to bring NUMA in on this, and Austin refused."

Therri bit her lower lip in frustration. Her loyalty toward Ryan was intense but not uncritical.

"Don't turn your sights on Kurt. If it weren't for him, you'd be eating sardines in a Danish prison cell."

Ryan beamed his lighthouse smile. "You're right. I'm out of line. But there's still time to call Bear and have him take you out of here."

"Not on your life, Ryan."

Mercer had finished organizing their backpacks. He strapped on a pistol belt and handed one to Ryan. Therri refused a weapon. They piled their supplies into the inflatable, shoved it off the beach and started the engine. It ran with a low hum and pushed them through the water at a slow but respectable speed. They hugged the shoreline even after they had passed through the channel into the larger lake.

Ryan was using a topographic map with notations based on Ben's information. He stopped the boat at one point and peered through his binoculars at the opposite side of the lake. He could make out a pier and several boats, but no structure matching Nighthawk's description.

"That's funny, I don't see any dome. Ben said it rose above the trees."

"What should we do?" Therri said.

"We'll go to Ben's village and wait there. Then we'll head across the lake, leave our calling cards where they will do the most good and set the timers for late morning, when we'll be well on our way out of here."

They got underway again. The sun was falling behind the

trees when they saw the clearing and the dozen or so houses that made up Ben's village. It was deathly quiet, with only a faint soughing in the trees and the lap of the waves against shore breaking the silence. They stopped about fifty yards offshore while Ryan, then the others, checked out the village with light-gathering glasses. Seeing nothing, they cruised straight on in, beached the boat and came ashore.

Ryan was careful, insisting that they check out the houses and store. The village was deserted, as Ben had described. They had something to eat. By the time they finished, darkness was complete, except for a blue-black sheen on the lake and pinpoints of light on the opposite shore. They took turns standing watch while the others slept. Around midnight they were all awake and preparing to move out. They slid the boat into the water and pushed off.

Halfway across the lake, Ryan peered through his glasses, and said, "Jesus!"

The sky across the lake was lit up. He handed the binocs to Therri, but even with her naked eye she could see the dully lit greenish-blue structure that mounded above the trees. It seemed to have dropped from space.

Ryan directed Mercer to steer off to one side, away from the pier. They beached a few minutes later, pulled the inflatable onshore and piled brush around it. Then they made their way along the beach toward the pier. When they were a few hundred feet away, they cut inland and came upon the road that Ben and Josh Green had used to get to the airship hangar. The muddy ruts Ben had described had since been graded and blacktopped.

They were looking for a particular type of building, and found what they were looking for in a structure that hummed with the sound of pumps. Mercer made short work of the padlocks with a tiny cutting torch.

Large glass tanks stretched from one side of the building to the other, and the air inside was heavy with the smell of fish and the hum of motors. The room was in semidarkness, but large pale shapes could be seen moving behind the glass. Mercer got right to work. He placed packets of C-4 in strategic places, molding the puttylike explosive around pumps and electrical conduits where explosions would do the most damage. What was left, he placed on the outside of the tanks.

They worked fast, arming the charges and setting the timers, and were done within thirty minutes. The only people they had seen were those moving in the distance, but Ryan wasn't going to press their luck. They made their way back toward the lakeshore, again without encountering anyone. Ryan was beginning to feel uneasy, but he pressed on. If all went as planned, Bear would be picking them up just before the big bang.

Unfortunately, all did not go as planned. Their boat was missing, to begin with. Thinking that they may have misjudged the distance in the dark, Ryan sent the others down the beach to look for the boat, while he stood watch. When five minutes had passed and they hadn't returned, he struck out after them, and he found Therri and Mercer standing side by side looking out toward the lake.

"Did you find it?" he said.

No answer. They remained motionless. When he moved in closer, he saw why. Their wrists were bound behind their backs with wire, and they had tape across their mouths. Before he could free his friends, the bushes behind the beach erupted and they were surrounded by a dozen burly figures.

One man took Ryan's gun away and another came closer and flicked on a flashlight, its beam illuminating the man's hand. Dangling in his fingers was one of the charges Ryan had set in the fish house. The man threw the explosives into the lake and put the beam on his own face so that Ryan could be sure to see the pockmarked jack-o'-lantern features and the fierce grin.

He drew a white-bladed knife from his belt and put it under Ryan's chin so that the point dimpled his skin and drew a droplet of blood. Then he uttered something in a strange language and returned the knife to its scabbard. Together, they began to march back toward the airship hangar.

31

AUSTIN EXAMINED THE satellite photograph through the magnifying glass and shook his head. He slid the picture and magnifier across his desk to Zavala. After studying the photo for a moment, Zavala said, "I can see a lake with a clearing on one side and some houses. Could be Nighthawk's village. There's a pier and some boats on the other side, but no airship hangar. Maybe it's hidden."

"Maybe we're setting off on a fool's mission, old chum."

"Wouldn't be the first time. Look at it this way: Max said this is the place, and I'd trust Max with my life."

"You may have to," Austin said. He checked his watch. "Our plane will be ready in a couple of hours. We'd better get packed."

"I never *un*packed from my last trip," Zavala said. "See you at the airport."

Austin did a quick turnaround at his boathouse and was heading out the door, when he saw the light blinking on his telephone answering machine. He debated whether to listen to the message, but when he pushed the button, he was glad he did. Ben Nighthawk had called and left a phone number.

Austin dropped his duffel bag and quickly punched out the

number. "Man, am I glad to hear from you," Nighthawk said. "I've been waiting by the phone hoping you'd call."

"I tried to get in touch with you a couple of times."

"Sorry for being such a jerk. That guy would have killed me if you hadn't stepped in. I wandered around and hung out with some pals, feeling sorry for myself. When I got back to my apartment, there was a message from Therri. She said that SOS was going off on its own. Ryan talked her into it, I guess."

"Damned fools. They'll get themselves killed."

"I feel the same way. I'm worried about my family, too. We've got to stop them."

"I'm willing to try, but I need your help."

"You've got it."

"How soon can you leave?"

"Whenever you want me to."

"How about now? I'll pick you up on the way to the airport."

"I'll be ready."

After Zavala left the NUMA building, he drove his 1961 Corvette convertible to his home in Arlington, Virginia. While the upstairs was spotless, as would be expected of someone who routinely dealt in microscopic tolerances, Zavala's basement looked like a cross between Captain Nemo's workshop and a redneck gas station. It was crammed with models of undersea craft, metal-cutting tools and piles of diagrams marked with greasy fingerprints.

The one exception to the jumble was a locked metal cabinet where Zavala kept his collection of weaponry. Technically, Zavala was a marine engineer, but his duties on the Special Assignments Team sometimes required firepower. Unlike Austin, who favored a custom-made Bowen revolver, Zavala employed whatever weapon was handy, usually with deadly efficiency. He eyed the collection of firearms in the cabinet—wondering what, short of a neutron bomb, would be effective against a ruthless multinational organization with its own private army—and reached for an Ithaca Model 37 repeating shotgun, the primary weapon used by the SEALs in

Vietnam. He liked the idea that the shotgun could be fired almost like an automatic weapon.

Zavala carefully packed the shotgun and an ample supply of ammunition into a case, and before long he was on his way to Dulles Airport. He drove with the top down, savoring the ride because he knew it would be his last in the 'Vette until his assignment was over. He pulled up to a hangar in an out-of-the-way corner of the airport where a crew of mechanics was doing last-minute checks on a NUMA executive jet. He kissed the Corvette's fender and said a sad good-bye, then climbed aboard the plane.

Zavala was going over his flight plan when Austin arrived a short time later with Ben Nighthawk in tow. Austin introduced the young Indian to Zavala. Nighthawk glanced around as if he were looking for something.

"Don't worry," Austin said, noting the expression of consternation on Nighthawk's face. "Joe just looks like a bandit. He really does know how to fly a plane."

"That's right," Zavala said, looking up from his clipboard. "I've passed a correspondence course, all except for the part about the landing."

The last thing Austin wanted was to have Ben bolt from the plane in fright. "Joe likes to kid around," he said.

"I wasn't worried about that, it's—well, is this all there is? I mean just *us*?"

Zavala's lips turned up in a smile. "We hear a lot of that sort of thing," he said, recalling Becker's skepticism when he and Austin had arrived to rescue the Danish sailors. "I'm starting to get an inferiority complex."

"This isn't a suicide squadron," Austin said. "We'll pick up some extra muscle on the way. In the meantime, make yourself comfortable. There's coffee in that carafe. I'll assist Joe in the cockpit."

They were quickly cleared for takeoff, and the plane headed north. At a cruising speed of five hundred miles an hour, they were over the waters of the Gulf of St. Lawrence in a little over three hours. They touched down at a small coastal airport. Rudi Gunn had checked earlier and found that there was a NUMA survey ship working in the gulf. The way had been smooth through Canadian customs, and before long Austin, Zavala and Ben were climbing aboard the ship, which had come into port. By previous arrangement, the *Navarra* was waiting ten miles offshore.

As they approached the yacht, Zavala eyed the long, sleek vessel with appreciation. "Pretty," he said. "And from her lines, I'd say she's fast, too, but she doesn't look tough enough to take on Oceanus."

"Wait," Austin said, with a knowing smile.

The *Navarra* sent over a launch to pick them up. Aguirrez was waiting on deck, his black beret, as usual, perched at a jaunty angle on his head. By his side were the two brawny men who had escorted Austin after he was plucked from the waters outside the Mermaid's Gate.

"Good to see you again, Mr. Austin," Aguirrez said, pumping Kurt's hand. "Glad you and your friends could make it aboard. These are my two sons, Diego and Pablo."

It was the first time Austin had seen the two men smile, and he noted the resemblance to their father. He introduced Zavala and Nighthawk. The yacht was already underway by that time, and he and the others followed Aguirrez to his grand salon. Aguirrez motioned for the men to take a seat, and a steward appeared with hot drinks and sandwiches. Aguirrez asked them about their trip and waited patiently for them to finish their lunch before he picked up a remote control. At a click of a button, a section of wall slid up to reveal a giant screen. Another click, and an aerial photograph filled the space. The photograph showed forest and water.

Nighthawk sucked in his breath. "That's my lake, and my village."

"I used the coordinates Mr. Austin gave me and fed them into a commercial satellite," Aguirrez said. "I'm puzzled, however. As you can see, there is no sign of this airship building that you mentioned."

"We had the same problem with the satellite photos we looked at," Austin said. "But our computer model indicates that this is the place."

Nighthawk rose and walked over to the screen. He pointed to a section of forest bordering the lake. "It's here, I *know* it is. Look, you can see where the woods have been cleared, and there's the pier." His confusion was evident. "But there's nothing but trees here where the blimp hangar should be."

"Tell us again what you saw that night," Austin said.

"The dome was huge, but we didn't see it until the airship appeared. The surface was covered with panels."

"Panels?" Zavala said.

"Yes, what you see on a geodesic dome, like the one they built for the Olympics in Montreal. Hundreds of sections."

Zavala nodded. "I didn't think that adaptive camouflage technology was that far advanced."

"Sounds more like invisibility we're talking about," Austin said, gesturing toward the screen.

"Not a bad guess. Adaptive camouflage is a new technique. The surface that you want to hide is blanketed with flat panels, which sense the scenery and changing light. Then what the sensors see is displayed on the panels. If you were standing at ground level looking at this thing, all you would see is trees, so the dome would blend into the local forest. Someone obviously took satellite imaging into account. It would be a simple matter to project treetops on the roof panels."

Austin shook his head. "Joe, you never cease to amaze me with your supply of arcane knowledge."

"I think I read about it in *Popular Mechanics*."

"Nonetheless, you may have solved the mystery," Aguirrez said. "At night, the panels Mr. Zavala talked about could be programmed for the ambient darkness. Mr. Nighthawk saw more than was intended when the dome opened for the zeppelin. There's something else that might interest you. I saved photos taken earlier." Aguirrez went back through the memory bank, and projected another aerial photo. "This picture was taken of the area yesterday. There in the corner, you see the outline of a small plane. I'll zoom in on that section."

The picture of a floatplane filled the entire screen. Four figures could be seen standing on the shore of the lake. "The plane disappeared a short time after the photo was taken, but look here." Another image appeared, showing a small boat with three people in it. One of them, a woman, was looking skyward as if she knew they were under surveillance from space.

The Basque's sharp ears picked up the sound of Austin swearing under his breath. Aguirrez raised his bushy eyebrows.

"I think I know who those people are," Austin said by way of explanation. "And if I'm right, it could complicate things. How soon can we jump off?"

"We're heading up the coast to a point that will enable you to go the shortest straight-line distance. Two hours maybe. In the meantime, I can show you what I have to offer."

With his sons taking up the rear, Aguirrez escorted the others down a companionway to a large, brightly lit belowdecks helicopter hangar. "We have two helicopters," he said. "The civilian one on the stern we use for getting about. This Sea-Cobra is held in reserve should the occasion arise. The Spanish Navy ordered a number of these aircraft. Through my connections, I was able to sidetrack one of them. It carries the standard armament." Aguirrez sounded like a car salesman touting the extras for a Buick.

Austin swept his eyes over the naval version of the army Huey, the rocket and Minigun pods slung under the stubby wings. "The standard armament will do just fine."

"Very good," Aguirrez said. "My sons will accompany you and your friend in the Eurocopter, and the SeaCobra will go along with you in case you need backup." He furrowed his brow. "I'm concerned that someone smart enough to use such clever camouflage would have the best detection technology. You could be greeted by a welcoming party, and even a heavily armed helicopter would be vulnerable."

"I agree," Austin said. "That's why we're going in by land. We'll put down at an abandoned logging camp, and Ben will guide us through the forest to our target. We think they will expect any intrusion to come across the lake, as Ben did before, so we'll come in from behind. We'll escape the same way—hopefully, with Ben's family and friends."

"I like it. Simple in planning and execution. What do you do when you get to your target?" Aguirrez asked.

"That's the hard part," Austin replied. "We don't have much other than Ben's account and the aerial photos. We'll have to improvise, but it wouldn't be the first time."

Aguirrez didn't seem worried.

"Well, then, I suggest we get started." He signaled Diego, who went over to a phone next to a battery of switches. He spoke a few words, then began to punch buttons. There was the hum of motors, an alarm horn sounded, and doors in the ceiling slid slowly apart. Next, the floor started to move upward, and moments later, they and the helicopter were lifted up to the deck, where crewmen, alerted by the call, hurried in to prepare the SeaCobra for action.

32

THE VESSEL THAT Dr. Throckmorton had comman-
deered for his survey was a stubby converted stern-
trawler used by the Canadian Fisheries Service. The
one-hundred-foot-long Cormorant was docked near where
Mike Neal's boat had been tied up on the Trouts' first visit to
the harbor.

"To quote the great Yogi Berra, 'This is like déjà vu, all
over again,'" Trout said, as he and Gamay walked up the
gangplank onto the deck of the survey vessel.

She gazed out at the sleepy harbor. "Strange being back
here. This place is so peaceful."

"So is a graveyard," Paul said.

Throckmorton bustled over and greeted them with his
usual effusiveness. "The Doctors Trout! What a pleasure it is
to have you aboard. I'm so glad you called. I had no idea after
our discussion in Montreal that we'd be seeing each other so
soon."

"Neither did we," Gamay said. "Your findings created
quite a stir with the people at NUMA. Thanks for having us
aboard on such short notice."

"Not at all, not at all." He lowered his voice. "I recruited a couple of my students to help out. A young man and woman. Brilliant kids. But I'm pleased to have adult scientific colleagues aboard, if you know what I mean. I see you're still wearing your cast. How's the arm?"

"It's fine," Paul said. He glanced around. "I don't see Dr. Barker on board."

"He couldn't make it," Throckmorton said. "Personal commitment of some sort. He may try to join us later. I hope he shows up. I could use his genetic expertise."

"Then the research hasn't been going well?" Gamay said.

"On the contrary, it's been going fine, but I'm more of a mechanic in this field, if I may use an analogy. I can bolt the frame and chassis together, but it's Frederick who designs the sports car."

"Even the most expensive sports car wouldn't run forever without the mechanic to make the engine go," Gamay said with a smile.

"You're very kind. But this is a complex matter, and I've run into a few aspects that have me puzzled." He frowned. "I've always found fishermen to be superb observers of what's going on at sea. The local fishing fleet has moved on to more productive grounds, as you know. But I talked to a few old-timers, shore captains who watched the fish stocks vanish and be replaced by these so-called devilfish. Now the devilfish have dribbled down to nothing. They're dying, and I don't know why."

"Too bad you haven't been able to catch any."

"Oh, I never said that. Come, I'll show you."

Throckmorton led the way through the "dry lab," where the computers and other electrical equipment were kept high and dry, and into the "wet lab," basically a small space with sinks, running water, tanks and table space used for the damp pursuits such as carving up specimens for investigation. He donned a pair of gloves and reached into an oversized cooler. With a hand from the Trouts, he pulled out the frozen carcass of a salmon about four feet long and placed it on a table.

"That's similar to the fish we caught," Paul said, bending low to inspect the pale-white scales.

"We would have liked to keep this specimen alive, but it was impossible. He tore the net apart and would have devoured the rest of the ship if he lived long enough."

"Now that you've seen one of these things up close, what are your conclusions?" Gamay said.

Throckmorton took a deep breath and puffed out his plump cheeks. "It's as I feared. Judging from his unusual physical size, I'd say he's definitely a genetically modified salmon. A lab-produced mutant, in other words. It's the same species as the one I showed you in my lab."

"But your fish was smaller and more normal-looking."

Throckmorton nodded. "They were both programmed with growth genes, I'd venture, but where my experiment was kept under control, there seems to have been no effort to restrain size with this fellow. It's almost as if someone wanted to see what would happen. But size and ferociousness led to its downfall. Once these creatures destroyed and replaced the natural stocks, they turned on each other."

"They were too hungry to breed, in other words?"

"That's possible. Or this design may simply have had a problem adapting to the wild, in the same way a big tree would be uprooted in a storm while a straggly little scrub pine survives. Nature tends to cull out mutants that don't fit into the scheme of things."

"There's another possibility," Gamay said. "I think Dr. Barker said something about producing neutered biofish so they couldn't breed."

"Yes, that's entirely possible, but it would involve some sophisticated bioengineering."

"What's next for your survey?" Paul said.

"We'll see what we can catch over the next few days, then I'll bring this specimen and anything else I catch back to Montreal, where we can map the genes. I may be able to match it up with some of the stuff I have in the computers. Maybe we can figure out who designed it."

"Is that possible?"

"Oh, sure. A genetic program is almost as good as a signature. I sent Dr. Barker a message telling him what I found. Frederick is a whiz at this sort of thing."

"You speak very highly of him," Paul said.

"He's brilliant, as I said before. I only wish that he weren't affiliated with a commercial venture."

"Speaking of commercial ventures, we heard there's a fish-processing plant of some sort up the coast. Could they have had anything to do with this?"

"In what way?"

"I don't know. Pollution, maybe. Like those two-headed frogs they sometimes find in contaminated waters."

"Interesting premise, but unlikely. You might see some deformed fish or fish kills, but this monster is no accident. And we would have seen deformities in other species, which doesn't seem to have been the case. Tell you what, though. We'll motor out and anchor for the night near the fish plant and make a few sets with the net in the morning. How long can you stay on board?"

"As long as you can stand us," Paul said. "We don't want to impose."

"No imposition at all." He put the salmon back into the cooler. "You may decide to cut your stay short after you see your cabin."

The cabin was slightly bigger than the two up-and-down bunks it contained. After Throckmorton left them to get settled, Paul tried to ease his six-foot-eight length into the lower bunk, but his legs hung over the side.

"I've been thinking about what Dr. Throckmorton told us," Gamay said, trying the mattress on top. "Suppose you were Dr. Barker and you were working for Oceanus on this biofish thing. Would you want anyone testing genetic material that could be traced to your doorstep?"

"Nope. Judging from our own experience, Oceanus is ruthless when it comes to snoops."

"Any suggestions?"

"Sure. We could suggest that Throckmorton find another location to anchor for the night. Fake a toothache, or make some other excuse."

"You don't really want to do that, do you?"

"As you recall, I whined the whole trip up here because I couldn't go play with Kurt and Joe."

"You don't have to remind me. You sounded as if you hadn't been picked for the Little League team."

"Dr. Throckmorton is a fine fellow, but I wasn't prepared to baby-sit him away from the action."

"And now you think the action may have moved to our doorstep."

Paul nodded and said, "Got a loony?" Gamay dug out a Canadian dollar coin with the picture of a loon on one side.

Paul tossed it in the air and caught it on the back of his cast. "Heads. I lose. You get to choose which watch you want."

"Okay, you can take the first two-hour shift, starting as soon as the rest of the crew turns in."

"Fine with me." He extracted himself from the bunk. "I wouldn't get much sleep in this torture rack." He lifted his injured arm in the air. "Maybe I can use this cast as a weapon."

"No need," Gamay said with a smile. She dug into her duffel bag and pulled out a holster that held a .22 caliber target pistol. "I brought this along in case I wanted to brush up on my target shooting."

Paul smiled. As a girl, his wife had been taught by her father to shoot skeet, and she was an expert marksman. He took the pistol and found that he could aim it if he propped up the cast with his other hand.

Gamay looked at his shaky aim. "Maybe we should both stand watch."

The ship dropped anchor about a mile from shore. The silhouettes of rooflines and a communication tower marked the Oceanus facility, which was located on a rocky hill overlooking the water. The Trouts had dinner in the small galley with Throckmorton, his students and some crew. Time went by quickly, hastened by talk about Throckmorton's work and the Trouts' NUMA experiences. Around eleven, they called it a night.

Paul and Gamay went to their cabin and waited until the ship was quiet. Then they crept up onto the deck and took a position on the side facing land. The night was cool. They stayed warm with the heavy sweaters under their windbreakers and blankets borrowed from their bunks. The water was flat calm, except for a lazy swell. Paul sat with his back to the cabin housing, and Gamay lay on the deck beside him.

The first two hours went quickly. Then Gamay took over and Paul stretched out on the deck. It seemed he was asleep only a few minutes before Gamay was shaking him by the shoulder. He came awake quickly and said, "What's up?"

"I need your eyes. I've been watching that dark smudge on the water. I thought it might be a patch of floating seaweed, but it's come closer."

Paul rubbed his eyes and followed the pointing finger. At first, he saw nothing but the blue-blackness of the sea. After a moment, he saw a darker mass, and it seemed to be moving in their direction. There was something else, the soft murmur of voices. "That's the first time I ever heard a patch of kelp talking. How about firing a shot across their bow."

They crawled forward, and Gamay assumed a prone firing position with her elbows resting on the deck, the pistol clasped in two hands. Paul fiddled with a flashlight, but finally got it into position. When Gamay gave him the go-ahead, he flicked the light on. The powerful beam fell upon the swarthy faces of four men. They were dressed in black and were sitting in two kayaks, their wooden paddles frozen in midstroke. Their almond eyes blinked with surprise in the light.

Crack!

The first shot shattered the paddle held by the lead man in one boat. There was a second shot, and a paddle in the second boat flew into pieces. The men in the rear of the kayaks back-paddled furiously, and the others dug their hands into the water to help. They got the boats turned around and headed back toward land, but Gamay wasn't about to let them off so easily. The boats were almost out of range of the light when she shot out the other two paddles.

"Good shootin', Annie Oakley," Paul said.

"Good spottin', Dead-Eye Dick. That should keep them busy for a while."

The gunfire wasn't loud by itself, but in the stillness of the night it must have sounded like cannon barrages, because Dr. Throckmorton and some of the crew came on deck.

"Oh, hullo," he said, when he saw the Trouts. "We heard a noise. My goodness—" he said, spying the pistol in Gamay's hand.

"Just thought I'd do some target practice."

They could hear voices out on the water. One of the crew went to the ship's rail and cocked his ear. "Sounds as if someone needs help. We'd better get a boat over the side."

"I wouldn't do that if I were you," Paul said, in his usual soft-spoken manner but with an unmistakable steeliness in his voice. "The folks out there are doing fine on their own."

Throckmorton hesitated, then said to the crewman: "It's all right. I want to talk to the Trouts for a moment."

After the others had shuffled back to their cabins, Throckmorton said, "Now if you wouldn't mind telling me, my friends, exactly what is going on?"

Gamay said to her husband, "I'll go get some coffee. It could be a long night." Minutes later, she returned with three steaming mugs. "I found a bottle of whiskey and poured in a few shots," she said. "I thought we might need it."

Taking turns, they laid out their suspicions of the Oceanus plot, backing them up with evidence gleaned from several sources.

"These are grave charges," Throckmorton said. "Do you have solid proof of this outrageous plan?"

"I'd say the proof is that thing in your lab cooler," Gamay said. "Do you have any more questions?"

"Yes," Throckmorton said after a moment. "Do you have any more whiskey?"

Gamay had thoughtfully stuck the pint in her pocket. After they refreshed his coffee and he had taken a sip, Throckmorton said, "Frederick's affiliations have always bothered me, but I had assumed, optimistically I suppose, that scientific reason would overrule his commercial interests in time."

"Let me ask you a question about the premise we're operating under," Gamay said. "Would it be possible to destroy the native fish populations and substitute these Frankenfish?"

"Entirely possible, and if anyone could do it, it would be Dr. Barker. This explains so much. It's still hard to believe Dr. Barker is with this bunch. But he has acted strangely." He blinked like someone coming out of a dream. "Those gun-shots I heard. Someone tried to board our ship!"

"It would seem so," Gamay said.

"Perhaps it would be better if we moved on and informed the authorities!"

"We don't know where that shore facility fits into the pic-ture," Gamay said, with a combination of feminine firmness and reassurance. "Kurt thinks it may be important and wants us to keep an eye on it until his mission is completed."

"Isn't that dangerous to the people on board this ship?"

"Not necessarily," Paul said. "Just as long as we keep watch. I'd suggest that you have the captain get the ship ready for a quick departure. But I doubt our friends will come back, now that we've spoiled the element of surprise."

"All right," Throckmorton said. He set his jaw in determi-nation. "But is there anything else I can do?"

"Yes," Paul said. He took the whiskey from Gamay and poured Throckmorton another shot to calm the professor's nerves. "You can wait."

33

THE SOS CREW stumbled blindly through deep woods, with the guards showing no mercy. Therri tried to get a better look at their tormenters, but a guard jammed a gun into her back with such force that it broke the skin. Tears of pain ran down her cheeks. She bit her lip, stifling the urge to cry out.

The forest was dark, except for lights glowing here and there through the trees. Then the trees thinned, and they were standing in front of a building whose large door was illuminated by an outside floodlight. They were shoved inside the building, the guards cut the wire binding their wrists, and the sliding door was slammed shut and locked behind them.

The air inside smelled of gasoline and there were oil stains on the floor, evidence that the structure had been built as an oversized garage. No vehicles were parked inside, but the garage was far from empty. More than three dozen people—men, women and a few children—huddled like frightened puppies against the far wall. Their misery was etched into their tired faces, and there was no mistaking the terror in their eyes at the sudden appearance of strangers.

The two groups stared warily at each other. After a moment, a man who had been sitting cross-legged on the floor got to his feet and came over. His face was as wrinkled as old leather and his long gray hair was tied in a ponytail. He had dark circles under his eyes and his clothes were filthy, yet he projected an aura of unmistakable dignity. When he spoke, Therri realized why the man looked so familiar.

"I'm Jesse Nighthawk," he said, extending his hand in greeting.

"*Nighthawk,*" she said. "You must be Ben's father."

His mouth dropped open. "You know my son?"

"Yes, I work with him in the SOS office in Washington."

The old man glanced past Therri's shoulder as if he were looking for someone. "Ben was here. I saw him run out of the woods. He was with another man, who was killed."

"Yes, I know. Ben is fine. I just saw him in Washington. He told us that you and the villagers were in trouble."

Ryan stepped forward and said, "We came to get you and the others out."

Jesse Nighthawk gazed at Ryan as if he were Dudley Do-Right, the cartoon Mountie who always arrived to save the day. Shaking his head, he said, "You seem to mean well, but I'm sorry you came. You have put yourself in great danger by coming here."

"We were captured as soon as we landed," Therri said. "It was as if they knew we were coming."

"They have watchers everywhere," Nighthawk said. "The evil one told me this."

"The 'evil one'?"

"You'll meet him, I'm afraid. He's like a monster in a heat dream. He killed Ben's cousin with a spear." Jesse's eyes grew moist at the recollection. "We've been working day and night clearing the forest. Even the women and children . . ." His voice trailed off in weariness.

"Who are these people?" Ryan said.

"They call themselves Kiolya. I think they're Eskimos. I don't know for sure. They started building in the woods across the lake from our village. We didn't much like it, but we're squatters on the land, so we don't have any say in things. Then one day they came across the lake with guns and brought us here. We've been cutting trees and dragging them off ever since. You have any idea what this is all about?"

Before Ryan could answer, there was the sound of the door being unlatched. Six men came into the garage, machine rifles draped in the crooks of their arms. Their dark faces were alike, wide with high cheekbones, and hard, almond-shaped eyes. The cruelty sculpted into their impassive expressions paled next to that of the seventh man to enter. He was built like a bull, with a short thick neck, his head sitting almost directly on powerful shoulders. His yellowish-red skin was pock-marked and his mouth was set in a leer. Vertical tattoo marks flanked his nose, which was bruised and misshapen. He was unarmed, except for the knife hanging in a scabbard at his belt.

Therri stared in disbelief at the man who had pursued Austin on the dogsled. There was no mistaking the ruined face and the body that looked as if it had been pumped up on steroids. She knew exactly who Jesse meant when he talked about the 'evil one.' The man swept his eyes over the new prisoners, sending chills along Therri's spine as his coal-black eyes lingered on her body. Jesse Nighthawk instinctively stepped back with the other villagers.

A brutish grin crossed the man's face as he saw the fear he inspired. He uttered a guttural command. The guards shoved Therri, Ryan and Mercer out of the building and marched them through the woods. Therri was completely disoriented. She had no idea where the lake was. If by some miracle she had the chance to escape, she wouldn't know which way to run.

Her confusion was further compounded seconds later. They were moving along a paved path toward a thick stand of fir trees that barred their way like a dark and impenetrable wall. The fat trunks and thickly grown branches were a shadowy interplay of blacks and grays. When they were yards away from the nearest trees, a section of forest disappeared. In its place was a rectangle of blinding white light. Therri shielded her eyes. When they adjusted after a moment, she saw people moving about as if she were looking through a doorway into another dimension.

They were herded through the door into an enormous, brightly lit space hundreds of feet across, and vaulted by a high, rounded ceiling. She looked behind her as the rectangle of forest vanished, and she realized that they had stepped into a building masked by a clever camouflage. While the structure itself was an architectural wonder, what caught their breath was the huge silvery-white airship that took up a good portion of the space inside the dome.

They gazed up in astonishment at the torpedo-shaped leviathan that was longer than two football fields. Its tail tapered down to a point that was surrounded by four triangular stabilizing fins, giving it a streamlined appearance despite its enormous size. Four massive engines in protective nacelles hung from struts below the belly of the aircraft. The airship rested on a complicated system of fixed and movable gantries. Dozens of men in coveralls swarmed around and over the airship. The air echoed with the sound of machinery and tools. The guards nudged the prisoners forward under the rounded nose of the airship, which loomed overhead as if it could crush them at any second. Therri had a fleeting image of what a bug must feel like just before a shoe comes down.

A long, narrow control cabin, ringed by big windows, was set into the aircraft's belly a short distance back from the nose, and they were ordered inside. The roomy interior reminded Therri of a ship, complete with its spoked wheel and binnacle. A man stood inside giving orders to several others. Unlike the guards, who all looked as if they had sprung from the same mold, he was tall and his skin looked as if it had been bleached. His head was shaved bald. He turned at the arrival of the prisoners and looked at them through dark sunglasses, then handed off the electronic clipboard he was holding.

"Well, well, what a pleasant surprise. SOS to the rescue." He smiled, but his voice had all the warmth of a wind blowing off a glacier.

Ryan responded as if he hadn't heard the taunt. "My name is Marcus Ryan, the director of Sentinels of the Sea. This is Therri Weld, our legal counsel, and Chuck Mercer, SOS operations director."

"There's no need to go through the routine of name, rank and serial number. I know perfectly well who you are," the man said. "Let's not waste time. In the white-man's world, I go by the name of Frederick Barker. I'm called Toonook by my own people."

"You and these others are Eskimos?" Ryan said.

"Ignorant people call us by that name, but we are Kiolya."

"You don't fit the stereotype for an Eskimo."

"I've inherited the genes of a New England whaling captain. What started as a humiliating liability has enabled me to pass myself off in the outside world without question, to the benefit of the Kiolya."

"What is this thing?" Ryan said, glancing above his head.

"Beautiful, isn't it? The *Nietzsche* was secretly built by the Germans to go to the North Pole. They planned to use it for commercial flight. It was all fitted out to take on passengers who would pay anything to fly aboard a real polar explorer. When it crashed, my people thought it was a gift from heaven. In a way, they were right. I've spent millions in restoration. We made improvements in the engines and their carrying capacity. The gas bags were replaced with new ones that can hold millions of cubic feet of hydrogen."

"I thought hydrogen went out with the *Hindenburg*," Mercer said.

"German airships safely traveled thousands of miles using hydrogen. I chose it because of the weight of my cargo. Hydrogen has twice the lifting power of helium. By the means of this simplest of atoms, the People of the Aurora Borealis will achieve their rightful destiny."

"You're talking in riddles," Ryan said.

"Not at all. Legend has it that the Kiolya were born in the aurora, which the Inuit tribes fear as a source of bad luck. Unfortunately, you and your friends will soon learn that this reputation is well-earned."

"You intend to kill us, don't you?"

"The Kiolya don't keep prisoners beyond their usefulness."

"What about the villagers?"

"As I said, we don't keep prisoners."

"Since we're doomed, why not indulge our curiosity and tell us where this aviation antique fits in."

A cold smile crossed the pale lips. "This is where the hero plays on the villain's vanity, hoping for the cavalry to arrive. Don't waste your time. You and your friends will live only as long as I need you."

"Aren't you interested in learning what we know about your plans?"

In answer, Barker said something in a strange language, and the leader of the guards stepped forward and handed him one of the C-4 explosive packets that Mercer had carefully prepared. "Did you intend to do some mining?"

Ryan shot back. "Hell no! We planned to sink your operation like you did our ship."

"Blunt and to the point as usual, Mr. Ryan. But I don't think you'll get the chance to ignite your little July Fourth display," he said, his words dripping with contempt. He tossed the explosives to his henchman. "And exactly what do you know about our 'operation'?"

"We know all about your experiments with biologically modified fish."

"That's only part of my grand plan," Barker said. "Let me explain what the future holds. Tonight, this airship will rise into the sky and head east. Its holding tanks will be filled with genetically modified fish in several species. It will spread my creations in the sea like a farmer planting seed. Within a few weeks and months, the native species will be wiped out. If this pilot project succeeds, as I expect it will, similar seedings will take place in all the world's oceans. In time, most of the fish on the world market will be those produced through our patented gene banks. We will have near-total monopoly."

Ryan laughed. "Do you really think this crazy scheme will work?"

"There's nothing crazy about it. Every computer model points to a resounding success. The natural fish stocks are doomed from overfishing and industrial pollution, anyway. I'm simply hastening the day when the oceans are turned into vast fish farms. Best of all, throwing fish into the sea isn't even against the law."

"*Killing* people is against the law," Ryan said, anger in his eyes. "You murdered my friend and colleague Josh Green."

Therri was unable to contain herself any longer. "Josh wasn't the only one. You killed the television reporter aboard the *Sentinel*. Your thugs shot one of your own men in Copenhagen. You murdered Ben Nighthawk's cousin and tried to kill Senator Graham. You're keeping people as slaves."

"The company lawyer has a tongue!" Barker's jaw hardened and the civilized tone he had been using turned into a snarl. "It's a pity you weren't around to argue the case for the Kiolya when they starved to death because the white men decimated the walrus. Or when the tribe was forced to leave its traditional hunting grounds, spreading throughout Canada, moving into the cities far from their homeland."

"None of that gives you the right to kill people or to mess up the oceans for your own good," she said, with unrestrained fury. "You can terrorize a bunch of poor Indians and push us around, but you're going to have to contend with NUMA."

"I'm not going to lose any sleep over Admiral Sandecker's collection of oddballs and geeks."

"Would you lose sleep over Kurt Austin?" Ryan said.

"I know all about Austin. He's a dangerous man—but NUMA regards SOS as an outlaw organization. No, you and your friends here are all alone. More alone than you have ever been in your life." Barker's tattooed henchman said something in the Kiolya language. "Umealiq reminds me that you wanted to see my pets."

With the guards taking up the rear, Barker led the way to a side door that opened to the outside. Moments later, they were back at the building where SOS had planted the explosive charges. Only this time, the interior was brightly lit up.

Barker paused in front of one of the tanks. The fish inside was nearly ten feet long. Barker cocked his head like an artist studying his canvas.

"I did most of my early work with salmon," Barker said. "It was comparatively easy to create giants like this. Although I actually came up with a fifty-pound sardine that lived a few months."

He moved on to the next tank. Therri sucked in her breath at the sight of the creature inside. It was a salmon, half the size of the fish in the first tank, but it had two identical heads on the same body. "This one didn't turn out the way I planned. You must admit it's interesting, though."

The fish in the next tank was even more deformed, its body

covered with round lumps that gave it a repulsive, pebbled appearance. In another tank was a fish with bulbous, protruding eyes. The same deformities were repeated with other species, haddock and cod and herring.

"These are hideous," Ryan said.

"Beauty is in the eye of the beholder." Barker stopped before a tank that held a silvery-white fish about five feet long. "This is an early prototype I developed before I found that aggression and size were getting out of control in my experiments. I let some into the wild to see what happened. Unfortunately, they started to devour each other after they wiped out the local species."

"These aren't experiments, they're monsters," Ryan said. "Why do you let them live?"

"Feeling sorry for a fish? That's stretching it, even for SOS. Let me tell you about this fellow. He's very handy. We threw the body of the Indian into the tank along with your friend, and he stripped them down to the bone in no time. We let the other Indians watch, and they haven't given us an ounce of trouble since."

Ryan lost his cool and launched himself at Barker. He had his hands around the man's throat, when Barker's henchman grabbed the rifle from one of the guards and slammed the butt into Ryan's head. Therri was showered with blood as Ryan slumped to the floor.

Therri felt the coldness in the pit of her stomach as she recognized the source of the fear she had seen in Jesse Nighthawk's eyes. She heard Barker say, "If Mr. Ryan and his friends are so concerned about their finny friends, maybe we can arrange dinner together later."

Then the guards closed in.

34

THE EUROCOPTER CARRYING Austin, Zavala, Ben
Nighthawk and the two Basques lifted off the *Navarra*'s
helicopter pad and wheeled above the yacht in a big circle.
Minutes later, the SeaCobra joined the circling chopper. Flying side by side, the choppers headed west toward the afternoon sun.

From his seat next to the pilot, Austin had a clear view of
the SeaCobra's lethal silhouette pacing the Eurocopter a few
hundred feet away. The combat helicopter carried enough
weaponry to level a small city. Austin was under no illusions.
Oceanus would be no pushover.

Cruising at a speed of one hundred twenty-five knots, the
helicopters soon passed over a rocky shoreline and left the sea
behind them. They were traveling over a dense forest of fir
trees, keeping a tight formation, hugging the treetops in the
hope of avoiding detection. Austin checked the load in his
Bowen revolver, then he sat back in his seat, closed his eyes
and worked through their plan in his head.

Zavala sometimes jokingly accused Austin of making
things up as he went along. There was some truth to the
charge. Austin knew planning could only go so far. Having

grown up on and around the water, his views were colored by his nautical experiences. He knew that a mission was like sailing a boat into foul weather; when things went wrong, they *really* went wrong. A good sailor kept his lines clear and his bailing can handy.

He was a strong believer in the KISS principle. Keep It Simple Stupid. Since his primary goal was to get Ben's family and friends out safely, the SeaCobra couldn't just swoop down and blast away at everything in sight. Austin knew there was no such thing as a surgical strike. The chopper's armament would have to be used sparingly, a fact which neutered its fearsome capability. He furrowed his brow at the wild card that fanatical idiot Marcus Ryan had dealt him. Austin didn't need his fondness for Therri Weld to cloud his judgment.

The Eurocopter's engine changed pitch as the aircraft cut speed and came to a hover over the forest. Ben, who was sitting behind Austin with Zavala and the Aguirrez brothers, was signaling the pilot to descend. The pilot shook his head and insisted that there was no place to land.

Pablo glanced out the window. "Do you trust the Indian?"

Austin checked the landing zone. Visibility was restricted, and he could see nothing but dark greenery in the lowering sun. They were now in Ben Nighthawk's backyard. "This is his country, not mine."

Pablo nodded, then barked in Spanish at the pilot, who muttered to himself and radioed the other helicopter of his plans to land. The SeaCobra peeled off and flew a back-and-forth pattern over the woods, using its infrared detectors to see if there were any warm bodies lurking in the vicinity. Detecting no sign of human life, the SeaCobra gave the okay to land.

The Eurocopter sank into the forest. No one except Ben would have been surprised to hear the rotors shred themselves in an unequal match with the sturdy tree trunks. But the only sound was a crackle and snap of thin branches and the soft thump of the skids hitting the ground. Ben's sharp eyes had seen what the others had not, that what appeared to be thick forest was in reality a cleared area overgrown with heavy underbrush. The SeaCobra dropped down a short distance away.

Austin let out the breath he had been holding and jumped

from the chopper with Zavala and the Aguirrez brothers right behind him. They ducked into a combat crouch with guns at the ready, despite the infrared sweep. As the rotors spun to a stop, a silence so complete that it seemed to have substance settled on them. Ben climbed out of the chopper and glanced at the upheld machine rifles.

"You won't find anyone here," he said. "This place hasn't been used since I was a kid. There's a river over there through the trees." He pointed to some ramshackle buildings that were barely visible in the dusky light. "That's the bunkhouse and the sawmill. It's a bad-luck place. My father said they had lots of accidents. They built a new camp downriver where they could float the logs to market quicker."

Austin had more temporal things on his mind. "The light's fading. We'd better get moving."

They rounded up their rucksacks and broke into two groups. The NUMA men, Nighthawk and the Aguirrez brothers would be the assault group. The muscular Basques moved with an air of assurance that suggested they were no strangers to clandestine missions.

The two pilots, who were also heavily armed, would wait for a call to provide backup. Ben led the way into the forest, and they went from dusk to darkness the second they were under the trees. Each man except the last in line carried a small halogen flashlight, which they held beam-pointed-down as they followed Ben, who moved through the woods as silently and as swiftly as a woodland wraith. They traveled between a walk and a trot for several miles, making good time on the soft carpet of pine needles, until Ben finally called a halt. They stood in the piney darkness, panting with exertion, sweat pouring down their faces.

Ben cocked his ear, listening. After a moment, he said, "We're less than a mile away."

Zavala slipped the shotgun off his shoulder. "Time to make sure our powder is dry."

"Don't worry about the guards," Ben said. "They're all on the lakeside. Nobody would expect us to come in this way."

"Why not?" Zavala replied.

"You'll see. Make sure you don't get ahead of me,"

Nighthawk said, and without another word, he pushed on. Ten minutes later, Ben slowed his pace to a walk. Advising them to proceed with care, he brought the group to an abrupt halt at the edge of a chasm. Austin flashed his light on the steep vertical walls, then pointed it downward toward the sound of rushing water. The beam exhausted itself before reaching the river far below.

"I think I know why there are no guards on this side," Zavala said. "We took a wrong turn and ended up on the north rim of the Grand Canyon."

"This is called 'Dead Man's Leap,'" Ben said. "The people around here aren't very original when it comes to naming things."

"They make their point well enough," Austin said.

Zavala looked to the right and the left. "Can we detour around this little ditch?"

"We'd have to travel another ten miles through thick forest," Ben said. "This is the narrowest point. The lake is a half mile from here."

"I remember an Indiana Jones movie where they crossed a chasm on an invisible bridge," Zavala said.

"Ask and you shall receive," Austin said, as he removed his backpack. He unsnapped the flap and pulled out a coil of nylon rope and a compact folding grapnel.

Zavala's eyes widened. "You never cease to amaze me, amigo. Here I was thinking I was well prepared because I brought a Swiss army knife with the corkscrew. I'll bet you have a bottle of fine wine in your little baggie as well."

Austin produced a pulley and rappelling harness. "Before you nominate me for a Boy Scout merit badge, I should confess that Ben told me we'd have to cross this moat before we scaled the castle walls."

Austin warned everyone to give him room. He stepped dangerously close to the rim, whirled the grapnel over his head and let it fly. The first try fell short and clanged against the chasm wall. Two other tosses landed on the other side but failed to hook on. On the fourth throw, the hooks wedged into a cleft between some rocks. Austin belayed the other end of the rope to a tree and tested his weight to see if the grapnel would hold. Then he attached the pulley and rappelling harness to the rope, took a deep breath and stepped out into space.

By the time he reached the other side, he seemed to be moving at Mach 2. A clump of bushes cushioned his landing. Using a retrieval line, Zavala pulled the pulley back, attached Austin's backpack and sent it over. After the rest of their gear was transported the same way, Zavala and Ben made the next crossing, then the two Basques followed.

They gathered up their packs and kept on moving through the woods until they began to see will-o'-the-wisp lights sprinkled among the trees like the campfires of a gypsy encampment. They could hear the muffled sounds of machinery.

Ben brought them to a halt. "*Now* you can worry about the guards," he whispered.

Zavala and the Basques slipped their weapons off their shoulders, and Austin loosened the flap on his belt holster. He had studied the satellite photos of the complex, trying to glean the layout as best he could even without the dome. Ben had helped fill in the gaps.

The zeppelin dome lay a short distance from the lake, surrounded by a network of paved walkways and roads that connected several smaller buildings hidden in the woods. He asked Ben to take him to where he saw the dome. While the others waited, the Indian led the way through the woods to the edge of a tarmac path that was lit by low-intensity, ankle-high lights. Seeing that the way was clear, they quickly crossed the tarred path into another patch of woods.

At one point, Ben stopped, then raised his hands like a sleepwalker and began to move toward the trees barring their way. He stopped again and whispered for Austin to do the same. Austin followed with arms outstretched until his hands were about to touch the shadowy tree trunks. But instead of rough bark, his palm encountered a smooth, cold surface. He put his ear against the exterior and heard a low humming. He backed off and saw the tree trunks again. Adaptive camouflage has a great future, he thought.

He and Ben quickly retraced their path and rejoined the others. Austin suggested that they investigate the outbuildings. They would regroup in fifteen minutes.

"Don't take any wooden Eskimo Pies," Zavala said, as he slipped away into the darkness.

Pablo hesitated. "What if we're discovered?"

"If you can do so quietly, neutralize anyone who sees you," Austin said. "If not, and all hell breaks loose, escape the way we came."

"What about me?" Ben asked.

"You've done enough leading us here. Take a rest."

"I can't rest until my family is safe."

Austin didn't blame Ben for wanting to find his family. "Stay close behind me." He drew his Bowen from its holster and waited until the others had melted into the darkness. Then he motioned for Ben to follow, and they struck off along the pathway, sacrificing the cover of the woods for speed.

They could hear activity from the direction of the lake, but the way was clear, and before long, they came across a long, low building. It was unguarded.

"Shall we?" Austin said to Ben. They stepped inside. The building was only a storage warehouse. They made a quick inspection and headed back to the rendezvous. Zavala showed up a few minutes later.

"We checked out a warehouse," Austin said. "Did you find anything exciting?"

"I wish I *hadn't*," Zavala said. "I'm swearing off fish and chips forever. I think I hit the Frankenfish mother lode."

He described the strange, deformed creatures that he had seen in the building he'd investigated. It took a lot to disrupt Zavala's natural calm, but from the tone of his voice, he was clearly rattled by the mutant monsters in the fish tanks. "Sounds like the things in your finny freak show constitute the prototype models," Austin said.

He stopped talking at a soft rustling in the woods. It was only Pablo returning. He said that he had found what looked like an empty garage. Inside there were signs of human habitation, scraps of food, slop buckets and blankets that might have been used to sleep on. He handed Austin an object that made Austin's jaw go hard. It was a child's doll.

They waited for Diego to appear, and when he did show up, they saw why he was late. He was bent low, carrying a heavy burden across his shoulders. He stood up, and an un-

conscious guard crashed to the ground. "You said to neutralize anyone who got in the way, but I thought this pig might be
more useful alive."

"Where did you find him?"

"He was in a barracks for the guards. Maybe one or two
hundred bunks. This thing was taking a siesta."

"Bet it's the last time he sleeps on the job," Austin said. He
got down on one knee and flashed his light in the guard's face.
The high cheekbones and wide mouth were indistinguishable
from the other guards he had seen, except that he had a
bruised forehead. Austin stood and unscrewed the top of a
canteen. He took a sip, then poured water onto the guard's
face. The heavy features stirred and the eyes fluttered open.
They widened when they saw the guns pointed at his head.

"Where are the prisoners?" Austin said. He held the doll
out so the guard could see what he wanted.

The man's lips spread wide in a mirthless grin, and the
dark eyes seemed to glow like fanned coals. He snarled something in an incomprehensible language. Diego added a little
persuasion, putting his boot on the man's crotch and placing
the muzzle between the fierce eyes. The grin vanished, but it
was clear to Austin that the guard was bound by a fanaticism
that would withstand all the threats and pain that could be
brought to bear.

Diego saw that he was getting nowhere, and switched
around, putting his foot on the man's face and his gun jammed
into the man's crotch. The man's eyes widened and he mumbled something in his language.

"Speak English," Diego said, and jammed the gun harder.

The guard caught his breath. "The lake," he gasped. "In the
lake."

Diego smiled. "Even a pig wants to keep his *cojones*," he
said.

He removed the gun, turned it around and slammed the
butt down. There was a sickening hollow sound, and the
guard's head lolled like that of the doll still clutched in
Austin's hand.

Austin flinched, but he had no sympathy for the guard. He
was too busy pondering the frightful possibilities for the prisoners. "Sweet dreams," he said with a shrug.

"Lead the way," Pablo said.

"Since we're slightly outnumbered, this may be a good time to call in the reserves," Zavala said.

Pablo unclipped the radio from his belt and ordered the SeaCobra pilot to hover a mile away. Austin tucked the doll inside his shirt. Then, with the others following, he hurried in the direction of the lake, determined to return the doll to its rightful owner.

35

WHEN THE GUARDS had burst into the garage prison brandishing truncheons, Marcus Ryan was huddled with Jesse Nighthawk. He had been probing the Indian's knowledge of the forest so that he could put together an escape plan. Ryan's hopes were dashed as the guards, at least two dozen of them, clubbed the prisoners at random. Most of the Indians were used to the sporadic beatings aimed to discourage resistance, and they cowered against the far wall. But Ryan was slow to move, and blows rained down on his shoulders and head.

Therri had been playing with a little girl named Rachael, when the door burst open and the makeshift prison was suddenly filled with shouts and swinging clubs. Rachael was about five years old, the youngest child in the group, and like many of the villagers, she was part of Ben's extended family. Therri stepped between one of the attackers and the little girl, and braced herself for the blow to come. The guard froze, confused at the unexpected show of defiance. Then he laughed and lowered his upraised club. He glared at Therri with pitiless eyes. "For that, you and the girl will go first."

He called out to one of his companions, who grabbed

Therri by the hair. She was pushed facedown onto the floor, and a club was pressed across the back of her neck. Her hands were bound behind her back with wire that cut painfully into her wrists. Then she was pulled to her feet and saw Marcus and Chuck, whose heads were bloodied from the club blows.

When all the prisoners had been trussed like hogs, the guards herded them through the doorway and marched them through the woods. They walked through the woods for several minutes, until the dull sheen of the lake was visible through the trees. Although it seemed like several days, only a few hours had passed since they had been captured.

They were shoved into a shed near the lake and left alone. They stood in the darkened building, the children whimpering, the older people trying to comfort the younger ones with their stoic attitude. The fear of the unknown was even more torturous than being beaten. Then there was a commotion at the door, which opened to admit Barker, surrounded by a contingent of his inscrutable guards. He had removed his sunglasses, and Therri saw the strangely pale eyes for the first time. They were the color of a rattlesnake belly, she thought. Some of the guards carried blazing torches, and Barker's eyes seemed to glitter in the flickering light. His face was wreathed in a Satanic smile.

"Good evening, ladies and gentlemen," he said, with the geniality of a tour guide. "Thank you for coming. Within a few minutes, I will rise high above this place on the first phase of a journey into the future. I wish to thank you all for helping to get this project launched. To those of you from SOS, I wish you'd been in my hands earlier, so that by the sweat of your labor you would come to appreciate the brilliance of this plan."

Ryan had regained his composure. "Cut the crap. What do you intend to do with us?"

Barker surveyed Ryan's bloodied face as if he were seeing it for the first time. "Why, Mr. Ryan, you're looking a little rumpled these days. Not your usual blow-dried self."

"You haven't answered my question."

"To the contrary, I answered it when you were first brought to me. I said you and your friends would remain alive as long as I found you useful." He smiled again. "I no longer find you useful. I'm having the air dome lit up for your entertainment. It will be the last thing your dying brain will record."

The words chilled Therri to the bone. "What about the children?" she said.

"What about them?" Barker's icy gaze swept the prisoners as if surveying cattle being led to slaughter. "Do you think I care for any one of you, young or old? You are nothing more to me than snowflakes. You'll all be forgotten once the world learns that an insignificant Eskimo tribe controls a significant portion of the ocean. Sorry I can't stay. Our timetable is very precise."

He spun on his heel and disappeared into the night. The prisoners were rounded up and herded outside and toward the lake. Moments later, their steps echoed on the long wooden pier. The dock was in darkness, except for the lights on what looked like a barge, only with a catamaran hull. As they moved closer, Therri saw that a conveyor belt, flush with the deck, led from a bin in the bow to a wide chute at the stern end. She surmised that the strange craft must be used as a moveable feeding station. The feed went into the bin, and was transported via the belt and dumped into the fish cages through the chute. An awful thought came to her, and she yelled a warning:

"They're going to drown us!"

Marcus and Chuck had seen the barge as well, and at her words, they struggled against their captors. All they got for their trouble were club blows that took the fight out of them. Rough hands grabbed Therri and pushed her onto the barge. She stumbled and crashed onto the deck. She managed to twist her body so that she didn't come down face first on the hard surface, and most of the shock was absorbed at great painful cost by her right arm. Her knee hurt like hell, too. She didn't have time to dwell on her injuries. Duct tape was slapped across her mouth so she couldn't cry out. Then her ankles were bound, a heavy weight was tied onto her wrist bindings, and she was dragged along to the end of the barge and stretched crosswise across the belt.

She felt another, smaller body against hers. She looked over, and to her horror she saw that the next victim in line was Rachael, the little girl she had befriended. Then came the SOS men and the other prisoners. The preparations for multiple murder went on until all the prisoners were laid across the belt like cordwood. Then the barge's inboard motors rumbled into life.

The lines were cast off the pier and the barge began to move. Therri couldn't see where they were going, but she managed to turn to face the child and tried to comfort the girl with her eyes, although she was sure they were filled with terror. In the distance, she could see the light from the dome rising above the trees, as Barker had promised. She vowed that if she ever got the chance, she would kill him personally.

The motors went for only a short while, then they cut out and there was the splash of an anchor in the water. Therri struggled against her bindings, to no avail. She tensed, preparing for the worst. It came a minute later, when the motor that powered the conveyor belt started. The belt began to move, carrying her closer to the lip of the chute and to the cold dark water beyond.

36

AUSTIN HAD LED his ragtag assault group through the woods, skirting the darkened plaza, using the dimly lit footpath visible through the trees as a rough guide. He moved slowly and with great deliberation, making sure his path was free of twigs and branches before he put his full weight on his advancing foot.

The slow pace was maddening, but while they had seen no one since encountering the guard, Austin had the creepy feeling that they were not alone. His instincts were vindicated when the airship dome lit up like a giant lightbulb and a low roar arose from the plaza.

Austin and the others froze like living statues. Then a delayed reaction set in and they hit the ground belly-first, their weapons cocked and ready to repel an assault. The hail of bullets they expected never came. Instead, the roar grew in intensity and volume and flowed around them in a vast rushing river of sound. The noise came from the mouths of hundreds of Kiolya men, their broad, upturned faces cast in bluish light, zombie eyes transfixed on Barker, who stood on a raised dais in front of the dome.

Then came the monotonous chorus of a dozen tom-toms ringing in the plaza, and the crowd began to chant:

"Toonook . . . Toonook . . . Toonook . . ."

Barker bathed in the adulation, letting it wash over him, drinking it in as if it were an elixir before he raised his arms to the sky. Then the chanting and the drumbeat stopped as if a switch had been pulled. Barker began to speak in a strange tongue that had its origins beyond the far reaches of the aurora borealis. He started speaking slowly, his voice growing in power.

Zavala crawled up beside Austin. "What's going on?"

"Looks like our friend is having a high school pep rally."

"Ugh. Those cheerleaders wouldn't win any beauty contests," Zavala said.

Austin stared through the trees, mesmerized by the barbaric spectacle. As Ben had said, the dome actually did resemble a huge igloo. Barker was doing them a favor by whipping his gang of cutthroats into a murderous frenzy. With all its attention focused on their leader, Barker's private army would hardly notice a handful of intruders sneaking through the woods. Austin scrambled to his feet and signaled to the others to do the same. Crouching low, they made their way through the forest until at last they broke into the open at the edge of the lake.

The area around the dock seemed to be deserted. Austin assumed that all of Barker's men had been summoned back to the big igloo for their leader's command performance. He wasn't about to take any chances, though. The shed near the dock was large enough to harbor dozens of assassins. He edged along one side of the building and peered around the corner. The shed's twin doors facing the water were wide open, as if the last person out had been in a hurry.

With Zavala and the Basques keeping watch, Austin stepped inside and flashed his light around. The shed was empty, except for some lines, anchors, buoys and other boating paraphernalia. After a quick glance around, he was about to leave, when Ben, who had followed him inside, said, "Wait."

The Indian pointed to the concrete floor. All Austin saw were mounds of dirt tracked in by those using the building.

Ben got down on one knee, and with his finger, traced the small footprint of a child. Austin's eyes hardened, and he strode back outside to find Zavala and the Aguirrez brothers staring at some lights that were moving in the lake. Austin thought he heard the sound of a motor. He couldn't be sure, because the sound of Barker's voice was still being carried on the wind. He reached into his pack and pulled out a pair of night-vision goggles, which he put to his eyes. "It's some sort of boat. Square-built with low sides."

He handed the goggles to Ben, who peered through the lenses and said, "That's the catamaran I saw the first time I was here."

"I don't recall you mentioning it."

"Sorry. There was so much happening that night. When Josh Green and I brought my canoe in, we saw it tied up to the dock. Didn't seem important at the time."

"It could be *very* important. Tell me about it."

Ben shrugged. "I'd say it was more than fifty feet long. Kind of a barge, but with a catamaran hull. A conveyor belt a couple of yards across ran down the center from a big bin at the bow back to the stern, which slopes down. We figured it was used to feed the fish."

"Feed the fish," Austin murmured.

"You remember what I told you about the fish cages I saw."

Austin wasn't thinking about fish in cages. Ben's words had conjured up the Mafia cliché associated with concrete overshoes and a trip to the bottom of the East River. He cursed as he recalled the nasty habit that had got the Kiolya in trouble with its neighbor tribes. Barker had cooked up a mass human sacrifice to go along with his send-off.

Austin trotted to the end of the dock. He stopped and squinted through the night-vision goggles again. With Ben's description running through his mind, he had a better understanding of what he was seeing. The low-slung craft was moving slowly and had almost reached the middle of the lake. In the illumination cast by the running lights, he could see people moving around the deck. He couldn't tell what they were up to, but he had a good idea.

Pablo had followed him. "What is it?" he said, looking out at the lights reflected in the water.

"Trouble," Austin replied. "Call in the SeaCobra."

Pablo unclipped the radio from his belt and barked an order in Spanish.

"They're on their way," he said. "What do you want them to do when they get here?"

"Tell them to thaw out that big igloo for starters."

Pablo smiled and relayed the order.

Austin called Zavala over and they talked briefly. While Zavala set off along the pier, Austin got the others together. "I want you to head for Ben's village on the far side of the lake. Wait for us there. If things get too hot after the fireworks start, lose yourselves in the woods."

"Are those my people out there on the barge?" Ben said anxiously.

"I think so. Joe and I will take a closer look."

"I want to go."

"I know you do. But we're going to need your knowledge of the forest to get us out of here." Seeing the stubborn set to Ben's jaw, he added: "The danger to your people becomes greater with every second we spend talking."

The rumble of a motor came from where Zavala had been at work on one of the boats tied up at the dock. Barker's men had taken no chances after Ben's last visit, and there were no keys left in the ignition, but Zavala could take a marine engine apart in his sleep. Moments later, the husky power plant of a Jet Ski could be heard purring. Zavala came back to where the others were standing. "I knew my Swiss army knife would come in handy," he said.

Austin glanced anxiously out into the lake, then climbed down from the pier onto the Jet Ski. Zavala got on behind to ride shotgun, literally. Austin pushed off from the pier and twisted the throttle, and seconds later, the Jet Ski was scudding across the lake at fifty miles per hour in pursuit of the distant lights.

Austin was ambivalent about personal watercraft. They were noisy polluters with no purpose beyond disturbing beachgoers, wildlife and sailboats. At the same time, he had to admit, riding a Jet Ski was like tearing around on a waterborne motorcycle. Within minutes, he could see the outlines of the catamaran without the use of the night goggles. The barge seemed to have stopped. Those aboard the craft heard the sound of the fast-approaching watercraft and saw the foamy rooster tail it was creating in its wake. A spotlight blinked on.

Temporarily blinded by the bright light, Austin ducked low over the handlebars, knowing that his reaction came too late. He had hoped to get close to the barge before being discovered. Even the shortest glimpse of his Caucasian features and pale hair would have identified him as a stranger, and by definition, as the enemy. He put the Jet Ski into a sharp turn that kicked up a wall of foam. The light found them within seconds. Austin swerved in the opposite direction, not knowing how long he could keep up the water acrobatics, or even if the slalom turns would do any good. He yelled over his shoulder.

"Can you douse that light?"

"Keep this thing steady and I will," Zavala shouted back.

Austin obliged by slowing the Jet Ski and putting it broadside to the catamaran. He knew he was giving those on board an easy shot, but felt he had to risk it. Zavala raised his shotgun to his shoulder and squeezed the trigger. The gun boomed. The light stayed on, and the beam found them again. Ears still ringing from the first blast, Austin felt rather than heard the second shot. The light blinked out.

The men on the boat broke out their flashlights. Soon, thin beams probed the darkness, and Austin could hear the rattle and snap of small-arms fire. By then, he was outside the range of the lights, keeping the Jet Ski at a low speed so its wake wouldn't be so obvious. They could hear the bullets ripping up nearby sections of water. The catamaran had pulled anchor and was moving again.

Austin was certain that the encounter had not delayed the evil task of those on board, but only hastened it. He suspected that if he tried to pull the boat over like a traffic cop, he and Zavala would end up with more holes than a sieve. Precious seconds went by as he scoured his brains. He recalled what Ben had said about the catamaran, and an idea came to him. He outlined his plan to Zavala.

"I'm starting to worry," Zavala said.

"I don't blame you. I know it's risky."

"You don't understand. I *like* the plan. *That's* what worries me."

"I'll make an appointment with a NUMA shrink when we get back. See if you can soften up the opposition in the meantime."

Zavala nodded and leveled his shotgun at a figure of a man who had the bad judgment to stand where he was silhouetted by the running lights. The shotgun thundered and the man threw his arms up and disappeared from view like a duck in a shooting gallery.

Austin throttled up, and seconds later, when a fusillade from the boat lacerated the surface of the lake, he was well away from the spot. The shotgun thundered and another body toppled over. The men aboard the barge finally figured out that they were easy targets and doused the running lights. It was exactly the reaction Austin had counted on.

The catamaran was starting to pick up speed. Austin ran the Jet Ski parallel to the barge for a moment, then circled around until he was a couple of hundred yards astern. Eyes riveted on the twin wakes ahead, he accelerated the Jet Ski. He aimed directly off to one side of the stern and cut power at the last second.

The front of the Jet Ski hit the catamaran's stern with a loud and hollow thump, then the watercraft made a horrible scraping noise as it slid up and onto the sloping deck. A crewman who had heard the approaching watercraft stood in the stern with his machine pistol at the ready. The Jet Ski's rounded bow slammed into his legs. There was the audible snap of bone, and he was catapulted halfway down the length of the deck. Zavala had rolled off before the Jet Ski had come to a stop. Austin dismounted and yanked the Bowen from its holster.

The Jet Ski had skidded so that it was sideways on the deck, offering them some protection. Austin drew a quick bead on a figure moving in the darkness and fired off a shot. He missed, but the muzzle flash illuminated a horrifying sight. Bodies—he couldn't tell if they were alive or dead in the dark—were lined up crosswise on the conveyor belt and were slowly moving toward the stern, where they would slide down a chute into the lake.

He yelled at Zavala to cover him. The shotgun fired off three shots in rapid succession. From the screams at the other end of the boat, one or more rounds found their deadly mark. Austin holstered his revolver, launched himself at the nearest struggling form and pulled it off the belt. Another, smaller body took its place on the nightmarish assembly line. Austin pulled it aside out of harm's way and saw that it was a child.

More bodies were coming at him. He wondered how long he could pull them to safety, but he was determined to try. He grabbed another by the legs. From the weight, he guessed that it was a man, and he grunted with exertion as he pulled him to safety. He had his hands around the ankles of another, when the belt stopped. He stood up. Sweat poured down his face, and he was breathing hard. He felt a twinge of pain from his old chest wound. He looked up and saw a figure holding a flashlight coming his way. The Bowen filled Austin's hand.

"Don't shoot, amigo," came the familiar voice of his partner.

Austin lowered the Bowen. "I thought you were covering me."

"I *was*. Then there was nothing left to cover you from. After I nailed a couple of guys, the rest of them jumped ship. I found the OFF switch on the belt controls."

The first body Austin had pulled from an almost certain death was making muffled sounds behind the duct tape. Austin borrowed the flashlight and found himself looking into the unmistakable gentian eyes of Therri Weld. He carefully stripped the duct tape from her mouth, then freed her hands and feet. She gave him a quick thanks, then freed the little girl who had almost been her companion in death. Austin handed over the doll, and the girl hugged it in a crushing embrace.

Working together, they quickly freed the others. Ryan beamed his smile at Austin and started to shower him with praise. Austin had had enough of the egotistic activist. He was angry at Ryan for getting in the way of the rescue and for risking Therri's life. A wrong look from Ryan and he would have thrown him overboard.

"Just shut up for now," he said.

Ryan saw that Austin was in a no-nonsense mood, and he clamped his lips together.

The last prisoners were being freed, when Austin heard a boat motor. He grabbed for his Bowen, and he and Zavala crouched behind the rail. They heard the boat shut its motor down and bump against the hull. Austin stood and flicked on the light. The bull's-eye fell on the anxious face of Ben Nighthawk.

"Come ahead," Austin yelled out. "Everyone's okay here."

A look of relief crossed Ben's face. He and the Aguirrez brothers climbed onto the catamaran. Pablo was bent over and seemed to be having some problems moving, and the other men had to help him. The Basque's sleeve was stained with blood above the elbow.

"What happened?" Austin said.

Diego smiled and said, "While you were out here, some of the guards saw us taking their boat and wanted us to pay rent. We gave them what we had. Pablo was wounded, but we killed the pigs." He looked around the boat and saw at least three bodies. "I see you have been busy, too."

"Busier than I would have liked." Austin glanced toward the dock, where lights were moving about. "Looks like you stirred up a hornets' nest."

"A very *big* hornets' nest," Pablo replied. He looked up at the *thut-thut* sound of a helicopter. "But *we* have stingers as well."

Austin saw a flitting shadow against the blue-blackness of the night sky. The SeaCobra had arrived in the nick of time. It flew like an arrow toward land. As it drew near Barker's complex, it slowed and, instead of unleashing the expected destruction on the igloo, went into a circle. It was searching for its target and not finding it. The igloo's camouflage had been turned on, and the huge building blended in with the dark forest.

It was a fatal moment of indecision. Searchlights illuminated the helicopter like a German bomber in the London blitzkrieg. Seeing that they had been discovered, the helicopter crew launched a missile at the plaza. Too late. The missile smashed into the plaza and killed a handful of Barker's men, but at the same time, a streak of light shot upward. The heat-seeking ground-to-air missile couldn't miss at such close range. It zeroed in on the helicopter's exhaust. There was a brilliant flash of hot yellow-and-red light, and the chopper fell in fiery, sizzling pieces into the lake.

It happened so fast that the people watching from the catamaran could hardly believe what they saw. It was as if the cavalry had come to the rescue, only to be wiped out in an Indian ambush. Even Austin, who knew the tide of battle could turn in an instant, was in a state of shock, but he quickly got over it. There was no time to waste. Barker's murderous myrmidons could be on them within minutes. He called Ben over and told him to ferry those on board to land, where they could hide in the woods.

Ryan came over and said, "Look, I'm sorry about all this, but I do owe you again."

"This one's on the house, but the next time you get into trouble, you're on your own."

"Maybe I can repay you by lending a hand."

"Maybe you can repay me by getting your butt out of here. Make sure Therri and the others make it safely to shore."

"And what are you going to do?" Therri said. She had come up behind Ryan.

"I intend to have a few words with Dr. Barker, or Toonook."

She stared at him in disbelief. "*Now* who's being reckless? You're the one who scolded me for putting myself in needless danger. He and his men will kill you."

"You're not getting out of our dinner date that easily."

"*Dinner?* How can you think about such a thing with all this insanity going on? You're crazy!"

"I'm quite sane, but I'm determined to get through a romantic meal for two without interruption."

Her face softened and a faint smile came to her lips. "I'd like that, too. So be careful."

He kissed her lightly on the mouth. Then he and Zavala pushed the Jet Ski back into the water. It had suffered a few dents and bullet holes during the rescue assault on the catamaran, but the motor was in fine shape and Zavala had no trouble getting it running again. As Austin pointed the watercraft back toward the vortex of violence, he realized that he didn't know what he was going to do when he finally met up with Dr. Barker. But he was certain he'd come up with something.

• • •

Austin and Zavala landed on the beach a few hundred yards from the dock and made their way back toward the plaza, where Barker had addressed his gang of thugs. The plaza was empty. Many of the defenders had scattered into the forest when the helicopter attacked. Austin and Zavala made their way around a crater and several bodies.

With its electronic camouflage in use, the dome itself was invisible, but light streamed from a slim rectangular opening in the forest where the portal had been left open. No one barred the way as Austin and Zavala stepped inside and got their first breathtaking glance of the huge silver torpedo that filled most of the hangar. Powerful floodlights reflected off the zeppelin's shiny aluminum skin, leaving the perimeter of the dome in darkness. They slipped into the shadows and hid behind a scaffold on wheels, where they had a good view of the scene.

The men scurrying around the zeppelin, apparently making last-minute preparations for takeoff, lent scale to the gigantic aircraft. Launch crews strained at the anchor lines like contestants engaged in a tug-of-war game. High above, the dome's roof was slowly opening, and stars were visible through the gap. Austin ran his eyes along the zeppelin's length, coolly taking in every detail, from the blunt nose to the tapering tail, his gaze lingering for a second on the triangular top fin and the word *Nietzsche*. The airship was a beautiful example of form following function, but aesthetics were secondary in his mind.

The control cabin was only a few feet above the floor, but it was surrounded by guards. He surveyed the airship again and saw what he was looking for. He pointed to the nearest engine nacelle and quickly outlined his idea to Zavala, who nodded and gave him the okay sign, signifying he understood. Zavala radioed Diego that they were boarding the airship. The roof opening was almost big enough to let the airship through. In another few seconds, the launch crews would begin to let up the slack on the anchor lines.

The zeppelin rested on tapering supports that resembled old-fashioned oil derricks. Other towers were arranged closer to the aircraft. With Zavala close on his heels, Austin made his way from tower to tower, finally reaching two scaffolds that supported the starboard rear nacelle. He glanced around. The crews were still intent on keeping the zeppelin down as it strained against the anchor lines. Satisfied that they had not been seen, he climbed to the top of the tower.

The egg-shaped engine housing was about the size of an SUV and attached to the fuselage by metal struts. The spinning propeller was the height of two men. Austin grabbed on to a strut and pulled himself onto the top of the nacelle. He could feel the vibration from the powerful engine through the soles of his boots. As the propeller picked up speed, it created a backwash, and he had to hold on tightly to prevent being blown off. He reached down to lend a hand to Zavala, who was still scrambling onto the engine housing, when the launch crew slacked the lines and the zeppelin began to rise. Zavala's legs dangled as he tried to get a foot up on the rounded side of the nacelle. Holding on with one hand, Austin used the considerable strength in his shoulders to give Zavala the lift he needed.

By then, the zeppelin was halfway to the roof. From their position atop the nacelle, they were shielded from eyes below. But the prop-wash was picking up, and it was becoming harder to hold on to the slick, rounded surface. Austin looked up and saw a rectangular opening where the struts disappeared into the fuselage. He yelled at Zavala, but his words were blown away by the wind, so he simply pointed. Zavala answered, and although Austin couldn't hear his partner's reply, he was sure Joe was saying, "After you."

Austin began to climb. The strut had been made with ladder rungs to allow an engineer access to the engine pod for midair repairs. With the prop turning and the zeppelin rising, the journey of several feet was the ultimate challenge. Austin's progress wasn't pretty, but he made it through the rectangular opening in the zeppelin's belly.

Once out of the main force of the prop wash, he hung on the ladder and looked back. Zavala was right behind him. The zeppelin had risen through the top of the dome, and the doors in the roof were closing. The people in the dome looked to be the size of ants. By the time Zavala made it into the fuselage, the dome was closed completely. Having made their decision to stow away, he and Zavala had no other choice. They began to climb into the darkness.

37

THE *NIETZSCHE* WAS a miracle of aeronautical design. Twice as long as a Boeing 747 Jumbo Jet, it had been built in an age before computers and space-age materials. The *Nietzsche* had been modeled after the *Graf Zeppelin,* the 776-foot-long silver cigar built in 1928 by airship pioneer Hugo Eckener, but innovations that would later be part of the *Hindenburg* had also been incorporated into the design. In the *Graf,* passenger quarters were behind the control room. But the *Nietzsche* had been designed with living space within the fuselage itself.

Once inside the fuselage, Austin and Zavala found themselves in a small room, after their perilous climb from the nacelle. Hanging on the wall were machinists' tools and spare parts and long black leather coats like those favored by aviators of a bygone era. The room was unheated, and the coats would come in handy for those who worked there. Austin tried a coat on and found that it fit.

"You look like the Red Baron," Zavala said.

Austin slipped a leather cap down on his head. "I prefer to think of myself as a master of disguise." Seeing the skepticism in his partner's face, Austin said: "Maybe you've noticed that we're somewhat different in appearance from the Eskimo gentlemen we've seen on this little adventure. If these ridiculous outfits give us a second's edge, they might be worth it."

"The sacrifices I make for NUMA," Zavala said, searching for a coat that fit him.

The room's single door opened onto a long corridor. The walls of the plushly carpeted passageway were decorated with fanciful scenes of men in top hats flying a variety of odd-shaped hot-air balloons and flying machines. Antique crystal lamps hung from the ceiling. At the end of the corridor was a passenger area of comfortably appointed staterooms, each with two berths and its own unique pattern of flowery wallpaper.

A short walk led to an elegant dining salon. There were about a dozen small rectangular tables, each covered with a white tablecloth, neatly creased napkins set in place. Two upholstered chairs with mahogany arms and legs were pulled slightly back from each table, as if guests were to arrive momentarily.

Tall curtained windows would have given the diners a God's-eye view of the world below. Next to the dining room was a lounge, complete with bar and bandstand, and a dance floor of highly polished wood. Like the dining salon, the lounge was decorated in Art Deco motif. Geometric patterns prevailed. The wall behind the bar was an art gallery of zeppelin photos.

The lounge was hushed except for the muted rumble of engines. Zavala looked around in wonder. "This is like being on an old ocean liner."

"Just pray that it isn't the *Titanic*," Austin said.

Austin led the way toward a room furnished with leather sofas and chairs. His knowledge of German was limited, but he guessed that the sign on the wall designated the area as the smoking room. They left the room and followed another corridor that led to an expansive space that seemed to be a work area. They could see a large functional table illuminated by halogen lamps, computers and several chairs that were designed more for function than comfort. Part of the room was in shadow. Austin found a wall light switch and flicked it on. The entire room was flooded with light, and both men tensed when they discovered that they were not alone. Two figures stood against the far wall, and Zavala swore in Spanish. Out of the corner of his eye, Austin saw the shotgun coming to bear.

"Wait!" he said.

Zavala lowered the gun and smiled as he studied the figures. He was looking at the mummified bodies of two men, propped up on metal stands. They stood in a natural position, arms hanging down by their sides. Their skin was as dark as leather and stretched tightly against their skulls. The eye sockets were empty, but the faces were remarkably well preserved. Austin and Zavala moved in for a closer look.

Zavala said, "I don't think these guys are the Blues Brothers."

"I don't think they're brothers at all. Judging from their clothing, I'd say they come from different eras."

One man was dressed in a heavy shirt and leggings of coarse material. His dark hair hung down to his shoulders. The taller man had short blond hair and wore a pre–World War II leather coat, not unlike the ones Austin and Zavala were wearing. Hanging above the mummies was a large, ragged-edged piece of aluminum. The word *Nietzsche* was printed on it.

Next to the mummies was a glass display case like those found in museums. Inside the case were a Leica 35mm still camera and several lenses, a Zeiss movie camera, charts of the northern hemisphere and a leather-bound book. Austin opened the case and leafed through the pages of the book. It was filled with entries in German, stopping in 1935. He stuffed the book into his pocket. He was examining a display of Eskimo harpoons and knives, when Zavala called him over.

"Kurt. You've got to see this."

Zavala had wandered over to the long ebony chest that rested on a waist-high platform. On top of the chest was a horn that looked as if it had been made from an elephant's tusk. The instrument was studded with gems and banded in gold. Austin carefully removed the horn and handed it to Zavala, who marveled at the detail of the battle scenes carved into the ivory.

Austin opened the chest and pushed back the lid. Lying on purple velvet inside the chest was a sword in its scabbard. He lifted the leather scabbard from the chest and inspected the gold-clad hilt and hand guard. Set into the heavy triangular pommel was a huge ruby. The elaborate hand guard was etched with flowers. He mused at the incongruity of the beautiful decoration on a weapon with such deadly potential.

He hefted the two-edged sword, feeling the perfect balance, then gingerly drew the weapon from the scabbard. An electric thrill seemed to run through his arm. Could this be *Durendal,* the fabled weapon that Roland swung against the Saracens? The blade was chipped here and there. A picture flitted through his mind of Roland banging the sword against a stone so that it wouldn't fall into the hands of the enemy.

Zavala whistled. "That thing must be worth a fortune."

Austin thought about all the time and money Balthazar Aguirrez had expended in his search for the object in his hand. "It's worth a lot more than that," he said.

He removed his coat and buckled the scabbard around his waist. He took a few steps as an experiment and found that the scabbard slapped against his leg. The thick leather belt hindered access to his revolver holster as well. He tried another position, slipping the scabbard belt over his shoulder so that the sword hung down by his left side. Then he got back into his coat.

"Planning to do some fencing?" Zavala said.

"Maybe. You must admit it beats your army knife."

"My knife has a corkscrew," Zavala reminded him. "What about the overgrown bugle?"

"We'd better put it back. I don't want to advertise the fact that I've absconded with the toothpick under my coat."

They carefully replaced the horn the way it was found and moved to the other side of the room, where a map of the world was spread out on the worktable. Austin bent over the map and saw that coastal areas on all the continents were blocked out in red pen. Noted next to each red section was a date and a listing of various species of fish. A large star marked the lake site where they had boarded the airship. He drew his finger from the star along a pencil line due east into the North Atlantic. The notation above the line was that day's date.

He straightened and said, "We've got to stop this ship before it gets to the Atlantic. This isn't a test run."

"Fine with me. I might point out that this thing is almost a thousand feet long and full of heavily armed thugs who might have other ideas."

"We don't have to take over the whole ship, just the control cabin."

"Why didn't you say so? It's as good as done."

"Think you can fly this old gasbag?"

"Can't be that hard," Zavala said. "You hit the throttle and point the nose where you want to go."

Despite the casual reply, Austin never doubted Zavala's words. His partner had hundreds of hours under his belt flying practically every aircraft built. Austin tried to picture where they were in the zeppelin. He guessed that they were about midway along the length of the great airship. If they kept moving forward and down, they would come to the control cabin.

They left the room and its strange museum display and followed a maze of passageways totally unlike those they had encountered when they first came aboard. Their surroundings were newer and more functional. They came to a set of stairs leading down. Austin thought they had come to the control cabin, but he changed his mind when his nose picked up a whiff of brine and fish. He was reminded uncomfortably of his first breath inside the Oceanus fish nursery in the Faroe Islands.

He hesitated at the top of the stairs, drew his Bowen, and slowly descended into the blackness below. His ears picked up the sound of motors and bubbling aerators, further convincing him that his fish-nursery theory was correct. He was about halfway down the stairs, when the lights went on and he saw that he had more than biofish to contend with.

Dr. Barker stood at the bottom of the stairs looking up at him, a cheerful smile on his thin face. His eyes were hidden behind dark sunglasses.

"Hello, Mr. Austin," Barker said. "We've been expecting you. Won't you join us?"

Any inclination to refuse Barker's offer was tempered by the sight of the stone-faced guards who surrounded the man, and the assault rifle muzzles pointed up the stairwell. The touch of a finger on even a single trigger would be enough to reduce Austin and Zavala to their basic molecules. Even more persuasive was the expression on the face of Barker's scar-faced henchman, who had tried on several occasions to kill Austin. His liver-colored lips were stretched in a wide grin that told Austin he was still the top target in the man's sights.

"I would be a fool to refuse such a warm invitation," Austin said, as he descended the rest of the way.

"Now drop your guns and kick them over," Barker said.

Austin and Zavala did as they were told. The guards picked the weapons up. One man came over and frisked Zavala. Scarface stepped up to Austin and ran his hands roughly down the front of the leather coat.

"I'm going to enjoy watching you die," he growled.

Durendal seemed to glow red hot against Austin's ribs. "I know a dentist who could do wonders for your teeth," he said.

Scarface stopped his search and grabbed Austin's lapel in a choking hold, only to back off at an order from Barker.

"That's no way to treat our guests," Barker said. Turning to Joe, he said, "You're Mr. Zavala, I presume?"

Zavala's mouth turned up slightly at the ends, and the softness of his dark brown eyes couldn't disguise the contempt in his voice. "And you're Dr. Barker, the mad scientist, I presume. Kurt has told me a lot about you."

"All good, I'm sure," Barker said. He seemed amused as he glanced back to Austin. "Are you gentlemen on your way to a costume ball?"

"Yes, as a matter of fact. If you don't mind, we'll be on our way," Austin said.

"Don't run off so soon. You just got here."

"If you insist. We'd like to lower our hands, if you don't mind."

"Go right ahead, but don't give my men an excuse to kill you on the spot."

"Thanks for the warning." Austin glanced around. "How did you know we were aboard, hidden surveillance cameras?"

"Nothing so sophisticated in this old relic. Purely as a safety measure, we installed sensors around the ship. A light in the control cabin indicated a change in air temperature in the starboard engine-maintenance room. When we went to investigate, we found the hatch open. We thought it was an accident until we noticed that the coats were missing."

"How careless of us."

"It's the kind of carelessness that can get you killed. That was a dangerous way to come aboard. If you wanted a tour, we would have been glad to accommodate you."

"Maybe next time."

"There won't be a next time." Barker stepped forward and removed his sunglasses, revealing the pale eyes Austin had first seen at the Smithsonian reception. The irises were almost as white as the rest of his eyes and reminded Austin of a venomous snake he had once seen. "You and NUMA have caused me a great deal of trouble," Barker said.

"Your troubles are just beginning," Austin said.

"Brave words for someone in your position. But not unexpected. Umealiq was disappointed when you foiled his plans for you in Washington."

"Umealiq?" said Zavala, who was hearing the name for the first time.

"That's Scarface's real name," Austin said. "It supposedly means 'stone lance.'"

Zavala's lips curled in a slight smile.

"You find something humorous in the situation?" Barker said.

"That's funny," Zavala said. "I thought it was Kiolyan for 'seal manure.'"

Scarface's hand went to the ivory knife at his belt, and he took a step forward. Barker stopped him with an outstretched arm. He gazed thoughtfully at the NUMA men.

"What do you know about the Kiolya?"

"I know that the Inuit consider you to be the scum of the Arctic," Austin said.

Barker's bloodless face flushed scarlet. "The Inuit are in no position to judge. They have let the world think that the people of the north are nothing but a bunch of blubber-chewing caricatures who run around in furs and live in ice houses."

Austin was pleased to see that he could get under Barker's cold skin. "I've heard the Kiolyan women smell like rancid whale blubber," he said.

Zavala sensed the opening and joined in. "Actually, they smell worse," he said. "That's why these goons prefer their own male company."

"Insult us all you want," Barker said. "Your feeble repartee is the ranting of the doomed. My men are a brotherhood, like the warrior monks of the past."

Austin's mind was racing madly. Barker was right. He and

Joe could summon up every insult possible, but they were still two unarmed men against several well-armed guards. He would have to try to change the equation. It took some willpower to do so, but he yawned and said, "What about that tour you promised?"

"How rude of me to forget."

Barker led the way onto a raised catwalk running down the middle of the chamber. The sound of bubbling water came from both sides, but the source of the noise was hidden by darkness. Barker replaced the sunglasses on his head and gave an order to one of his men. A second later, the chamber was flooded in a blue light that came from fish tanks on both sides and a couple of feet below the catwalk. The tanks were flush to the floor and were covered with sliding transparent plastic lids that allowed a view of the huge fish swimming inside.

"You look puzzled, Mr. Austin."

"Another miscalculation on my part. I thought your fish were being held at your coastal operation where they would have access to salt water."

"These are no ordinary fish," Barker said with pride in his voice. "They are designed to survive in salt or fresh water. The seed fish are improvements on the models I developed with Dr. Throckmorton. They are slightly larger and more aggressive than ordinary fish. Perfect breeding machines. The airship will fly within feet of the ocean's surface, and they will slide down special chutes built into the belly of the zeppelin." He spread his arms the way he had done at his pep rally. "Behold my creations. Soon, these beautiful creatures will be swimming in the sea."

"Where your monsters will create incredible havoc," Austin said.

"Monsters? I think not. I've simply used my genetic-engineering skills to produce a better commercial product. There's nothing illegal about it."

"*Murder* is illegal."

"Spare us your pitiful indignation. There were many casualties before you came onto the scene. There will be many more obstacles to be removed." He crossed to the tanks on the other side of the fish hold. "These are my special pets. I wanted to see how large and hungry I could make an ordinary fish. They are too aggressive for breeding purposes. They are separated by sluice gates now so they don't attack each other."

At a word from Barker, a guard went over to a cooler and extracted a frozen cod around two feet long. He slid back the plastic lid covering one of the tanks and tossed the carcass into the water. Within seconds, the cod disappeared in a bloody froth.

"I've made dinner reservations for you," Barker said.

"No thanks, we've already eaten," Austin said.

Barker studied the faces of the two men, but saw no sign of fear, only defiance. He frowned and said, "I'll give you and your partner time to think about your fate, to imagine what it feels like to be torn apart by razor-sharp teeth and scattered over the ocean. Our men will come for you shortly after we stop at our facility on the coast to refuel. Adieu, gentlemen."

Barker's men grabbed Austin and Zavala and hustled them down a corridor leading to a storage room. They were shoved inside, and the door was locked behind them.

Austin tried the lock, then found a seat on a pile of cardboard boxes.

"You don't seem very worried about being fed to the fishes," Zavala said.

"I have no intention of providing entertainment for that white-eyed freak and his cretinous henchmen. By the way, I liked your comment about Kiolyan women."

"It went against my grain. As you know, I love women of any kind. They have a lot to put up with, with their menfolk running around killing and sacrificing people. So, Mr. Houdini, how do we escape this little mess?"

"I guess we bust our way out of here."

"Uh-huh. And assuming we can get beyond that door, what chance do the two of us have against a battalion of armed men?"

"There are *three* of us, actually."

Zavala looked around. "An invisible friend, no doubt."

Austin peeled out of his coat and drew the sword from its scabbard. Even in the faint light inside the storage room, the blade seemed to glow. "This is my friend—*Durendal*."

38

THE CATAMARAN CAME in like a marine landing craft, and the twin hulls slid partway onto the shore with a shriek of fiberglass against gravel. The boat had no sooner come to a grinding halt than the people on board started to pile off. Ben Nighthawk was the first to hit the ground, followed by the Basques and the SOS crew. They helped the villagers climb down, and the group headed inland. Only Ben and Diego stayed behind.

Jesse Nighthawk turned and saw his son lingering on the beach. He shooed the other villagers into the woods and walked back to where Ben was standing.

"Why aren't you coming?" the old man said.

"Go on without me," Ben replied. "I've been talking to Diego. We have work to do."

"What do you mean? What sort of work?"

Ben looked across the lake. "Revenge."

"You can't go back!" Jesse said. "It's too dangerous."

Diego, who had been listening to the exchange, said, "The helicopter pilots who were shot down were our friends. Their deaths cannot go unanswered."

"Those people killed my cousin," Ben said. "They beat and

tortured my friends and family. They've raped our beautiful forest."

Jesse couldn't see his son's face in the shadows, but there was no mistaking the determination in Ben's voice. "Very well," he said sadly. "I will see the others to safety."

Marcus Ryan emerged from the woods, trailed by Chuck Mercer and Therri Weld. "What's going on?" he said, sensing the somber atmosphere.

"Ben and this man are going back," Jesse said. "I tried to stop them. They want to get themselves killed."

Ben put his hand on his father's shoulder. "That's the last thing I want to do, Pop. I can't speak for Diego, but at the very least, I want to wipe that big fake igloo off the face of the earth."

"That's a tall order for two men," Ryan said. "You'll need help."

"Thanks, Mark, I know you mean well, but the others need you more than we do."

"You're not the only one who has a score to settle," Ryan said. His voice gained a steely edge. "Barker killed Joshua, and he sank my ship. Now he's trying to kill the oceans. I owe him big-time. That thing on the other side of the lake is no grass hut. You're not going to blow it down with a huff and a puff."

"We know that. We'll figure it out."

"You don't have time for trial and error. I know how we can send that dome into the stratosphere." Ryan turned to Mercer. "You remember what we talked about?"

"Yeah, I remember. We said we could give Barker a big hotfoot if we got the chance."

"Well, Ben, how about it?" Ryan said. "Are we in?"

"It's not my decision alone." He turned to Diego.

The Basque said, "There are many of them and only a few of us. Pablo is out of action. We would have to be very lucky merely to stay alive."

Ben hesitated. "Okay, Mark. You're in."

Ryan's mouth widened in a triumphant grin. "We'll need some explosives. Our C-4 was taken away when we were captured."

"My brother and I have some hand grenades," Diego said, reaching over to tap his backpack. "Three apiece. Enough?"

In answer, Ryan glanced at Mercer, who said, "It could work if they're positioned in the right place."

"What can I do?" said Therri, who had been listening to the discussion.

"Ben's people are in pretty tough shape," Ryan said. "They'll need your help, especially the kids."

"I'll do my best," Therri said. She kissed him and gave Mercer and Ben a peck on the cheek as well. "Take care of yourselves."

As Therri made her way back into the forest, Ben and the other men pushed the catamaran off the beach and climbed aboard. The boat's twin hulls and powerful motors gave it a respectable speed. They scudded over the surface of the lake and soon reached the opposite shore. Pablo and Diego rode shotgun in the bow as the boat coasted up to the pier. They quickly tied up and headed inland.

Mercer made a stop at the boat shed and emerged with two reels of three-eighths docking line, some cord and a roll of duct tape. Walking single file, they detoured around the plaza. With Ryan in the lead, the group made its way undetected to the side of the dome. Ryan found what he was looking for: a tall, cylindrical fuel tank located in a clearing surrounded by dense woods. Painted on the side was a warning that the tank contained highly flammable contents. A steel pipe about six inches in diameter ran from the tank to the side of the building. Next to where the pipe entered the airship hangar was a locked door. Like the dome itself, the door was made of a plastic material and easily gave way to the strength and determination behind Diego's shoulders.

Then he and the others stepped into a short passageway that ran parallel to the pipe for several yards. The conduit disappeared through a wall next to another door, this one unlocked. Ryan took the lead and opened the door a crack, giving him a view of the interior of the airship hangar. Men milled around in the middle of the building, where the airship had been tied down. Others were coiling lines or moving gantries and scaffolding. A few guards were drifting out the hangar's main door.

Ryan motioned for the others to stay put while he and Mercer stepped into the hangar. They crawled along the wall behind tall stacks of coiled hose until they came to where the pipe entered the building. Barker had gestured toward the hose when he had explained why he used hydrogen rather than helium to fill the airship's gasbags. A valve controlled by a large hand-turned wheel allowed the flow of gas into the hose. Ryan turned the wheel on the pipe until they could hear the hiss of gas escaping through the nozzle.

The escaping gas rose to the roof, where it wouldn't be detected, they hoped, until it was too late. With their work done, they slipped out the door and followed the passageway into the open. Ben and Diego had been equally busy. Following Mercer's instructions, they had taped the hand grenades onto the tank. Short lengths of cord had been attached to the safety-pin rings and ganged to the line from one of the spools. Ryan and Mercer inspected the work, found it satisfactory, then walked back to the lake, uncoiling the line behind them. They tried to run the line straight back to the lake, keeping it clear of bushes and trees where it could snag.

When they'd emptied one two-hundred-foot-long spool, they spliced the free end onto another spool. They were still a dozen yards short of the lake when that spool gave out, too. Mercer ducked into the boat shed and came out with several lengths and sizes of rope that they spliced together until the rope reached to the water's edge. When all was ready, Diego headed back to the plaza and took a position behind a thick tree.

With their work inside the hangar done, Kiolyan men were streaming out into the plaza, some of them heading in the direction of their barracks. The Basque coldly took a bead on a guard and let off a short burst. The man fell to the ground. More guards came running from the direction of the barracks and began to fire indiscriminately into the woods where they saw muzzle flashes, but Diego moved after each kill and the bullets went far wide of their targets. When two more of their number were killed, the men in the plaza ran for the door of the giant igloo.

Diego had counted on exactly this reaction. He had tried to pick off the men who were making a break for the woods. The effect was to herd the guards into the "protection" of the structure. He knew that, given time, they would emerge from other exits in the dome and fan out into the woods and try a flanking maneuver. But as the last man disappeared into the airship hangar, leaving the plaza deserted, Diego was already sprinting back to the beach.

Waiting on shore, where he and the others had been alerted by the sound of gunfire, Ryan saw Diego running toward him and handed the end of the line to Ben.

"Would you like to do the honors?"

"Thanks," Ben said, taking the line. "Nothing would give me more pleasure."

Ryan turned to the other men. "When Ben yanks on that line, dive into the water and keep your head under for as long as you can. Okay, Ben. Let 'er rip!"

Ben jerked hard on the line, then dropped it and dove with the others into the lake. They filled their lungs with air, then ducked below the surface. Nothing happened. Ryan poked his head out and swore. He sloshed out of the lake onto the beach, picked up the loose end of the line and gave it a tug. It tugged back as if caught on a branch.

"I'll check. Must be hung up on something," he called out to the others, and followed the line inland.

Ryan was only partly right. The line was snagged on some*one*, not something. A stray guard had seen Diego bolt for the lake and had gone over to investigate. He was holding the line in his hand when he saw Ryan approach from the beach. Ryan was bent low, his eyes following the line, and he never saw the man level his gun. The first sign that he was not alone was the impact of the bullet hitting him in the shoulder like a fiery hammer blow. He dropped to his knees.

The guard never got off another shot. Diego, who had been following Ryan's trail, let off a burst that stitched its way across the guard's chest. The guard was thrown back by the impact, but his fingers clutched the line in a death grip. Ryan watched through filmy eyes as the guard fell, his weight pulling on the line. An alarm sounded in his brain, cutting through the pain and confusion, and he tried to rise, but his legs were made of rubber. Then he felt strong hands lifting him to his feet and guiding him back toward the lake. They were almost at the water's edge, when the lake lit up as if it had been sprayed with phosphorescent paint.

When the guard had toppled over, the tug had been transmitted along the line to the grenade rings. They'd popped out, and the levers had gone flying, igniting the fuse train. Six seconds later, the grenades went off simultaneously. A millisecond after that, the hydrogen in the tank ignited. The fiery gas rushed along the short length of the pipe and exited through the nozzle as if it were expelled from the business end of a flamethrower. The spurting flames touched off the invisible cloud of hydrogen hanging under the dome.

The airship hangar became a hell for the Kiolyan guards. Saturated with hydrogen, the superheated air exploded inside the dome, instantly incinerating flesh and bone. The dome contained the heat for only a few seconds, glowing white hot, before the thick plastic cells that formed the walls evaporated. But the delay before the final explosion of flames gave Ryan and Diego the time they needed. They gained the water's edge and dove into the lake as the dome exploded and sent out sheets of flame that vaporized the surrounding forest and outbuildings. Blistering waves of heat rippled out in every direction.

Hampered by his wound, Ryan had only taken a quick gulp of air before plunging into the lake, and his lungs were only partially filled. He saw the water light up and heard a muffled roar, and he stayed under for as long as he could before popping his head up. When he surfaced, thick smoke from the burning forest stung his eyes, but he paid no attention to the pain. He stared in awe at the mushroom cloud rising high in the sky from the field of orange-glowing embers that marked the place where he had last seen the dome. It made the *Hindenburg* explosion look like a candle flame.

Like otters coming up for air, Ben, Mercer and Diego stuck their heads out of the water and shared his wonder. Each of them had lost a friend or a relative to the schemes of Barker and his Kiolyan henchmen. But there was no smugness or satisfaction at the destruction they had caused. They knew that justice had been only partially served. The mad geneticist had been hurt but not stopped. By the flickering light of the burning trees, they swam to the catamaran, the three of them helping Ryan through the water. Minutes later, the boat was moving across the water, leaving the smoldering funeral pyre in its wake.

39

A USTIN SAT ON the box of fish antibiotics, holding the sword blade between his knees, his head bent against the hilt. A stranger would have seen this pose as one of dejection, but Zavala knew better. Austin would act when he was ready.

Zavala was keeping himself occupied with a set of exercises that were part yoga, part Zen and part old-fashioned shadowboxing to loosen him up and focus his mind. He finished demolishing an imaginary opponent with a left uppercut and a quick right cross, brushed his palms together and said, "I've just knocked out Rocky Marciano, Sugar Ray Robinson and Muhammad Ali in quick succession."

Austin looked up and said, "Save some punches for Barker and his pals. We're starting to descend."

Austin had been gambling that Barker was telling the truth when he said that he intended to feed them to his so-called pets and dump what was left into the Atlantic Ocean. A murderer like Barker would resort to any form of violence and duplicity to achieve his goals, but his inflated vision of himself extended to his godlike pronouncements of life and death. If Barker said he would kill them over the Atlantic, he meant it.

Austin had been waiting for the refueling stop, hoping the

zeppelin's crew would be distracted as the great airship came in for a landing. The guards had taken the men's wrist-watches, and it was impossible to keep accurate track of the passage of time. After seeing that they were cut off from sight and sound, Austin had stuck the sword point into the floor and put his ear against the hilt. The sword picked up the engine vibrations like a stylus on a record player. In the last few minutes, the pitch had changed. The engines had slowed. He stood and walked over to the sturdy wood-paneled door. They had put their shoulders against it earlier, but all they had gotten for their trouble were bruises.

Austin knocked softly on the door. He wanted to be sure no guard was standing on the other side. When there was no reply, he gripped the sword hilt in two hands, lifted the blade over his head and brought it down, putting all the considerable strength in his thick arms behind the thrust.

The wood splintered, but the blade didn't go through the door. Using the point, he pried off a section as big as his hand, then enlarged it. Working furiously, he opened a hole big enough to slip his arm through. The latch had been padlocked. After several more minutes, taking turns hacking at the wood with Zavala, they cut the latch off and pushed the door open. Seeing no guards, they cautiously made their way back to the fish hold. Austin leaned over the gangway.

"Sorry to disappoint you boys," he said to the milky shapes swimming around in the tanks, "but we have other dinner plans."

"They probably don't like Mexican food anyhow," Zavala said. "Check out the water level."

The surface of the water was at a slant, indicating that the zeppelin was inclined at a forward angle. They were on their way down. Austin wanted to get into the control car but suspected it would be heavily defended. They would have to be more creative. Again he looked for an answer in Barker's psychotic personality. In his rambling discourse, Barker had revealed more than he should have.

"Hey, Joe," Austin said thoughtfully, "do you remember what our host said about the sluice gates?"

"They keep the more aggressive fish separated. Otherwise, his little pets would chew themselves to pieces."

"He also said that the systems on this gasbag are hotwired. I'll bet that when the sluice gates are removed, an alarm goes off. How would you like to create a little chaos?"

Austin pulled up one of the gates. The fish on either side of the gate had come to the top of the tank, thinking that the presence of a human meant they were about to be fed. When the gate was removed, they all froze for an instant. Then their fins became a blur. There was a flash of silvery white and snapping jaws. Recalling the fate Barker had planned for them, Austin and Zavala watched the silent battle with a cold feeling in the pits of their stomachs. Within seconds, the tanks were filled with blood and fish parts. The creatures had ripped each other to shreds.

A red light on the wall had started to flash when the gate was removed. Austin waited by the door while Zavala lounged on the catwalk. He almost shouted for joy when only one guard showed up. The guard stopped short when he saw Zavala, and raised his rifle. Austin stepped up from behind and said, "Hello." When the guard turned, Austin jammed his elbow into the man's jaw. The guard crumpled to the floor like a sack of blubber. Austin scooped up the rifle and tossed it to Zavala. Then he found a switch that turned the alarm off.

With Zavala rearmed and Austin clenching his sword as if he were about to lay siege to a castle, they left the fish hold and followed a short corridor that led to a set of stairs going down to the control cabin. From their elevated vantage point, they could see through the open door. Men were moving about the cabin or were at the controls, but Barker wasn't among them. Austin signaled for Zavala to back away. The control cabin could wait. It made no sense to tangle with the claws and teeth of the monster called Oceanus when it might be easier to cut off its head.

Austin had a pretty good idea where he might find Barker. They hurried back through the fish hold and along a passageway until they came to the combination work area and museum where Austin had found *Durendal*. Austin's guess as to Barker's whereabouts was correct. The scientist and his scarfaced henchman were bent over the chart table.

With his animal instincts, Scarface sensed their intrusion and raised his head. He saw the two NUMA men, and his face contorted in an expression of savage fury. Barker heard his henchman snarl and looked up. After his initial surprise, he broke out in a smile. Austin couldn't see the eyes behind the sunglasses, but he could tell that they were fixed on the sword. Without a word, Barker went over and picked up the horn, then looked inside the chest.

"Well, well, Mr. Austin. It seems that you're a thief as well as a stowaway."

He closed the lid and went to replace the horn on top. But first he glanced over at Scarface, who replied with an almost imperceptible nod. Before Austin could move, Barker threw the horn at Zavala's head. Zavala ducked and the horn missed him by a few inches. Taking advantage of the distraction, Umealiq dropped down behind the desk. With the agility of a cat, he gained the protection of the heavy sofa. He popped up like an ugly jack-in-the-box, let off a wild shot from a handgun, then disappeared through a doorway.

"Get him before he alerts the others!" Austin shouted. But Zavala was already on his way.

Austin and Barker were left alone. With the smile still pasted on his ghostly face, Barker said, "Seems as if this is between you and me, Mr. Austin."

Austin returned the smile. "If that's the case, you're through."

"Brave words. But consider your position. Umealiq will kill your partner, and within moments, armed men will come pouring through that door."

"Consider *your* position, Barker." He raised the sword and advanced. "I'm about to cut your cold heart out and toss it to your mutant monsters."

Barker spun around like a ballet dancer, snatched a harpoon off the wall of the Eskimo display and, with a flick of his wrist, hurled it at Austin with amazing accuracy. Austin stooped to avoid the missile. The harpoon buried itself in the chest of one of the mummies. The stand holding the mummified body in leather crashed over, pulling down the section of airship skin with the word *Nietzsche* on it. Barker snatched another harpoon off the wall and charged at Austin, with an ivory knife from the display in his other hand.

Austin lopped off the harpoon point with a quick swing of the sword, but the movement left him open. He stepped backward to avoid the knife and stepped on the horn, which was lying on the floor. His ankle buckled and he fell. Barker yelled in triumph and lunged. Austin had landed with the sword under him and couldn't bring it to a defensive position. The knife slashed down. Austin blocked Barker's wrist with the edge of his hand. He tried to grip it, but his palm was sweaty. He let go of the sword and brought his other hand around and used it to push the knife point away from his throat.

Frustrated by Austin's superior strength, Barker jerked his hand back and brought it up to strike again. Austin rolled out of the way, leaving the sword behind him. They both scrambled to their feet at the same time.

When Austin went to retrieve the sword, the knife slashed the air a few inches from his chest. Barker kicked the sword out of reach, then advanced on Austin. He stepped back and felt the edge of the desk behind him. He could go no farther. Barker was so close, Austin could see his face reflected in the sunglasses.

Barker smiled and raised his knife to strike.

Zavala had bounded through the doorway and stopped short. He expected to find himself in another corridor. Instead, he was in a small chamber, not much bigger than a telephone booth, with ladder rungs running up one wall. A single wall lamp lit the cramped space. Under the lamp was a flashlight rack. One of the lights was missing. He grabbed one of the remaining flashlights and pointed it up. He thought he saw a flicker of movement in its beam, then nothing but darkness. He slung the rifle over his shoulder, tucked the light in his belt and began to climb. The shaft opened onto a passageway constructed in a triangle of interlocking girders. Probably part of a keel that kept the airship rigid and allowed access to its innards.

The keel intersected another passageway. Zavala held his breath and heard a slight *ting* that could have been made by a boot or shoe slapping against metal. He stepped into the new passageway and found that it curved up against the inside of the zeppelin's skin. The white fabric of the inflated gasbags was pressed tightly against the framework on the other side.

He guessed that he was inside a ring that worked with the keels to give the airship further support.

His theory proved out, as the passageway began to curve back on itself, so that he was climbing directly over the huge bags. Zavala was in good shape, but he was panting heavily when, at the top of the zeppelin, he came to another triangular passageway running lengthwise from the front to the back of the airship. The choice was easier this time. He pointed his light along the transverse support. He could see movement and hear heavy footsteps echoing in the distance.

Zavala dashed along the keel, knowing he had to stop Scarface before he made it to the control car and raised the alarm. He came to another juncture where the transverse corridor intersected a supporting ring. There was no sign or sound of Scarface to reveal where he had gone. Zavala's mind assembled a picture of the inside of the great airship.

If he were looking at a clock, the corridor he was in would be in the noon position. The transverse passageway he had seen earlier was at eight o'clock. To keep the rings rigid, there must be a third horizontal passageway at four o'clock. Maybe he could cut Scarface off at the pass.

He descended the ring, half climbing, half falling. He almost shouted in exultation when he came upon the third transverse passageway. He ran down the corridor, pausing at each ring to listen. He was guessing that Scarface would make his way as far forward as he could before descending to the control car using another ring.

At the third juncture of a keel and a ring, Zavala heard a *ting-ting* as someone climbed down the metal ladder. He waited patiently until he could hear heavy breathing. He flicked on the light. The beam caught Scarface clinging to the ladder like a large, ugly spider. Scarface saw that he'd been intercepted and began to climb up the ladder.

"Hold it right there!" Zavala ordered. He brought the shotgun to his shoulder.

Umealiq halted and looked down at Zavala with an ugly leer on his face. "Fool!" he shouted. "Go ahead and fire. You'll be signing your death warrant. If you miss me and hit a hydrogen bag, the airship will go up in flames and you and your partner will die."

Zavala's lips twitched at the ends. As an engineer, he was well-acquainted with the properties of various elements. He knew that hydrogen was volatile, but unless he was using a tracer bullet, combustion was unlikely. "That's where you're wrong," he said. "I'd just end up punching a hole in the gasbag."

The evil smile vanished. Umealiq bent off the ladder and pointed his gun at Zavala. The shotgun boomed once. The heavy shell hit Umealiq squarely in his broad chest and knocked him off the ladder. Zavala stepped back to avoid the body that crashed to his feet. As his life ebbed, Umealiq's face was twisted in disbelief.

"That's something else you were wrong about," Zavala said. "I don't miss."

While Zavala was chasing Scarface, Austin had been fighting for his life. Again, he had thrown his left hand up so that the edge of it caught Barker's wrist and stopped the descending knife inches from his neck. With his right hand, he reached up to grab Barker by the throat, but the other man jerked back. Austin's groping fingers yanked off the sunglasses. He found himself staring into Barker's pale-gray snake-eyes. Austin froze for a second and lost his grip on the wrist. Barker jerked his arm back, prepared to make another thrust.

Austin reached back onto the desk, his fingers in a desperate search for a paperweight or something else he could use to brain Barker with. He felt a searing sensation. His hand had touched one of the halogen lamps that illuminated the map. He grabbed the lamp, brought it around and shoved it in Barker's face, hoping to burn him. Barker blocked the lamp, but he couldn't stop the light. It was as if Austin had thrown acid into Barker's light-sensitive eyes. He screamed and threw his hand in front of his eyes to shield them. He stumbled back, screaming in the Kiolyan language. Austin watched dumbfounded at the damage he had wrought with a single lightbulb.

Barker groped his way out of the room. Austin picked up the sword and went after him. In his haste to catch Barker before he could get back to the control car, Austin was less careful than he should have been, and Barker was waiting for him in the fish hold. He ambushed Austin from just inside the door, and his slashing knife caught the rib cage on the side opposite from his existing wound. Austin dropped the sword and tumbled off the gangway onto the plastic lids that covered the fish tanks. He felt a warm dampness soaking his shirt.

He heard a nasty laugh from Barker, who stood on the gangway visible in the blue glow from the tanks. He was looking up and down, and Austin realized with relief that he was still blind. Austin tried to pull himself along the top of the tanks. The creatures under the plastic stirred in the water as they saw him moving and smelled the blood. Barker jerked his head in Austin's direction.

"That's right, Mr. Austin. I still can't see. But my acute sense of hearing gives me a different kind of sight. In the land of the blind, the man with the best hearing is king."

Barker was trying to goad Austin into a fatal response. Austin was losing blood and didn't know how long he could stay conscious. Zavala could be dead. He was on his own. There was only one chance. He slid back the lid of the tank next to him, groaning to cover the noise.

Barker's head stopped like a radar antenna with a fix on its target. He smiled, his pale eyes staring directly at Austin.

Barker smiled. "Are you hurt, Mr. Austin?"

He took a few steps toward Austin on the catwalk. Austin groaned again and slid back the top of the tank another few inches. Barker stepped off the catwalk and walked slowly along the tops of the fish tanks. Austin glanced at the opening. The gap was still less than a foot. He groaned again and brought it back another few inches.

Barker stopped and listened as if he suspected something.

"Screw you, Barker," Austin said. "I'm opening the sluice gates."

Barker's face fell, and he let out a feral snarl and charged forward. He never heard Austin pull the lid back another foot—and then he had stepped into the tank. He sank out of sight, then his head bobbed back up to the surface. His face turned into a mask of fear as he realized where he was, and he clung to the edge of the tank and tried to pull himself out. The mutant fish in the tank had been startled by the intrusion, but now it was nosing around Barker's legs. It was being excited as well by blood from Austin's wound that had seeped down into the water.

Austin rose to his feet and coolly pulled up the adjoining sluice gates. Barker was halfway out of the tank when the fish from the other tanks found him. His face turned even whiter, and then he slipped back into the tank. There was a flurry and commotion . . . and his body disappeared in bloody foam.

Austin turned off the alarm switch and staggered back to Barker's quarters, where he had found a medicine cabinet with a first-aid kit. Using tape and bandages, he stanched the bleeding. Then he retrieved the sword and was about to follow Zavala to see if he could help him, when his partner stepped through the door.

"Where's Barker?" Zavala said.

"We had a disagreement and he went to pieces." Austin's lips tightened in a mirthless smile. "I'll tell you later. What about Scarface?"

"Fatal gas attack." He glanced around. "We might want to get off this thing."

"I was just starting to enjoy the ride, but I see your point."

They hurried forward to the control car. There were only three men in the cabin. One man stood in front of a spoked wheel at the forward end of the car. Another manned a similar wheel on the port side. A third, who seemed to be in command, was directing them. He went for a pistol in his belt when he saw Austin and Zavala enter the cabin. Austin was in no mood for fooling around.

He stuck the sword's razor-sharp blade under the commander's Adam's apple and said, "Where are the others?"

Fear replaced the hatred in the man's dark eyes. "They're manning mooring lines for the landing."

While Zavala kept him covered, Austin lowered the sword and went over to one of the gondola windows. Lines dangled from a dozen points along the length of the great zeppelin. The zeppelin's lights illuminated the upturned faces of the men who waited below to grab the lines and pull the airship down to a mooring tower. He turned and ordered the commander to take his men and leave the control car. Then he locked the door behind them.

"What do you think?" he said to Zavala. "Can you fly this antique?"

Zavala nodded. "It's like a big ship. The wheel up front is the rudder control. The one on the side controls the elevators. I'd better take that. It might require a gentle hand."

Austin stepped over to the rudder wheel. The zeppelin was angled forward, giving him a clear view of the scene below. Some of the mooring lines were in the hands of the ground crew.

He took a deep breath and turned to Zavala. "Let's fly."

Zavala turned the elevator wheel, but the zeppelin refused to rise. Austin cranked the engine controls over to half speed ahead. The airship began to move forward, but the mooring lines were holding it down.

"We need more lift," Zavala said.

"What if we dump some weight?"

"That might work."

Austin scanned the control panel until he found what he was looking for. "Hold on," he said.

He punched the button. There was a gushing noise as the fish tanks emptied. Hundreds of wriggling fish and thousands of gallons of water poured out of the chutes under the airship and rained down on the men below. The ground crew scattered, releasing the mooring lines. Those men who didn't let go found themselves lifted in the air when the airship rose suddenly with the loss of ballast. Then they, too, dropped off.

The zeppelin moved forward and up until it was in the clear. Austin found that the rudder controls, as Zavala said, were not unlike those used to steer a ship. There was a delay before the great mass above their heads responded to the turn of the wheel. Austin steered the zeppelin out to sea. In the golden sparkle cast by the dawning sun, he could see the silhouette of a boat a few miles offshore. Then, he was distracted by a loud banging on the control-cabin door.

He yelled over his shoulder. "I think we've worn out our welcome, Joe."

"I wasn't aware we'd ever *had* a welcome, but I won't argue with you."

Austin steered toward the boat, and when they were closer,

he brought the engine speed down to SLOW. Zavala turned the elevator wheel so that the zeppelin would move up. Then they climbed through the windows and grabbed a couple of mooring lines. Austin had some trouble holding on because of his latest wound, but he was able to wrap his legs around the rope and control his descent fairly well. They started to rappel to the sea as the zeppelin began to regain altitude.

Paul had been standing watch a few minutes earlier when he heard the unmistakable sound of big engines. Something was going on in the air over the Oceanus facility. A minute before, beams of light had stabbed the sky. He saw a huge shadow, then lights were bouncing off the metallic skin of the airship. The airship turned seaward, gradually moving lower as it approached the boat.

He awakened Gamay and asked her to alert the rest of the crew. He was afraid Oceanus might have called in aerial support. The sleepy-eyed captain was on deck a moment later.

"What's going on?" he said.

Paul pointed at the approaching zeppelin, which glowed as if it were on fire from the golden rays of the new sun. "We'd better get moving. I don't know whether that's a friend or enemy."

The captain was fully awake now. He ran for the bridge.

Professor Throckmorton was on deck as well. "Dear God," the professor said. "That's the biggest thing I've ever seen."

The engines growled and the boat began to move. They watched nervously as the airship cut the distance between them. It was moving erratically, left and right, then its nose would go high and low. But one thing was clear, it was coming right at them. It was so low now that the lines dangling from below touched the waves.

Gamay had been focused on the control cabin. She saw heads appear in the windows, then two men climbed out and slid down the ropes. She pointed them out to Paul, and a broad grin crossed his face. The captain had returned to the deck. Paul told him to bring the boat to a stop.

"But they'll catch us."

"Exactly right, Captain, exactly right."

Mumbling to himself, the captain raced back to the bridge. Paul and Gamay grabbed some crew members and readied the vessel's inflatable outboard boat. The engines cut to an idle, and the boat plowed to a halt as the zeppelin's gigantic silhouette filled the sky. As the airship came abeam, the figures hanging from the lines dropped into the sea with two great splashes. The inflatable came alongside the heads bobbing in the waves. Paul and Gamay pulled Zavala and Austin aboard.

"Nice of you to drop in," Paul said. .

"Nice of you to pick us up," Austin said.

Even as he grinned with pleasure, Austin was keeping an eye on the zeppelin. To his relief, after the airship leveled out, it steered on a course away from the ship. Barker's men must have broken back into the control car. They would have made short work of the boat and everyone on it with their automatic weapons. But the Kiolya were headless now, without Toonook, their great leader.

Within minutes, friendly hands were helping Austin and the others back onto the research vessel. Austin and Zavala were taken below and provided with dry clothes. Gamay did a professional job patching up Austin's latest wound with bandages. The injury might require a few stitches, but it looked worse than it was. On the plus side, Austin consoled himself, he would have matching scars on either side of his rib cage. He and Zavala were sitting in the galley with the Trouts, enjoying strong coffee and the warmth from the stove, when the cook, a Newfoundlander, asked if they wanted breakfast.

Austin realized they hadn't eaten since the jerky they had had the previous day. From the look in Zavala's eyes, he was equally hungry.

"Anything you can rustle up," Austin said. "Just make sure there's a lot of it."

"I can give you fish cakes and eggs," the cook said.

"*Fish* cakes?" Zavala said.

"Sure. It's a Newfie specialty."

Austin and Zavala exchanged glances. "No, thanks," they said.

40

BEAR CAME THROUGH as promised.

Therri had called the bush pilot on the radio, told him she needed to evacuate nearly fifty people and pleaded for his help. Asking no questions, Bear had rallied every bush pilot within a hundred-mile radius. Floatplanes streamed in from every direction to airlift the passengers from the shore of the lake. The sick and elderly went on first, then the young. Therri stood on the beach, feeling a mixture of relief and sadness, and waved good-bye to her new friend Rachael.

Ryan's bloody badge of courage qualified him for a ride on one of the first planes out. With his shoulder wound patched up to stem the bleeding and prevent infection, he and the others were taken to a small but well-equipped provincial hospital. The Aguirrez brothers arranged their own transportation, calling in the EuroCopter to fly them back to the yacht with the news of their loss.

Before they left, Ben and some of the younger men in the tribe went back across the lake to see what was left of Barker's complex. On their return, they reported that nothing remained. When Therri asked about the fate of the monster fish she had seen, Ben simply smiled and said, "Barbecued."

Therri, Ben and Mercer were among the last to leave. This time, the fuzzy dice in Bear's cockpit were reassuring. As the floatplane wheeled over the vast forest, she looked down at the huge blackened area around the devastated site of Barker's incredible building.

"Looks like we had a little forest fire down there," Bear yelled over the drone of the engine. "You folks know anything about that?"

"Someone must have been careless with a match," Mercer said. Seeing the skeptical expression in Bear's eyes, Mercer grinned and said, "When we get back, I'll tell you the whole story over a beer."

It actually took quite a few beers.

Austin and Zavala, in the meantime, enjoyed their reunion with the Trouts and the leisurely cruise back to port on Throckmorton's research vessel. Throckmorton was still in a state of shock at the revelation of Barker's mad scheme, and he promised to testify before Senator Graham's Congressional committee once he had filled in Parliament about the dangers of genetically modified fish.

Back in Washington, Austin met with Sandecker to fill him in on the mission. The admiral listened to the story of Barker's demise with rapt attention, but he saved most of his fascination for *Durendal*. He held the sword gingerly in his hands.

Unlike many men of the sea, Sandecker was not superstitious, so Austin hiked an eyebrow when the admiral gazed at the shimmering blade and murmured, "This weapon is haunted, Kurt. It seems to have a life of its own."

"I had the same feeling," Austin said. "When I first picked it up, an electric current seemed to flow from the hilt into my arm."

Sandecker blinked as if he were coming out of a spell, and slid the sword back into its scabbard. "Superstitious rubbish, of course."

"Of course. What do you suggest we do with it?"

"There's no question in my mind. We return it to its last rightful owner."

"Roland is dead, and if the mummy I saw is Diego's, he won't be putting any claims on *Durendal* any time soon."

"Let me think about it. Do you mind if I borrow the sword in the meantime?"

"Not at all, although I could use it to cut through the mounds of paperwork."

Sandecker lit his cigar and tossed the match into his fireplace. Flashing his familiar crocodile grin, he said, "I've always found fire to be much more effective in dealing with the effluent of our federal bureaucracy."

Sandecker's summons came a couple of days later. The admiral's voice crackled over the phone. "Kurt, if you have a minute, could you please come up to my office. Round up Joe, too. There are some people here who want to see you."

Austin tracked down Zavala in the deep-submergence design lab and gave him Sandecker's message. They arrived outside the admiral's office at the same time. The receptionist smiled and waved them through. Sandecker greeted them at the door and ushered them into the nerve center of NUMA.

"Kurt. Joe. Good of you to come," he said effusively, taking them by the arm.

Austin smiled at Sandecker's disingenuous welcome. One had little choice when Sandecker called. Those who arrived late or not at all suffered the full weight of the admiral's wrath.

Standing behind Sandecker were Balthazar Aguirrez and his two sons. Balthazar roared with pleasure when he saw Austin. He pumped Austin's hand and then Zavala's in his lobster grip.

"I asked Mr. Aguirrez and his sons to stop by so we could thank them for helping us in Canada," Sandecker said. "I've been telling them about your mission."

"We couldn't have done it without your help," Austin said. "Sorry for the loss of your pilots and helicopter. And for Pablo's injury."

Aguirrez waved his hand in dismissal. "Thank you, my friend. The helicopter was only a machine and can easily be replaced. As you can see, my son's wound is healing nicely. The death of the pilots was a shame, but like all the men on my boat, they were highly paid mercenaries and well aware of the dangers of their chosen profession."

"Nonetheless, a tragic loss."

"Agreed. I'm pleased with the success of your mission, but do you have any news of the sword and the horn?"

"It seems your relics had a long and arduous journey," Sandecker said. "With the help of the log Kurt discovered in Barker's macabre museum, we've been able to piece the story together. Your ancestor, Diego, sailed across the Atlantic from the Faroe Islands. But he never reached land. He and his crew died, most likely from disease. The ship drifted into the polar ice. The zeppelin discovered the caravel hundreds of years later after a secret flight to the North Pole, and removed the body of your ancestor. Mechanical problems forced the airship down on the ice. The Kiolya found it, and removed the bodies of Diego and the zeppelin's captain, Heinrich Braun."

"Kurt has told me this story," Aguirrez said impatiently. "But what of the relics?"

Sandecker said, "Gentlemen, I'm being rude. Please sit down. I think it's time for some brandy."

The admiral waved his guests to the comfortable leather chairs in front of his massive desk and went over to a bar hidden behind a wall panel. He brought back a bottle of B and B and poured each man a snifter of brandy. He stuck his nose in the wide-mouthed glass, closed his eyes and took a deep breath. Then he unlocked his humidor and produced a handful of his specially rolled cigars. He passed the cigars around and patted the breast pocket of his navy blazer.

"I seem to have lost my cigar clipper. You gentlemen don't happen to have a knife? Never mind." He reached into the chair well of his desk, pulled out a scabbard and laid it on the desk. "Perhaps this will do."

Balthazar's dark eyes widened in disbelief. He rose from his chair and reached out for the scabbard, cradling it with both hands as if it were made of glass. With shaking fingers, he slid the sword from the scabbard and held it high above his head as if he were rallying Charlemagne's legions to battle.

His lips formed a single whispered word. *"Durendal."*

"The horn will arrive in a few days, along with the remains of your ancestor," Sandecker said. "I thought you might be able to put these priceless relics together with their rightful owner."

Balthazar slid the sword back into the scabbard and passed it on to his sons.

"The rightful owners are the Basque people. I will use the sword and horn of Roland to ensure that the Basques finally attain their sovereignty." He smiled. "But in a peaceful manner."

The glee at the success of his theatrical gesture was evident in Sandecker's clear blue eyes. He raised his glass high. "Let's drink to that," he said.

Ryan called Austin later that day and said he was back in Washington. He asked Austin to meet him at the "usual place." Austin arrived at Roosevelt Island a few minutes early, and was waiting in front of the statue, when he saw Ryan coming his way. Austin noticed that Ryan was still pale and gaunt from his wound. There was something else. The arrogant tilt of the chin and the boyish know-it-all grin that had flawed Ryan's good looks and irritated Austin were gone. Ryan seemed more serious and mature.

He smiled and extended his hand. "Thanks for coming, Kurt."

"How do you feel?"

"Like I've been used for target practice."

"I wish I could say you get used to it," Austin said, recalling the bullet and knife scars that marked his own body. "Knowing that you drove a spike into Barker's plans must help ease the pain. Congratulations."

"Couldn't have done it without the help of Ben and Chuck, and Diego Aguirrez."

"Don't be modest."

"*You*'re the one who's being modest. I heard about your adventures aboard the zeppelin."

"I hope this isn't turning into a mutual admiration society," Austin said. "I wouldn't want to ruin a wonderful relationship."

Ryan laughed. "I asked you here so I could apologize. I know I've been more than a little overbearing and self-righteous."

"Happens to the best of us."

"There's something else. I tried to use Therri to leverage your help."

"I know. I also know that Therri is too independent-minded to be used."

"I had to apologize, anyhow, before I leave."

"You sound as if you're heading off into the sunset."

"Like *Shane*? No, I'm not quite ready for that. I'm off to Bali in a few days to see if SOS can stop the illegal trade in sea turtles. Then I've got to help with a sea lion rescue in South Africa and see what we can do about poaching in the Galapagos Marine Reserve. In between, I'll be raising funds to replace the *Sentinel*."

"An ambitious schedule. Good luck."

"I'll need it." Ryan checked his watch. "Sorry to run, but I've got to line up the troops."

They walked back to the parking lot, where they shook hands once more.

"I understand you're seeing Therri later this week."

"We're having dinner, as soon as we crawl out from our office work."

"I promise not to interrupt you the way I did back in Copenhagen."

"Don't worry," Austin said. He glanced at the sky, a mysterious smile on his lips. "Where I'm taking Therri for dinner this time, *no* one will interrupt us."

41

MAY I POUR you more champagne, mademoiselle?" the waiter said.

"Thank you," Therri said with a smile. "I'd like that."

The waiter refilled the fine crystal champagne glass and gave the bottle of Moët a professional twist. Then, with a click of his heels, he walked back to his station, ready to be summoned with the slightest hike of an eyebrow. He was impeccably dressed, his black hair was slicked back with shiny pomade, and a pencil-thin mustache adorned his upper lip. He possessed the perfect attitude, a bored detachment combined with undivided attention.

"He's *wonderful*," Therri whispered. "Where did you get him?"

"Straight from the Orient Express," Austin said. Seeing the doubt in Therri's face, he added, "I confess. I borrowed him from NUMA food services. He worked as a maître d' at La Tour d'Argent in Paris before Sandecker hired him away to organize the NUMA dining room."

"He's done an outstanding job organizing our dinner," she said. They were sitting at a table for two. The tablecloth was white starched linen. The dishes and silverware were Art

Deco. Dress was formal. Therri wore a knockout strapless black evening dress, and Austin had replaced the tux he'd ruined in the Washington dogsled race. She nodded in the direction of a string quartet that was playing Mozart in the background. "I suppose the musicians are from the National Symphony Orchestra."

Austin's mouth widened in a sheepish grin. "They're friends from the NUMA engineering division who get together on weekends. Quite good, aren't they?"

"Yes. And so was dinner. I don't know who your chef was, but—" She paused, catching the look in Austin's eye. "Don't tell me. The chef was NUMA, too."

"No. He's a friend of mine, St. Julien Perlmutter. He insisted on cooking for us tonight. I'll introduce you later."

She sipped her champagne, and her mood grew somber. "I'm sorry, but I can't help thinking from time to time of Dr. Barker and the monstrous creatures he created. It seems like a nightmare."

"I wish it were a bad dream. Barker and his pals were very real. So were his Frankenfish."

"What a strange, terrible man he was. I suppose we'll never know how someone so brilliant could become so evil."

"All the more amazing when you consider that his ancestor, from all accounts, was a decent human being. The original Frederick Barker saw that the Eskimos were starving and tried to stop his fellow whaling captains from killing walrus."

"His genes must have been twisted during their passage from generation to generation," she said.

"Add a little God syndrome into the genetic stew and you get a mad scientist who fancies himself the personification of an evil spirit."

"It's ironic, isn't it?" she said, after a moment's thought. "Barker was a product of genes gone wrong. It was precisely the process he used in his laboratory to create monsters from normally docile fish. I shudder every time I think of those poor deformed creatures." An anxious look came to her eyes. "This *is* the end of that insane research, isn't it?"

Austin nodded. "Barker was a true genius. He wrote nothing down. He kept the notes for his genetic tinkering stored in his head. That knowledge died with him."

"Still, it wouldn't prevent someone else, equally as brilliant, from duplicating his work."

"No, but the loopholes in the law will soon be closed. Biofish will not be allowed into the U.S. The Europeans are equally determined that Frankenfish and chips will never be on their menu. Without a market, there's no incentive."

"What about the others in the Kiolya tribe?"

"Arrested, dead or on the run. Without Barker to whip them into a murderous frenzy, I'd say it's the end of that bunch as a threat. Barker's holdings are up for grabs. The wolves are tearing his giant corporation to pieces. Now let me ask you a question. What's the future hold for you and SOS?"

"We're parting ways. I've decided that commando raids aren't my style. I've been offered a staff position as environmental counsel with Senator Graham."

"Glad to hear you'll be around."

The waiter carried a black telephone over to the table. "Mr. Zavala would like to talk to you," he said.

Joe's voice came on the line. "Sorry to interrupt dinner. I thought you should know that we're going to start to make the approach soon."

"Thanks for the heads-up. How long do we have?"

"Enough for one very long dance."

Austin smiled and hung up. "That was Joe calling from the control car. We'll be landing soon."

Therri stared out the large observation window at the tapestry of lights far below. "It's beautiful. I'll never forget this night. But please tell me how you wrangled the use of the zeppelin for a dinner date?"

"I had to pull a few strings. The Germans are anxious to reclaim the first airship to have landed on the North Pole. When I heard the zeppelin was being flown from Canada to Washington, I offered the services of an experienced pilot, and in return reserved the dining room for a few hours. It seemed the only way we could have dinner undisturbed." He looked at his watch. "The pilot says we have time for one dance."

"I'd love to."

They rose from the table and Austin offered his arm, and they strolled into the dimly lit lounge. Austin turned on a record player, and the mellow tunes of the Glenn Miller band flowed from the speaker. "Thought we should have a little period music."

Therri was staring out the observation window at the lights of the great East Coast megalopolis. She turned and said, "Thank you for an exceptional evening."

"It's not over yet. After we land, we can have a nightcap at my place. Who knows where the evening will lead?"

"Oh, I know *exactly* where it will lead," she said with a dreamy smile.

He took her in his arms, inhaling the scent of her perfume, and high above the earth, they danced among the stars.

Carnival Elation

7 Day Exotic Western Caribbean Itinerary

DAY	PORT	ARRIVE	DEPART
Sun	Galveston		4:00 P.M.
Mon	"Fun Day" at Sea		
Tue	Progreso/Merida	8:00 A.M.	4:00 P.M.
Wed	Cozumel	9:00 A.M.	5:00 P.M.
Thu	Belize	8:00 A.M.	6:00 P.M.
Fri	"Fun Day" at Sea		
Sat	"Fun Day" at Sea		
Sun	Galveston	8:00 A.M.	

TERMS AND CONDITIONS

PAYMENT SCHEDULE:
50% due upon booking
Full and final payment due by July 26, 2004

Acceptable forms of payment are Visa, MasterCard, American Express, Discover and checks. The cardholder must be one of the passengers traveling. A fee of $25 will apply for all returned checks. Check payments must be made payable to **Advantage International, LLC** and sent to: Advantage International, LLC, 195 North Harbor Drive, Suite 4206, Chicago, IL 60601

CHANGE/CANCELLATION:
Notice of change/cancellation must be made in writing to Advantage International, LLC.

Change:
Changes in cabin category may be requested and can result in increased rate and penalties. A name change is permitted 60 days or more prior to departure and will incur a penalty of $50 per name change. Deviation from the group schedule and package is a cancellation.

Cancellation:

181 days or more prior to departure	$250 per person
121 - 180 days or more prior to departure	50% of the package price
120 - 61 days prior to departure	75% of the package price
60 days or less prior to departure	100% of the package price (nonrefundable)

US and Canadian citizens are required to present a valid passport or the original birth certificate and state issued photo ID (drivers license). All other nationalities must contact the consulate of the various ports that are visited for verification of documentation.

We strongly recommend trip cancellation insurance!

For further details call 1-877-ADV-NTGE or visit www.GetCaughtReadingatSea.com

---

For booking form and complete information
go to **www.getcaughtreadingatsea.com** or call **1-877-ADV-NTGE**

Complete coupon and booking form and mail both to:
**Advantage International, LLC,
195 North Harbor Drive, Suite 4206, Chicago, IL 60601**